GREENBERG'S GUIDE TO LIONEL® TRAINS: 1901 - 1942

Volume I

By Bruce C. Greenberg

Edited by
Christian F. Rohlfing

Cover photograph: The Lionel Blue Comet Standard Gauge Engine. Photographed by Mettee Studio, M. Wolfe Collection.

Greenberg Publishing Company, Inc.
7566 Main Street
Sykesville, MD 21784
(301) 795-7447

First Edition

Manufactured in the United States of America

Greenberg Publishing Company, Inc. offers the world's largest selection of Lionel, American Flyer, LGB, Ives, and other toy train publications as well as a selection of books on model and prototype railroading, dollhouse miniatures, and toys. For a copy of our current catalogue, please send a large self-addressed stamped envelope to Greenberg Publishing Company, Inc. at the above address.

Greenberg Shows, Inc. sponsors the world's largest public train, dollhouse, and toy shows. They feature extravagant operating model railroads for N, HO, O, Standard, and 1 Gauges as well as a huge marketplace for buying and selling nearly all model railroad equipment. The shows also feature, a large selection of dollhouses and dollhouse furnishings. Shows are currently offered in metropolitan Baltimore, Boston, Ft. Lauderdale, Cherry Hill and Wayne in New Jersey, Long Island in New York, Norfolk, Philadelphia, Pittsburgh, and Tampa. To receive our current show listing, please send a self-addressed stamped envelope marked "Train Show Schedule" to the address above.

Greenberg, Bruce C.
Greenberg's guide to Lionel trains, 1901-1942.

Rev. ed. of: Greenberg's price guide to Lionel trains, 1901-1942 / by Robert Pauli ... [et al.]. 3rd ed. c1983.
Includes indexes.
1. Railroads--Models. 2. Lionel Corporation. I. Rohlfing, Christian F. II. Greenberg's price guide to Lionel trains, 1901-1942. III. Title.
TF197.G67 1987 625.1'9'0294 87-29452
ISBN 0-89778-069-X (v. 1)
ISBN 0-89778-101-5 (v. 2)

ISBN: 0-89778-069-X

Table Of Contents

ACKNOWLEDGMENTS

The intent of this book is to provide as comprehensive a guide as possible to the collector, indicating historical developments, variations, and current market values. We have included Lionel locomotives, rolling stock, and accessories in Standard, 2-7/8", and OO Gauges manufactured between 1901 and 1942.

A work of this magnitude could not be completed without the research and writing efforts of many talented and generous people. This work was built on the foundation established in the previous edition by **Roland LaVoie**. Roland also catalogued a good portion of the information gathered since publishing the 1983 edition. In addition, Roland reread the entire manuscript for both content and style. His considerable skill substantially improved the work.

Dr. Charles Weber examined his entire collection and submitted over fifty pages of notes. The number of items credited to him will attest to the importance of his contributions. He is largely responsible for the reclassification of the 1677-1682 lithographed cars. In addition, Charlie proofread the entire text and made many final suggestions to insure accuracy.

Dave Ely generously gave of his time to review text and point out examples of many variations of pre-classic period Standard Gauge. Dave also contributed listings throughout the book from his vast knowledge and collection. The hours spent with Dave viewing his collection were particularly helpful to the editor. The number of listings attributed to him show his significant contributions to this book. Dave, along with **Dave Christianson**, provided an analytical framework for classifying four-wheel freight cars.

Jim Flynn reviewed the entire text with the editor, making suggestions for additions, corrections, and revisions. In addition, Jim provided input on market price information for most of the listings.

William Schilling established a new standard of research with his study of the 100-series freight cars. His research, combined with the work of Dave Ely and Jim Flynn, has provided a valuable insight into manufacturing techniques as a guide to chronology of variations.

George Koff's collection is a key resource for the study of Standard freight cars.

Dr. Robert Friedman wrote the comprehensive report on OO Lionel and provided interesting photographs as well. **James Sattler**, who wrote the chapter on 2-7/8" Gauge, is the leading authority on that subject.

Lou Bohn reread the entire manuscript and made extensive very helpful additions to the listings.

Al Weaver provided us with many color slides which helped confirm existing variations and add new ones.

Joe Kotil provided an extensive listing of new variations.

Frank Hare, publisher of **Toy Train Treasure** Volumes I and II, made available his magnificent color plates. His generosity and support are very much appreciated.

Tom McComas and **James Touhy** permitted us to use their fine color plates from **Lionel: A Collector's Guide and History, Volumes I and III.**

Philip Graves provided excellent line drawings of couplers and provided many Standard listings. Philip also reviewed the entire manuscript and made additional comments and corrections which were very helpful.

Jack Edwards reported a number of new variations in the 650/2650 Series of freight cars.

Steven Blotner made a number of contributions to the accessory listings.

Richard Vagner was most helpful in organizing the listings of the early 800-series Cars.

Gordon Thomson reread the entire manuscript and made additional very helpful comments.

Roger Bartelt reviewed the entire manuscript and identified several important problems which consequently we solved. His ability to see inconsistencies and subtle error is remarkable.

Ken Starke read the entire manuscript for style and consistency. His skills as a proofreader were very important to the quality of the final book.

Ed Prendeville, who is a major toy train dealer and has a very large inventory of toy trains, provided very helpful market information.

Richard Sullens generously welcomed us to photograph and describe his magnificent collection. He was a most gracious host.

Trip Riley graciously made available to us many pieces from his collection to photograph. He also shared his great fund of information about toy trains with us. We appreciate very much his great assistance on this project.

Ken Fremont assisted us in reviewing his collection. He pointed out a number of heretofore unknown varieties. His expertise on Lionel Standard Gauge Trains his very impressive.

Richard Shanfeld, who has a remarkable fund of knowledge about Lionel trains, reviewed the entire manuscript and made a number of very helpful suggestions.

Lou Koehler very generously allowed us to photograph his red Lionel 251 and other equipment.

Charles Phillips, who is well-known as a toy train dealer, "Have trains, will travel", reviewed the manuscript for us and made a number of very helpful suggestions.

Fred Wasserman assisted us by bringing some of his exceptional Lionel Trains to Sykesville for us to photograph and study.

And finally, **Fred Schlipf** very graciously read the final manuscript for us. He found a number of errors. I appreciate very much his careful reading.

The following people (in alphabetical order) also assisted in this book: **W. Adkins, D. Anderson, W. Mark Anderson III, L. Bertram, Warren Blackmar, Robert Bowes, H. Brandt, J. Bratspis, Nelson Brueckl, P. Catalano, Bob Cirrillo, David Clayton, Richard Clement, W. Davis, M. Diamond, D. Dudley, B. Edson, H. M. Exter, R. K. Fincham, R. Flanagan, Michael Foster, J. Gillander, J. A. Grams, Ronald Griesbeck, Richard S. Hahn, P. Haidvogle, W. Harrison, Woody Hoffman, Eric Hundertmark, J. Juratovic, R. Kirchner, T. Lemieux, B. Liep, R. Mancus, E. Manthos, Donald McErlean, Jack McLaren, Richard R. Menken, R. Merrill, W. Miles, P. Miller, P. Murray, R. Neidhammer, Bob Peca, D. Pickard, F. Reichenbach, Bill Schuppner, L. Shaeffer, LaRue Shempp, A. Simon, R. Sinkule, I. D. Smith, J. Spivak, J. Szasz, K. Wills, Jerry Williams, D. Witman**, and **M. Wolfe.**

At Greenberg Publishing Company, Inc., **Cindy Lee Floyd** was project administrator and responsible for the voluminous correspondence, typesetting, and layout of the book. She also compiled the Index with the assistance of **Fred Schlipf.** Her organizational skills were essential to the timely and professional completion of the work.

Marsha Davis and **Jerry Kiley** entered necessary corrections on the word processor.

Maureen Crum, staff artist, was responsible for the layout and design of the book and its preparation for the printer. The attractiveness of this book is due to her expertise and skill.

Donna Price proofread the book both as initially typeset and in final form. Her skills contributed to the quality of the work.

Maury Feinstein, staff photographer, provided most of the new color plates. These plates provide some of the finest train photography that has ever been published. **Roger Bartelt**, took many of the black and white photographs for the book.

Chris Rohlfing edited this edition. He had a monumental task because of the tremendous amount of new information that had been acquired since 1983. He spent an entire summer and most of his spare time for over a year in this project. Although we encourage our readers to report in a uniform manner, nevertheless the data often is inconsistent or incomplete. It is the editor's responsiblity to work with these materials and produce a reliable final product. Chris accomplished this task in a highly professional manner. But Chris did not define his task simply as editing the volume. He also engaged in further research in collaboration with Dave Ely, Jim Flynn, and William Schilling. Their continued efforts have substantially advanced our knowledge. Chris also undertook to rewrite most of the entries in the work to put them in chronological order.

FOREWORD

The train values in this book are based on prices obtained at train shows and meets during the fall of 1987 and from private transactions reported by our panel of reviewers. Meets are our primary data source since the greatest dollar volume of transactions occur there.

As we indicated, prices in this book were derived from large train shows. If you have trains to sell and you sell them to a person planning to resell them at another train show, you will NOT obtain the prices reported in this book. Rather you may expect to achieve about 50 percent of these prices. Basically, for your items to be of interest to such a buyer, he must buy them for considerably less than the prices listed here.

For each item we usually provide three conditions. Good, Excellent, and Restored.

GOOD — Scratches, small dents, dirty

EXCELLENT — Minute scratches or nicks, no dents or rust

RESTORED — Professionally refinished to a color that very closely approximates the original finish. All trim and ornament are present and in like-new condition. The finish appears in like-new condition.

Early Lionel equipment (pre-1923) is very hard to find in excellent or better condition. Most pieces grade good or very good. Most collectors readily accept good or very good pieces since this is what is available. However, collectors are still avidly seeking that elusive "like-new" item.

In the toy train field there is a great deal of concern with exterior appearance and less concern with operation. If operation is important to you, you should ask the seller whether the train runs. If the seller indicates that he does not know whether the equipment operates, you should test it. Most train meets have test track provided for that purpose.

In this book we do not show a value for Very Good. Generally, Very Good items are valued between those listed as Good and Excellent. We have not listed Mint since these items are extremely rare, and market values are difficult to establish. We have included the term "Restored" since such items are becoming an increasingly important part of the market. Restorations differ in quality. The values quoted are for professionally restored items.

We have had a number of inquiries as to whether or not a particular piece is a "good value". This book will help you to answer that question and will sensitize you to factors affecting that value. But, there is NO substitute for experience in the marketplace.

WE STRONGLY RECOMMEND THAT NOVICES DO NOT MAKE MAJOR PURCHASES WITHOUT THE ASSISTANCE OF FRIENDS WHO HAVE EXPERIENCE IN BUYING AND SELLING TRAINS.

If you are at a train meet and do not know who to ask about a train's value, look for the people running the meet and discuss with them your goal of getting assistance. Usually they can refer you to an experienced collector who will be willing to examine the piece and offer his opinion.

The **Prewar Guide** involved the collaboration of many people who generously gave their time and efforts. Only through such cooperative ventures can studies of this kind be carried out — it is impossible for one person to put together what the factory and the market dispersed to the four corners of the country (or more properly to the nooks and crannies of our basements and attics). I can only express my very deep appreciation to my fellow enthusiasts for their willingness to share their information and knowledge with me. This work is not finished; fortunately, there is always more to be learned. If you discover items that are omitted or errors, please tell me about them on the form provided so that the correct or additional information may be incorporated into the book's next edition.

Better grade and condition Standard and O Gauge items have substantially increased in value since 1983. Hence, these investment grade items have done better than the inflation rate and other collectibles. The most important changes are the increasing fussiness of buyers about condition. One prominent East Coast dealer told me that his customers ask not only about a locomotive's condition, but the condition of the inside wrapper and insert and the outside box. Some buyers demand original signal flags on the front of these steam locomotives! This is quite a change from the customs of 20 or 30 years ago when collectors sought one of each and were happy with a shiny piece.

Because of these changes in taste, I expect that the price differentiation between good and excellent will continue to expand for several years. By that time, the more common pieces — good and very good — will appear "cheap" in relation to the "true" excellents and generate increased demand.

Bruce C. Greenberg

PREFACE

When Bruce Greenberg first approached me in early 1986 about rewriting the Prewar Lionel Guide, I agreed with enthusiastic reluctance. The thought of learning how to use a computer for something other than games, not to mention the organization of all of the tidbits of information that had been gathered since the last printing, was enough to cause severe apprehension. Nevertheless, I entered into the project in the summer of 1986.

Bruce's original estimate was that the project would take about a month. As it turned out, it took exactly a year to complete the editing. On numerous occasions, just when we thought a section was complete, the mailman would bring more information that would necessitate a complete redoing of the section just completed. After reciting a few unprintable words to myself, I began anew. Ultimately we completed the project before the mailman came back again.

As we worked on the book, we had to make a few basic editorial decisions concerning existing listings and color descriptions. When the original Prewar guide was prepared, a number of generic listings were placed in this guide. In time, as more accurate descriptions were entered, these generic listings remained without any verification as to whether they ever existed that way. In this volume, we have attempted to eliminate generic listings where we are certain that they in fact did not exist. Where we are not certain, we have asked for reader verification.

We have also attempted to rearrange the previous listings where necessary in order to place the listings in a more accurate chronological order. While this may cause some initial confusion for those comparing this volume with the previous edition, in the long run, we believe that it will be more helpful to have the listings in proper chronological order.

A WORD ABOUT COLOR

Throughout this new edition, an effort has been made to describe the color variations in accordance with the colors of the color chart developed some years ago by the Train Collectors Association. This chart provides a readily available standard for color comparison. At times these colors are different from what is the common perception of a color. For example, what is commonly called "bright red" or just "red" is really "light red" on the TCA chart. Sometimes colors defy definition from the chart and a descriptive term has to be used like "brown-orange". The TCA chart refers to the color "aluminum". We have generally changed this to "silver-painted" so as not to confuse color with the metal used in the construction of the item. Finally, different kinds of light can make colors appear entirely different. When checking items for color, it is best to look in sunlight, in incandescent light, or under color-corrected 3000K florescents. It is hoped that by using the TCA color chart as a standard, we can achieve accurate reporting of variations.

This book began as an editorial task. It ended as a labor of love. With the help of many contributors, over 700 new variations and corrections have been entered. It could not have been done without their help. I also could not have completed the task without the encouragement and understanding of my wife and family as I labored away many late nights hunched over the computer. Is this edition the last word on Prewar Lionel? Of course not. Experience has shown that as more accurate descriptions are generated, even more variations are realized and new discoveries are made. We encourage you, the reader, to contribute these discoveries to the next edition.

Chris Rohlfing

Introduction

AN OVERVIEW: FOUR VITAL CONCEPTS IN UNDERSTANDING LIONEL TOY TRAINS

This book is the result of many enthusiasts sharing their knowledge. This commitment to scholarship has enabled us to make great progress in our documentation of Lionel production since our first publications in 1975. Despite a multitude of discoveries, we still have much to learn. To assume that this book is an absolutely complete document would be sheer folly.

Due to the diligence and scholarship of enthusiasts like Charles Weber, Dave Ely, Jim Flynn, William Schilling, and Roland LaVoie and many others like them we have identified hundreds of new varieties for this edition. However, we do not know the relative scarcity of most of these new varieties. You, our readers, would be of great assistance if you would compare your collections with the descriptions in this book and report to us which variations you have. We will compile this information and provide relative frequency counts for our next edition.

Since we are in the knowledge generation business, we are trying to learn what the Lionel factory produced on a year-to-year basis. Our problems have been compounded because the dust of years of history has settled upon the facts. The workers who could enlighten us have, for the most part, gone to their final rewards, leaving only their magnificent trains as testimony to their craftsmanship and skill. If there is one major difference between prewar and postwar research, it is the lack of first-hand knowledge of the factory production in the early years.

However, if direct testimony is lacking, many indirect clues exist which allow us to draw reasonable deductions based upon evidence. One major data source is the annual consumer catalogue. Through these catalogues, Lionel provided reasonably reliable reports about its products. Many times, the sets are found with the exact components in the exact colors shown in the catalogues. However, other items clearly shown in the catalogue have never been found. Although we have not confirmed an item's existence, we still cannot assume it was not made. Any item pictured in the catalogue signifies that, at the very least, a pre-production mock-up was made. These mock-ups might have been a previous production run hand-painted with the new design, or even a wood and/or plastic model of the proposed piece. This practice persists even today.

In the text, we generally report major catalogued items which we believe never reached production. We do this because people often have the catalogues and wonder if an item they have seen catalogued was actually made. We also do this expecting that, on occasion, a previously unreported item will be found and the finder will let us know that we were apparently in error in listing the item as not manufactured. This has happened more than once!

Although the consumer catalogues have been the major research tool for model train historians, other "paper" produced by the factory can be as important or more important than the consumer catalogue. Factory wholesale price sheets often contain corrections to the consumer catalogue and report that an item was not made, although catalogued (or, conversely, made although uncatalogued). Two cases in point are the 1916 catalogue insert and the 1946 catalogue insert 30 years later. These sheets retain their importance even today. For example, as recently as 1980, the Lionel Catalogue showed a Texas and Pacific diesel freight set which was never produced as the factory wholesale sheets have confirmed.

This book examines in considerable detail many Lionel pieces. However, there are relationships between these pieces which are not explicit in our descriptions. Lionel trains compose a "system" (to use the contemporary jargon) of interrelated and interdependent units which "interface" in definite patterns. Unlike most toys, model trains form a complex interdependent system. Not only must the track fit together tightly to carry current, it must also hold its shape within certain tolerances so that a train runs easily. The locomotive wheels and middle rail pickups require spacing, or "gauge", within certain physical limits. The middle rail pickup must press against the center rail with a predetermined pressure. The cars of the train need couplers which match in both height and type; they must also have weight relationships so that cars can be placed at different locations in the train, without undue stress causing derailment.

The systematic aspects of model railroading are potentially delightful; the railroad can grow and become more complex, and its parts will work together. Yet these aspects are also a potential nightmare for a designer or a manufacturer. Relatively small changes in some component could have unforeseen consequences which cause operating difficulties or — even worse — the end of operation.

Besides the systematic nature of Lionel's production, Lionel's technology must be given closer examination. Lionel, of course, always claimed to be a leader in toy train technology — not without good reason. But there is a broader question which must be addressed, especially in relation to the technology used by Lionel's competitors. Was Joshua Lionel Cowen, in the last analysis, like the ancient Greeks, a true innovator and pioneer of toy train technology? Or was Cowen more like the ancient Romans — one of the great synthesizers and adapters of technology pioneered by others? Although this question is very difficult to answer (evidence for both sides abounds), the attempt should be made. When we understand the nature of Lionel's technology, we will begin to understand why one path was chosen over another. For instance, we may come to a better understanding concerning Lionel's abandonment of OO Gauge trains after World War II.

We must also recognize that Lionel trains were made and sold in competitive markets. The relationship between Lionel's products and those of its competitors is crucial to understanding the Lionel phenomenon itself, and the descriptive mode of our book gives short shrift to that concept. What marketing strategies worked — or failed? Was Joshua Lionel Cowen's advertising skill the crucial element in making Lionel the preeminent maker of toy trains in the prewar era, rather than the innate quality of the trains themselves? Joshua Lionel Cowen was, after all, the prototype of the American entrepreneur in a time when the entrepreneurial spirit was unchecked by government regulation. What elements enabled Lionel to succeed where Ives did not?

The competitive nature of Lionel's market leads to one final element which must be discussed: the relationship of Lionel to its time and its place within American society. Like all other businesses, Lionel was a product of its time — and that society is far removed from us now. Significantly, Lionel's beginnings pre-date Henry Ford's mass production ideas. Additionally, the catalogue prices can cause amazement unless they are seen as part of the whole. Six dollars for a fine locomotive looks irresistible unless one remembers that in these times, other prices were just as mind-boggling. In Theodore Roosevelt's time, 1907, a good dress shirt would sell for 25 cents, and the nickel beer was a reality. One might also buy a real brass bed for about fourteen dollars, and if a man wanted to jollify his family, he could lay out $4.50 for bonded Kentucky bourbon — a gallon of it! Even in the 1930s when Lionel was selling its Blue Comet for about $75, the same amount could purchase a decent-running used car. Lionel trains were, in reality, very expensive. Lionel's famous advertising statements that "control of a Lionel train today by a boy means control of his life as an adult", or that Lionel trains were the "best way for a father to know his son", may seem preposterous to us now — yet Lionel successfully "sold" these ideas for decades. The nearly complete absence of women from the world of Lionel is another hallmark of a vanished era.

These four elements — the systematic nature of model railroading, the technology, the marketplace, and the historical era — are crucial to an understanding of Lionel production before World War II. In the introductory chapters to the various production areas, we will attempt to tie together some of these elements.

In fact, an examination of all these elements leads to a theme and a thesis for the entire book: Lionel was a very well-organized company which made consistent products for a given year. In other words, the characteristics of a particular item always went together — wheels, couplers, brakewheels, underframe lettering, etc. When people see variations of these characteristics, they may assume that all is confusion. Any confusion comes from inadequate data collection and analysis, not from the trains themselves. As this book clearly illustrates, the changes had definite patterns. Lionel consistently used the same elements together for a time and then changed the set to improve the design, save money, or enhance the item's appearance.

The pattern is there. It is up to us to find it!

THE EARLY YEARS OF LIONEL: 1901-1905

It is easy to romanticize in our minds the moment when Joshua Lionel Cowen first hit upon the idea of the miniature electric train. One can visualize him standing before a static, lifeless window display and, with his fertile imagination, contemplating how motion would attract potential customers. Eureka! The muse of inspiration strikes! "I'll produce an electric car which will carry the goods around the window!" Cowen remarks. A "Fabulous Career" ensues.

If only the truth were that simple! The Lionel researcher could then assume, safely, that Cowen built the toy train industry almost single-handedly, and everyone else feebly copied his ideas — much to his displeasure. Unfortunately, the facts get in the way of such an idealized, uncluttered scenario. The truth even confirms to some extent that Joshua Lionel Cowen was ignorant of a thriving toy train industry in those days, much less the inventor of a new toy industry. Despite this, two points are quite clear: Cowen did make a high-quality product, and he was clearly the most innovative marketer of toy trains in the world. His entrepreneurial reputation best rests upon those two elements rather than his work as a pioneer of the industry. This is not meant to belittle Cowen's numerous technical innovations. Rather, it is an attempt at perspective. One of the more fascinating speculations for the Lionel historian would be whether Cowen would have proceeded differently had he known more about his competition in the early years. The answer is, of course, forever denied to us.

The toy train industry was very well established by 1901, when Cowen supposedly stood before that store window. Most of the toy train pioneers were of German origin. The Marklin Company had been manufacturing trains since the 1850s, not too long after the first real German railroad was built between Nuremberg and Furth in December of 1835. The Bing and Carette companies, also in Germany, were well established and had very extensive lines. In fact, the Bing line for 1902 included locomotives which were powered by clockwork or live steam in different gauges. Significantly, Bing also offered two electrically-powered sets! Bing completed its line with the production of many different buildings and trackside accessories.

The German companies, although they were the most advanced, did not have the American market to themselves. The Ives Company had been producing toy trains in America since 1868. In 1902, Ives offered mechanical locomotives in two gauges as well as trackside buildings, although Ives did not produce live steam models at that time. In addition, the Carlisle and Finch Company, makers of electrical apparatus, had been offering electrically-powered trains and trolleys beginning in 1896. The Voltamp Company began its train production somewhat later, but it too offered excellent trains and trolleys during these years.

As this analysis indicates, the European toy manufacturers were much further advanced in the production of toy trains than were their American counterparts; their lines were far more extensive. As a result, the dominant American toy train producer of the time, Ives, did what any good competitor would do — it copied its competition. The Carlisle and Finch Company — and, ultimately, Lionel — appeared to be far less influenced by European competition.

Electricity was the new wonder of the age throughout the world for the society of 1900; it represented the equivalent of today's computer and "high-tech" revolutions for the society of 1900. For example, one of the biggest attractions of the Paris Exposition of 1900 was the huge Palace of Electricity, with lighted fountains and thousands of multicolored lights to beckon the visitor. In the American world of toy trains, Carlisle and Finch achieved a major American innovation with its trolley of 1896. This relatively small trolley was made of lightweight material. It ran on strip track, which was composed of ties named after British "sleepers" and thin continuous metal strips placed within slots in the ties.

It was with this strip track that Lionel launched its modest toy train line in 1901. With such a track system, Lionel was already behind the times. Sectional track, which was far more reliable and easy to handle, had been introduced in Europe well before 1900 and apparently was introduced to America by Ives in 1901. It is important to emphasize Lionel's use of strip track, because this type of track system had major shortcomings.

Among the problems inherent to a strip track system was that the metal strips resisted being put back in a straight line after being formed into a curve. In addition, connections between the strips were not reliable, whether there were overlapping connections or some sort of metal fastener. Moreover, the track had to be fastened to a hard surface in order to be used successfully. Worse than any of these problems, however, was the fact that the contact surface between track and wheel was extremely small, making for rather haphazard connections and transfer of track power to the motor. This is especially noteworthy when strip track is compared to the surface area of the tubular track which replaced it and the T-rail track which is the standard track for scale model railroads.

The founding of Lionel in New York City was a stroke of good fortune because there was probably a larger market for electrical goods there than in any other turn-of-the-century American city. Soon after, Thomas Edison built the nation's first public power distribution system in lower Manhattan. New York became a center for the manufacture and sale of electrical devices.

With such a ready market for that new and not fully understood marvel, electricity, we need to consider Lionel's earliest marketing concepts as compared with those of Bing, Marklin, Ives, and Carlisle and Finch. It appears from a review of the recently discovered 1902 catalogue, as well as the catalogues for the 1903-1906 period, that Cowen's original and primary marketing concept was to produce goods for sale and use by "mechanical institutions for demonstrating purposes, as they give a thorough insight into the workings of the electric cars now so universally used" and that the original concept was expanded in 1902 and later: (1) to meet previously unanticipated demand "from the students and their friends for duplicate outfits"; (2) to attempt to create a new market consisting of retailers for "Window Display" purposes; and (3) to attempt to create a second new market for "Holiday Gifts" and "toys".

The covers of the 1902 and 1903 catalogues boldly announce "MINIATURE ELECTRIC CARS WITH FULL ACCESSORIES FOR WINDOW DISPLAY AND HOLIDAY GIFTS". Cowen obviously wanted to pitch his products to the retailers of New York and other rapidly growing American cities. The idea was to have the retailer put the track and the operating equipment in the window to attract the attention of passersby by loading the cars with small items of merchandise. It is, therefore, understandable that Cowen's first product was not a locomotive or trolley, but rather an open, motorized gondola. Such a product would serve the original marketing objective of "demonstrating" while also accommodating a "Window Display".

The new toy aspect of Cowen's "goods" is emphasized on page 5 of the 1902 catalogue where, in reference to the No. 200 hardwood "ELECTRIC EXPRESS" open gondola car, it is stated: "As a toy it will afford the user much greater pleasure than the trolley car, as it may be loaded and unloaded." It is unclear from the 1902 catalogue whether the "Holiday Gifts" aspect referred to making gifts of Cowen's "goods" themselves or to the displaying of small "Holiday Gifts" in the open cars.

For some unknown reason, but probably due to the greater demand for the goods as "toys", the emphasis was reversed on the covers of the 1904 and 1905 catalogues from "Window Display" and "Holiday Gifts" to "MINIATURE ELECTRIC CARS, MOTORS, Etc. for Holiday Presents and Window Display". The implication of the word change from "Gifts" to "Presents" is that the "goods" themselves would be "Presents" rather than vehicles for the display of "Holiday Gifts".

Interestingly, the words "train" and "trains" do not appear in any Lionel catalogue before 1909 (other than in passing in the description of the No. 100 Electric Locomotive which was introduced in 1903 as a "faithful reproduction of the 1,800 horsepower electric locomotives used by the B. & O. R. R. for hauling trains through the tunnels of Baltimore"). In the 1909 catalogue, the cover announced for the first time "LIONEL Miniature Electric Trains and New Departure Battery Motors". Thus, it would appear that Cowen did not originally intend to compete with the established manufacturers of toy "trains" at all, but rather got into that business by a process of evolution. It appears that it was only after the demand for Cowen's "goods" as "toys" manifested itself that he correctly perceived that people were more interested in the gondola itself than in whatever small "Holiday Gifts" it may have carried in a "Window Display". This is not the only instance of a product differing from its original marketing concept. A few years later, a young printer's apprentice solved a serious printing problem with a new device. It seems that color printing blurred in the extreme summer humidity of New York City. The apprentice's device drew moisture out of the air and thus prevented the print from blurring. As a by-product, print shops became the most comfortable places in the city. The apprentice's name was Willis Carrier, and he had invented air conditioning. By the time Cowen introduced Standard Gauge in 1906, something similar had occurred to his original marketing concept. His trains had become sophisticated, attractive playthings for the general public.

One of the ongoing themes in Lionel's history is the changing of Lionel's roster to match innovation within the real transportation world. Did Joshua Lionel Cowen actually see an electrically-operated gondola to serve as a model for his miniature version? There is strong evidence that he did indeed observe a prototype. Research into the early records of American trolley and traction systems has been extensively documented by trolley enthusiasts. This research has shown that some trolley systems of the period were built with power from underground contact rails in the street rather than from overhead wires. The system built by New York's Metropolitan Street Railway Company along Third Avenue in 1894 was such a system. Cowen almost certainly was able to observe this system, which eventually became the Third Avenue Line.

It is one of the intriguing stories of American traction that the traction companies not only moved people in large numbers, but also served as urban freight transit networks. This being the case, we are certain that work cars once existed which carried equipment and goods along transit lines. Philadelphia used traction lines to haul city garbage. Recently, an underground electric railway for just such transportation has been unearthed in Chicago after being forgotten for many years. Cowen almost certainly observed the freight gondolas used by these transit companies; such cars could have given him the model for his window display gondola. There is further evidence in a later 2-7/8" Gauge car known as the "jail car" because of the bars on its windows. This is a very fine model of the baggage cars used to transport goods in the early 1900s.

Lionel's second powered unit was a trolley; this obviously reflected the latest thing at the turn of the century, when trolley lines were growing rapidly and innovation in trolley design was widely heralded. The trolleys of the time, only recently freed from the horses which first drew them, were becoming larger, faster, and more comfortable. It made sense for Lionel to imitate the real world.

Of course, Lionel, as a beginning manufacturer, had a very small plant and only a few employees. Therefore, it made good sense for Lionel to mate its drive train with a body from another manufacturer. Very fortunately for Lionel, the Morton E. Converse Company made a trolley of approximately the correct proportions to fit the Lionel drive train. The Converse trolley body was big — 16-1/2" long by 5" wide — and it was handsomely decorated. Most of the trolley bodies made by Converse for Lionel were painted quite differently from those used by Converse itself, although at least two original specimens of Converse "pull toy" trolleys are known to exist in paint colors identical to those supplied to Lionel. How many of these trolley bodies did Lionel use? We probably will never know for sure, although one of the dreams of the Lionel historian is to stumble over a carton of Converse records in some dingy bookstore or second-hand shop of lower Manhattan including correspondence between Lionel and Converse.

Historians have asked why Lionel chose such an odd gauge for its 1901-1905 production. Why did Lionel space its rails 2-7/8" apart, when toy train gauges of 0, 1, 2, and 3 had already been established by toy train makers? Was Joshua Lionel Cowen's idea to differentiate his product so that it could not be used by other systems? Or, was Cowen simply ignorant of the current practices of the toy train industry? (If so, such ignorance certainly did not last very long!) Was it just a coincidence that the then readily-available Converse trolley bodies happened to fit well on the previously determined 2-7/8" Gauge system? Or was the decision to adopt the 2-7/8" Gauge system dictated in whole or in part by the size of the Converse trolley bodies? Until the very earliest Lionel production can be satisfactorily documented, it will not be known for certain what all of the motivating reasons were for Cowen's decision to go with a 2-7/8" gauge system as opposed to one of the existing gauges.

LIONEL'S PREWAR TECHNOLOGY: PROBLEMS BEGET SOLUTIONS BEGET PROBLEMS...

"LIONEL ALWAYS LEADS", trumpeted the Lionel catalogues from the firm's earliest days. One might append the words . . . "IN WHAT?" to the statement, however. Did Lionel's greatest strengths lie in the firm's technological innovation? Or, was the admitted marketing genius of Joshua Lionel Cowen the real reason for Lionel's dominance over its competition? It would be very foolish to make a choice. Yet, Lionel was not nearly as innovative a firm as it claimed to be, although the Lionel Corporation did come up with some ingenious mechanisms over the years, such as the whistle and the non-derailing turnout.

It was not so much that an individual element of a Lionel product was truly innovative. The real technical genius of Lionel came about because the parts fit together into a systematic whole as well. In addition, Lionel very early committed itself to quality of the product — and hang the expense if necessary. That quality of manufacturing was trumpeted ceaselessly — and sometimes a little unfairly. In the 1923 catalogue (indeed, in much earlier ones), Lionel would show a picture of a competitor's car (usually the cheapest Ives car) twisted beyond recognition. In the same catalogue, on page 5, there appeared two pictures of tracks being tested by weight support. The competitor's track has snapped under a 20-pound weight, while Lionel's track is unscathed by a 110-pound weight. Look closely, because there are two misleading elements to these pictures. In the first place, Lionel's Standard Gauge track is being compared to the competitor's O27-style track — obviously much smaller and more lightly built. Additionally, the 20-pound weight is fastened to the competitor's track with a piece of wire at one small point of the rail. The 110-pound weight is hanging from a much larger leather strap which distributes the pull over the rail much more evenly. To say the least, Lionel is playing with a stacked deck!

Such one-sided comparisons tend to obscure the real quality of much of Lionel's production, and that is too bad, because Lionel did establish technical leadership as well as marketing genius. Before World War I, the German firms of Marklin and Bing pioneered nearly every basic element of toy train railroading, and Lionel was a follower rather than a leader. The war with Germany gave Lionel a chance to overcome this early lead, and Lionel was able to establish a technical dominance it never relinquished. The only real challenge to Lionel after World War I came from the Ives Company, and it was the fate of that organization to be led by old-fashioned leadership which was slow to take up marketing challenges. Ives and the later American Flyer were no match for Lionel in the 1920s.

During the 1920s, Lionel's technical dominance rested largely upon the systemic quality of its trains rather than any single innovation. That was to change dramatically during the 1920s. Lionel had introduced remote-control switches in 1926, for example, but these were not made non-derailing until 1931. Lionel's "Chugger", a relatively crude imitation of the sound of a steam engine, came out in 1933. Lionel's whistle, a truly ingenious device which worked from a spurt of DC current, appeared in 1935. The first automatic uncoupler appeared in 1938.

Technical innovation in model railroading sometimes causes mechanical and electrical problems because of the complexity and interdependence of a model railroad. A change to one part of a locomotive or a car can cause unanticipated problems elsewhere. A less charitable way of stating this fact is to say that Lionel's engineers were so smart that they sometimes outsmarted themselves. Nowhere was this more true than in the checkered history of Lionel's O Gauge automatic coupler systems.

At the onset of O Gauge trains by Lionel in 1915, Lionel offered two series of O Gauge cars. The premium cars of the 820 freight series came with two four-wheel trucks, while the lower-priced 800-series freight cars had only four wheels. The frames of these cars stood at different heights atop the rails, with the 820 cars being quite a bit higher. As long as Lionel continued to use its simple hook couplers, these height different cars did not matter very much because the hook couplers have half an inch of vertical play. There is enough stretch within this system to compensate for the height differences between the two series of cars.

In 1924, however, Lionel introduced a new degree of complexity — and confusion — when it brought the latch coupler to the O Gauge cars. This coupler, which had been used on Standard Gauge cars a year earlier, makes a horizontal connection rather than a vertical connection. The play or stretch is usually more horizontal than the vertical. (This reflects where the play actually exists in prototype equipment.) Since both lines of freight cars were continued, Lionel now had four lines of moderately incompatible O Gauge cars — low and high hooks, low and high latches!

To solve at least part of the problem, Lionel made transitional latch couplers known as combination couplers. These couplers had a slotted tab which would accept the earlier hook couplers. After a few years, Lionel only made regular latch couplers (we are not sure when the combination coupler was dropped). Lionel did make attempts to steer customers to compatible equipment, as can be seen on page 31 of the 1924 catalogue.

One of the greatest innovations in Lionel's history was the introduction of remote-control electrically-operated couplers in 1938. Although Lionel had advertised that its older latch couplers were automatic, they were virtually impossible to couple by backing the train into a car. (The similar Ives couplers were, ironically, much more likely to work in this fashion.) The new mechanism would permit the operator to uncouple a car at the touch of a button.

This mechanism used a box coupler with a lip on the leading lower edge of the box which caught the pin of the adjacent coupler. The initial mechanism consisted of an electromagnet with a cone-shaped core end which, when energized, attracted the bottom back flap of the box coupler towards the core. This would lift the front edge of the box coupler and permit the pin of the adjacent cars to slip out. Lionel had been using a non-automatic version of this box coupler since 1935. This improvement on the latch coupler provided secure attachment, yet ease of unlatching and a more realistic appearance.

So far, so good. However, Lionel's engineers had short memories which would embarrass the company severely. The power for the 1938 automatic couplers electromagnet came from a metal shoe on one side of the truck. This was essentially a resurrection of the sliding shoe pickups from the early Standard Gauge motors of 1906-1923. In 1923, Lionel "improved" its switches. However, as the sliding shoe touched the outside rail of the switch, it shorted out. Lionel solved that problem by adding a piece of fiber to the rail surfaces. Lionel's engineers forgot about this when they reintroduced the sliding shoe for the uncoupling mechanism in 1938. The pickup shoe contacted a center rail when going through the curved section of the switch. Therefore, the electromagnet was energized and the cars uncoupled.

Lionel's red-faced engineers changed the pickup shoe in 1939. The new shoe had only a small rivet head for electrical contact; the rivet head was encased within a plastic shoe. Although the small contact area was prone to oxidation, which would prevent current from reaching the electromagnet, this redesigned shoe was successful enough to last into the postwar era. It became the energizing device for many of Lionel's postwar operating cars after its use on couplers was discontinued after 1948.

Many more changes were made to these coupler mechanisms. In 1938, Lionel produced two automatic coupler types, each with a different shape to its electromagnet. Larger trucks of the 2800 Series had large cylindrically-shaped electromagnets. The differentiation might be a simple matter of proper size for the truck. On the other hand, differences in the magnetic flux might be involved. We invite reader comments. In 1939, a rod was inserted through an electromagnet on the truck. When the coil was activated, the rod was pulled away from the car center towards the car end. The rod then pushed against a plate connected to the box lid, which then tilted and released its opposing coupler pin. This solenoid mechanism was very reliable; it continued into the postwar knuckle coupler.

Ironically, Lionel still had not solved the problem of coupler heights! In fact it became worse! As if the complexity and costs for all the design changes were not enough to crinkle an accountant's cost sheets, Lionel's O Gauge cars still came in two heights. The box coupler has even less tolerance for vertical play than does the latch coupler. Consequently, Lionel had to produce two different box coupling heights achieved through different shank and truck to frame configurations. These problems must have turned the hair of many salesmen prematurely gray. (Grandmom, you say you want a tank car for Billy's train set? Do his cars have four or eight wheels? Do they have this little hook or this little latch? You don't remember? Help!)

Even today, Lionel's engineers can outsmart themselves by failing to anticipate operating problems. When Fundimensions introduced its Geep diesels in 1970, it put hollow-roller power pickups on the power trucks. Such pickups had worked well for inexpensive late Lionel 027 production, but the Fundimensions people forgot that these engines often stalled when crossing switches. As howls of protest began to reach the factory, Fundimensions hurriedly installed sprung solid-roller assemblies on the trailing trucks until it produced a solid-roller pickup for the power truck.

For all the headaches and problems caused by an individual component, it must be remembered that these were only momentary lapses of an individual component within a model railroading system which always worked well. It was not an accident that Lionel's commitment to quality in the prewar years meant prompt attention to design problems and a constant search for improvement. Perhaps Lionel was never the innovator it claimed to be. Yet the fact remains that no other American firm ever developed a toy railroading system with the dependability and durability of those developed by the Lionel Corporation.

MAKING THE TRAINS MOVE: LIONEL'S ELECTRICAL POWER AND REVERSING SYSTEMS

Like many young men of his age and society, Joshua Lionel Cowen was an inveterate experimenter and tinkerer. In his later years, he was fond of pointing out that one of his earliest experiments went wrong and "blew up his parents' kitchen". He was also reported to have rewired a friend's apartment so that the light switch would turn on the toaster instead. It really does not matter whether these stories are true or not. What they do point out is the insatiable curiosity of an inventive mind.

We do know that Cowen's curiosity settled upon electricity very early. He patented a "photographer's flash light apparatus" which used a small dry cell battery to set off a charge of magnesium powder. In speaking of these early years, Cowen said that he sold off this patent to a man who used it as the foundation for the Ever-Ready Flash Light Company, but evidence for this tale is lacking. He also patented an electric fan motor which, while not very effective for a fan, was the basis for Cowen's "New Departure" motors used in his earliest trains.

Once Cowen settled upon the idea of a moving window display for merchants, he realized that he would need a reliable low voltage power supply. While the contemporary practice of the toy train market was usually to use wet cell batteries as a low-voltage source of direct current, Lionel offered two different sources of battery power in its 1902 catalogue, dry cell batteries and "OUR PLUNGE BATTERY" which was to be charged "with electric sand, which may be purchased at any electric supply house". A third power source was portrayed and described as "the proper way to operate our cars when utilizing direct electric current". This sinister-looking collection of two glass jars, lead plates, and wires called for filling the jars with water and adding "a sufficient amount of sulphuric acid". The bold warning was given to "NEVER ADD WATER TO THE ACID IN ANY EVENT, BUT POUR THE ACID ON TOP OF THE WATER". The apparatus was to be wired to a 110-volt direct current source and called for a 32-candle-power incandescent bulb to be used "or, if a higher speed is desired, a lamp of greater candle-power should be employed". The price of the jars and plates was a whopping 50 cents.

Sulphuric acid is a hideous substance to handle even for an experienced chemist, let alone an unskilled retailer of dry goods. In its concentrated form, it will eat through almost any substance rapidly, and when it touches skin it absorbs the water in the tissues, leaving horribly charred burns. This was not the stuff of a child's toy, to say the least! The 1903 and later catalogues contain the much safer and saner suggestion that "We have found it advisable when making up outfits complete with battery, to supply four dry cells, which work satisfactorily when used intermittently for from ten to fifteen hours. . . ." Such dry cell battery systems, with individual batteries about the size of a mortar shell, were well established by the time Standard Gauge trains made their appearance in 1906.

Cowen realized the danger of wet cells and the limitations of dry cells, and in his 1906 catalogue offered a light bulb and shunt mounted on a base to reduce the high voltage DC house current to low voltage. Unfortunately, this use of a light bulb as a resistor to reduce 110 volts of DC current to 15 volts DC was rife with hazard. There would still be a 110 volt potential in the track!

Add to these hazardous power methods the fact that some toy trains were powered by live steam, and one might readily observe that there was much left to chance in these toys, to say the least! Lack of electrical safety apparently was caused by the "buyer beware" mentality of business in those years. What a difference from today this is! The Consumer Products Safety Commission will not even let Lionel make an AC transformer with an output of more than 100 watts let alone resurrect the 275 watt ZW of postwar days. Had Cowen been foolish enough to distribute a wet cell system today, he would be serving a lengthy prison term!

By the early teens, however, Lionel had scrapped its earliest systems for power in favor of dry cell batteries with rheostats to control current. Since the electrical distribution systems in most American cities used alternating current, Lionel soon offered relatively safe AC transformers without rheostats — except in some sections of its own home base, New York, which continued to use batteries and rheostats because the main current remained DC for quite some time. These two power systems made the operation of toy trains relatively safe for children.

The early Lionel transformers worked, as all transformers do, by induction. They consisted of a primary and a secondary coil with three to five taps taken from the secondary. The combination of these taps and the return terminal gave a range of fixed voltages. Lionel's designers wired the secondary taps to the brass caps on the transformer's external face. Another set of taps was taken from the secondary coil and connected to various fixed terminal posts.

This method produced highly reliable voltage sequences. However, as the controller moved from one brass cap to the next, there was a momentary current interruption. As long as the locomotives were reversed by a hand lever on the locomotive itself, these momentary lapses were no problem, since the engine would merely glide for a split second. Clearly, this situation would no longer suffice when Lionel introduced its pendulum-type reversing switch unit in 1926. Any current interruption while the operator changed voltage taps would result in the immediate reversing of the locomotive with a two-position reversing unit. This, of course, would cause derailments, crashes, and generally unstable operation.

Curiously, Lionel chose not to redesign the transformer itself so that voltage would change consistently. Instead, Lionel redesigned the No. 88 Battery Rheostat and created the No. 81 Controlling Rheostat, which first appeared without a number on page 17 of the 1926 catalogue and with a number the next year. Because the AC current flow was heavier than the DC current from batteries, the coil for the No. 81 Rheostat was protected by a metal cover which was insulated from the resistance wire by a piece of asbestos. The No. 88 Rheostat had no such cover.

The use of a separate rheostat had one negative effect upon the Lionel line of trains: Lionel was very slow to modernize its transformers. In fact, the brass button type of transformer persisted until 1938, long after American Flyer and other train makers introduced a continuous voltage dial-type transformer. In this AC transformer, still used today, the controller slides continuously across the secondary coil, tapping infinitely variable voltage throughout the transformer's voltage range. However, all of Lionel's transformers from 1926 to 1938 required the use of a separate rheostat if the locomotive had a sequence reversing switch.

The combination of the transformer, the rheostat, and the reversing unit formed a system which Lionel called its "Electric Control System". The key element to this system was the pendulum reversing unit, which allowed the operator to change the direction of the locomotive without manually throwing a switch on the locomotive itself. According to the 1926 Lionel catalogue, this reversing unit was only offered with Standard Gauge trains. However, by the next year Lionel had re-engineered the unit to fit the smaller spaces of O Gauge equipment. In subsequent years, Lionel began to use Ives' drum reverse unit, and the system then was called "Distant Control".

The introduction of the pendulum reverse unit led to some curious anomalies in Lionel's roster of locomotives. The 254 Locomotive is sometimes found with both pendulum reverse units and hand reverse units — on the same locomotive! In fact, the 1927 catalogue takes advantage of promoting this feature. On page 10, the catalogue states that "Another desirable feature of the Lionel Electrically-Controlled Locomotives is the fact that they can also be reversed by hand, and the controlling unit may be disconnected by moving another small lever." The hand-reverse switch was wired as the cutout switch for the pendulum reverse unity.

Not surprisingly, Lionel claimed that its pendulum reversing unit was superior to that of Ives, which predated Lionel's unit. "The construction throughout is dependable and must not be confused with so-called 'Automatic Reversing Locomotives' ", claimed the catalogue. Was Lionel's unit in fact more reliable? Since nearly 60 years have passed, this question is difficult to answer. However, there is one piece of circumstantial evidence that Lionel's claim of superiority for its pendulum reversing unit was not well founded. The Ives reversing unit operated by a rotating drum and pawl arrangement quite similar to the more modern E-unit reversing switch. After Lionel acquired sole control of the Ives Company in 1930, the pendulum reversing unit persisted. Three years elapsed before a re-engineered Ives drum unit was introduced. This unit has been used in Lionel production ever since, even to the present day! Only in the last few years has a fully electronic reversing switch begun to replace the pawl-and-drum design solenoid switch. Amazingly, many operators still prefer the old design to the electronic unit! Perhaps tradition dictates this, because E-unit "buzz" is a sound so closely associated with Lionel production after all these years.

In 1927, Lionel made another interesting comparison between its pendulum unit and the Ives drum unit. The Lionel pendulum unit's coil is only momentarily energized to cause sequence reversing. However, like the famous E-unit, the Ives reversing mechanism's coil is continuously energized as long as power is present in the track. Lionel was quick to point out that its unit operated ". . . without using extra current, with the result that Lionel locomotives are the only ones made that will operate as perfectly on direct current as on alternating current, dry cells or storage batteries." This claim meant that the extra current draw of the Ives unit was a serious disadvantage when the locomotive was run on dry or wet cell batteries. Was the claim true? Perhaps. However, as the use of electricity rapidly spread throughout the country, especially with the massive electrification programs of the 1930s, fewer and fewer people ran their trains from batteries. Therefore, the question rapidly became academic.

Whatever flaws they may have had, Lionel's power delivery systems from 1906 onward offered reliable, safe control of the operation of Lionel trains. Without the properly controlled use of that wonderful power source, electricity, Joshua Lionel Cowen's idea for the best toy trains in history would have remained a pipe dream. Lionel's transformers, rheostats, and reversing units made a gigantic contribution to the ultimate success of the Lionel Corporation. Today, in the 1980s, the efficient control of power for these trains is with us still.

Chapter I

Standard Gauge Locomotives

Standard Gauge, a completely new gauge, was introduced by Lionel in 1906 and replaced Lionel's two-rail, 2-7/8" Gauge. Standard Gauge measures 2-1/4" between the rails, except on curves where the gauge is somewhat widened. According to Lionel catalogues, Standard Gauge sets were last offered in 1939 and cars were last listed in 1940. However, some equipment was available for sale through 1942.

Standard Gauge can be divided into two periods—an Early Period from 1906 to 1923 and the Classic Period from 1923 to 1940. Early Period locomotives include the 5, 50, 51, 6, 7, 1910, 1911, 1912, 53, 33, 34, 38, 42, and 54. Classic Period equipment includes the 8, 10, 318, 380, 402, 408, 9, 381, 384, 390, 385, 392, 400, and 1835. Early Period equipment usually appears in drab colors with rubber-stamped lettering. Initially, Classic Period equipment continued the drab colors of the earlier equipment. Then Lionel introduced bright colors. Classic period equipment is also characterized by extensive use of copper and brass trim, and brass and nickel number and nameplates.

Coupler types, as described below, are very useful in dating Standard Gauge equipment, especially where the equipment was manufactured over an extended time period:

1906-1914	Short and long straight hooks
1910-1918	Short and long crinkle hooks
1914-1925	Hook with ears
1924-1928	Combination latch (Latch with a slot for a hook coupler)
1925-1942	Latch

As far as can be determined, Standard Gauge equipment was not produced with manual or automatic box couplers.

Other design changes useful in dating equipment are: name changes, headlights, wheels, and motor construction. For example, in 1918, Lionel changed its name from the Lionel Manufacturing Company to the Lionel Corporation and the identification on some equipment and boxes also changed.

The earliest headlights were pedestal and slide-on types; these were followed by strap headlights in the late 1910s and by cast headlights in the mid-1920s.

The earliest Standard Gauge locomotives have cast-iron wheels with thin rims. These were followed by thick-rimmed iron wheels. In the early 1920s, die-cast wheels with bright steel rims and red spokes replaced the iron wheels. In 1934 the Lionel catalogue first illustrated steel-rimmed wheels with black spokes. Eventually, the 385E, 1835E, 392E, and 400E Locomotives were made with black-spoked wheels and nickeled rims. Unfortunately, die-cast wheels were subject to deterioration. In the mid or late 1930s, Lionel introduced, as replacement parts, new die-cast wheels with black tires replacing the bright metal tires. These black-rimmed wheels have resisted deterioration. Several small companies have also made replacement wheels including Model Engineering Works and McCoy Manufacturing. Replacement wheels are readily available today.

Motor construction is also a key in determining manufacturing dates. Lionel introduced the Super motor in 1923, with large gears on one side of the motor. The gears prevented engines from passing easily through switches. Consequently, in 1925, the gearing was changed and the small gear Super motor was introduced. Later, probably in 1927, the Bild-A-Loco motor was introduced for certain models. The Bild-A-Loco motor featured do-it-yourself assembly with only a screwdriver. Slots were provided for axle bushings which were already mounted on axles. The last Standard Gauge motor featured black-anodized sides.

Two versions of the pedestal headlight have been observed. One version has the pedestal soldered to the light cylinder on the ends while the other has the pedestal soldered to the light cylinder on the sides.

The earliest Lionel headlights were the pedestal type. Lionel introduced the pedestal headlight by 1907 according to a recently discovered catalogue. In the late teens, Lionel introduced the strap headlight which was simpler and less expensive to manufacture.

Two versions of the strap headlight have been observed. According to C. Weber, the early version has a hollow rivet (actually an eyelet) holding the insulated washers and socket to the outer shell. The center post lead is soldered to the rivet. The later version has a machine-threaded screw with hex nut holding the insulated washers and socket to the outer shell. The center post lead is fastened by the nut.

Later version of strap headlight with screw and nut holding assembly together. R. Bartelt photograph.

In 1923, Lionel introduced the celluloid insert headlight with an on-off switch. This headlight was an elaboration of the strap headlight with side windows and a switch. It appeared in the top-of-the-line 402 and 380, and the O Gauge 256.

Brass Beauties: 7 and 54

Celluloid insert headlight. Note tab for on-off switch. Some came without on-off switch. R. Bartelt photograph.

In 1928, Lionel announced the die-cast headlight with its red and green panels (1928 catalogue, page 6). The catalogue also shows for the first time an O Gauge motor with the fiber headlight connection that supplies power to the die-cast headlight (1928 catalogue, page 4). On page 7, the catalogue indicated that the die-cast headlight was patented June 12, 1928. However, a close analysis of the 1926 and 1927 catalogues shows die-cast headlights!

Cast headlight with red-painted and green-painted panels on sides of light. A fiber and metal assembly fits into a slot on the underside of the casting and provides power for the bulb center post. R. Bartelt photograph.

The Lionel Paint Department
By Louis Bohn

In the early period, Lionel purchased coils of thin steel that they prime-painted (undercoated) for locomotives, cars, and accessories, or was tin-plated (for rust resistance) and used as is for track rails and ties. Later, they used mostly tinplate for nearly everything and omitted the prime-painting operation.

The paint colors used in the early period mirrored the actual colors used by the railroads of the time. These were mostly dark colors made with low cost "earth" pigments then widely available, and most resistant to fading. After World War I, paint research produced brilliant color paints made with metallic pigments. One such pigment is chrome yellow — a lead chromate. Other metallic pigments provided brilliant emerald green, bright blues, and vermilion red, which were also fade resistant. All of these metallic pigments are considered toxic today and so are now no longer generally available. In the mid-1920s, Lionel decided to use these bright colors as they were attractive in what we call Classic Period production.

It becomes obvious to anyone that mixes their own paint to match the colors of the pre-World War II era, that the Lionel paint department seldom used a paint-maker's color directly out of the can, but did some mixing, and toned them down a bit. This allowed more flexibility as they could buy any paint-maker's product and then mix it to the Lionel color. A critical observer today will note variations in a given color and gloss. Some of the variation is due to the mixing of paints noted above, as well as varying amounts hand-sprayed on, different colors underneath (tinplate, bare steel, repaints, etc), aging, and separation. Separation can occur when a mixed paint is left for a time (as overnight) and not stirred prior to resumption of painting. Example; peacock can be made by mixing green and blue paints. However, if settling occurs, the blue floats to the surface, leaving green on the bottom. Resumption of spraying without stirring draws the green paint.

The hand-sprayed items were placed on racks and then in ovens to hasten drying. Later, items were hung from hooks and conveyed through drying tunnels. Paint runs, and beads of thick paint along the lower edge of pieces, were not unusual. Many Lionel trains were dipped and hung.

Flaking of these baked enamel paints is due to: 1) mill oil on the original metal coil, 2) no primer, 3) paint more brittle due to age, and 4) less than ideal storage conditions.

	Gd	Exc	Rst

5 STEAM: Catalogued 1906-26, 0-4-0, sheet steel, described by Lionel as a Russian iron boiler, soldered, black cab and red window trim and pilot, nickel-plated trim, rubber-stamped in gold "N.Y.C. and H.R.R.R.", or less frequently "PENNSYLVANIA" or "B. & O.R.R.", with wooden dome, stack, pilot beam, and boiler front, 11-1/2". Specials are not marked in any way on the locomotive. The 5 and 5 Specials both have large coal bunkers. The 5 was sold without a tender (available separately) while the 5 Special was sold with a tender. Without the original box it is impossible to distinguish a 5 from a 5 Special. The 51 had a low bunker and was sold with a tender. C. Weber comment. Also see 51 Steam entry.

(A) 1906-07, 5 Early with thin-rimmed drivers, short crinkle hook coupler, large coal bunker, split frame, dummy slide-on headlight, lettered "N.Y.C. & H.R.R." (note absence of third R), no tender. Sattler Collection. **800 1200 600**

(B) 1906-09, 5 Special with black and red trim, slope-back coal tender with one 10-series solid three-rivet truck, lettered "PENNSYLVANIA". **1100 1900 800**

(C) Same as (B), but lettered "N.Y.C. & H.R.R.R." **1000 1700 800**

(D) Same as (B), but lettered "B.&O.R.R." **1200 2000 800**

(E) 1907-09, 5 Special, same as (C), but tender has open, three-rivet truck. 1908-09, engine has slide-on headlight. **900 1600 800**

(F) 1910-11, 5 Special, same as (A), but with eight-wheel slope-back tender with two 100-series trucks, "LIONEL MFG. CO." embossed on tender base, renumbered 51 in 1912 catalogue. **800 1200 700**

(G) 1911, 5 Late, similar to (A), but thick-rimmed drivers, long crinkle hook coupler, large coal bunker, solid frame, pedestal headlight, terminal on coal bunker to illuminate passenger cars, lettered "PENNSYLVANIA", no tender, two holes in boiler under sand dome directly under handrails, apparently intended

Early Standard Steam

TOP SHELF: **Early 5 marked "B. & O. R.R." with thin-rimmed drivers and short straight hook coupler with single-truck slope-back tender marked "N.Y.C & H.R.R.R.", "Lake Shore" Gondola with closed three-rivet trucks, yellow underframe with no embossing on underside, short straight hook couplers "WEIGHT 35000 LBS". BOTTOM SHELF: "C.M. & St.P. / 19050." Boxcar and "N.Y.C. & H.R.R R. / 51906." Caboose with yellow underframe, no embossing. R. Sullens Collection, M. Feinstein photograph.**

Gd Exc Rst

for second set of handrail stanchions, but never installed. Sattler Collection. **400 700 400**

(H) 5 Special, same as (G), except lettered "N.Y.C. & H.R.R.R.", eight-wheel double-truck tender. C. Weber Collection. **450 700 400**

5 STEAM: Late, (see entry 51 Steam entry).

6 STEAM: Catalogued 1906-23, 4-4-0, sheet steel, described by Lionel as a Russian blue iron boiler, soldered body, black cab with red window trim and red pilot, nickel-plated trim, including two boiler bands. Gold rubber-stamped with various road names under cab window and on tender sides, black rectangular tender with red trim. Some tenders apparently were lettered "B. & M.R.R." See illustration of 6(C). Reader comments invited. Sattler observation.

(A) Early 6: thin-rimmed wheels, cast-iron pilot wheels, dummy headlight, split frame. **1200 1600 1000**

(B) 1908-11, Later 6: thin-rimmed wheels, cast-iron pilot wheels, operating slide-on headlight. Large bell, solid frame. Gold rubber-stamped "PENNSYLVANIA" in sans-serif lettering on cab, or "N.Y.C. & H.R.R.R." in large gold serif lettering. No "MFG." embossing on tender base and two holes in base, short straight hook couplers, 10-series solid three-rivet trucks. D. Ely Collection and comment.
1200 1900 900

(C) 1911, same as (B), but lettered "N.Y.C. & H.R.R.R." in sans-serif block lettering. Thin-rimmed wheels, cast-iron pilot wheels, solid frame, operating slide-on headlight, large bell (two screw holes), small frame vertical motor, car-lighting terminal in cab, long straight hook coupler on engine, short crinkle hook couplers on tender, gold-stamped sans-serif lettering on tender, 10-series Type IV trucks with hollow rivet on tender. R. Kirchner Collection. **1000 1500 900**

(D) Same as (B), but lettered "B.&O.R.R." in sans-serif block lettering. **1300 2100 900**

(E) 1912-17, thick-rimmed wheels, die-cast pilot wheels, pedestal headlight, large bell, gold rubber-stamped "NYC & HRRR" below cab window, tender gold rubber-stamped "NYC & HRRR" long crinkle hook coupler on tender, tender with 10-series trucks, Type 4. **800 1200 800**

(F) 1918-23, thick-rimmed wheels, die-cast pilot wheels, strap headlight, solid frame, regular hook couplers, small bell. Gold rubber-stamped on cab beneath window "N.Y.C. & H.R.R.R." in sans-serif block lettering. Tender is gold rubber-stamped "N.Y.C & HRRR" and "4351" Rubber-stamped lettering differs in size and thickness. **800 1200 800**

6 SPECIAL: Catalogued 1908-09, Steam, 4-4-0, Early 6 locomotive and tender constructed from heavy sheet brass and nickeled brass. Nickeled tender has either open or closed three-rivet trucks. No lettering on locomotive or tender sides, although shown lettered in catalogue. Engine boiler is brass while cab is nickel-finished. Red pilot, driver spokes, pilot wheels, and tender stripes. A 6 Special is indistinguishable from an Early 7. **2000 3000 2000**

7 STEAM: 1908-23, 4-4-0, early models same as 6 Special with/without binding post inside cab, pilot wheels cast-iron to 1920, then die-cast.

(A) 1908-14, brass engine, thin-rimmed wheels, 1910-11; with red spokes, red solid pilot wheels, large nickel bell 1908-14; nickel tender with single red bead line, tender with two open, three-rivet trucks with red solid wheels. **2000 3500 2000**

(B) 1912-23, brass boiler, nickel cab, thick-rimmed, red-painted spokes and pilot wheels, small nickel bell. Brass tender with unpainted wheels, no red bead line. **1800 2800 1800**

(C) Same as (B), but engine (excluding light, bell, stack, and dome) completely brass. Cab window outlined in red. Tender has double red bead trim, two open and spring-embossed trucks with solid red-painted wheels. Nickel sides on tender.
1800 2800 1800

Six different Lionel 8 Locomotives illustrating three major steps in its development. TOP SHELF: early maroon 8 with early motor, short wheelbase, nickel flagholders, nickel top trim including strap headlights; also early red 8 with early motor and similar trim to the maroon 8 with combination couplers. CENTER SHELF: mojave 8 with late motor with longer wheelbase, brass flagholders, cast headlights, and combination couplers; olive green 8. BOTTOM SHELF: pea green 8 with late motor, brass flagholders, cast headlights, and brass whistle and pantograph. It also has yellow-painted ventilators and windows which distinguishes it from the earlier 8s. This locomotive was part of a special Macy's set with 337, 337, and 338 Passenger Cars. The red 8 has similar trim to the pea green 8. R. Sullens and T. Riley Collections. M. Feinstein photograph.

Gd Exc Rst

(D) Brass boiler, nickel cab, thick-rimmed, red-painted spokes, pilot wheels, and pilot. Brass tender with nickel-painted outside and red interior, red wheels, red trim line along bottom edge, straight shank hook couplers. **1800 2800 1800**

NOTE: A number of reproduction 7s have been made. Extreme caution is required in purchasing what is purported to be an original 7. It is highly recommended that a 7 known to be an original be compared with any prospective purchase. Many reproductions are not marked in any way. One reproduction that is carefully marked was manufactured by McCoy Manufacturing Co. It is the 7 (R) McCoy Manufacturing Co., a 1962 reproduction. Various components are stamped "M" or "McCoy". It is almost an exact duplicate of a late 7 with red-spoked drivers, pilot and pilot wheels, and tender wheels. A serial number is stamped inside the boiler. It came with an original Lionel No. 33 motor. Reproductions sell for $300 to $400.

8 ELECTRIC: Catalogued 1925-32, 0-4-0, New York Central prototype, smallest of late series Standard Gauge electrics,

Lionel 8 with strap headlight and combination latch couplers. The ventilator inserts are unpainted brass and are part of the same sheet which forms the windows and number plates. R. Bartelt photograph.

11", combination latch or latch couplers, hand-reversing. Two headlights, either cast or steel strap, small pantograph and whistle.

(A) 1925-26, maroon with brass windows, ventilators, and plates, strap headlights, large gear Super motor, combination

TOP SHELF: Lionel 8E and Lionel 8E. BOTTOM SHELF: Lionel 10 and Lionel 10E. The 10E is part of a set built for Macy's Department Store in New York.

Gd Exc Rst

latch couplers, larger pantograph than later 8s, narrow axle spacing. **NOTE:** The narrow axle spacing on the early 8 places the axles directly behind the spring and journal trim. The later, more common variety has the axles outside the trim location. Therefore, the frame was not changed when the small gear Super motor was introduced. Came with 35 and 36 Passenger Cars or 100-series freight cars. Price for locomotive only. D. Ely Collection. **80 160 80**

(B) Dark olive green with brass windows, ventilators, and plates, strap headlights. **80 145 75**

(C) Olive green with brass windows, ventilators, and plates, cast headlights, latch couplers. **60 125 75**

(D) Mojave with brass windows, ventilators, and plates, cast headlights, latch couplers. **80 145 75**

(E) Red with cream windows and ventilators, brass name and number plates with black lettering, cream stripe, cast headlights, latch couplers, brass whistle and pantograph. **75 150 75**

The Lionel 8 has cast headlights, regular latch couplers, and hand reverse at pantograph end. The ventilator insert is painted brass and part of the same brass sheet which forms the windows and number plates. R. Bartelt photograph.

(F) Red with brass windows, ventilators, and plates. **75 150 75**

(G) Peacock with orange windows and ventilators, and brass plates. **200 450 75**

(H) Peacock, marked "Macy Special". **NRS**

(I) Maroon with cream windows and ventilators, cream stripe, regular latch couplers, cast headlights, wide axle small gear Super motor. Possibly part of a Macy Special passenger set including maroon 32, 35, and 36 cars with early 500-series trucks. D. Ely Collection. **NRS**

8E ELECTRIC: Catalogued 0-4-0, similar to 8, but with pendulum reversing unit. Some late variations came with drum-type reversing unit.

(A) Mojave with brass windows, ventilators, and plates, red lettering, die-cast headlights, brass pantograph, nickel whistle, latch couplers. **80 160 75**

(B) Red with brass windows, ventilators, and plates. **70 140 70**

(C) Red with cream windows, stripes, and ventilators, and brass plates, drum-type reversing unit. D. Ely Collection. **70 140 70**

(D) Peacock with orange windows and ventilators, and brass plates, orange stripe. **200 400 95**

(E) Pea green, cream stripe, red lettering. Specially painted for Macy's Department Store, but not so marked. **250 450 95**

(F) Olive green with brass windows, ventilators, and plates with block lettering. Reader verification requested. **NRS**

(G) Same as (F), but red serif lettering. D. Ely Collection. **70 140 70**

(H) Same as (C), but without cream stripe. C. Weber Collection. **70 140 70**

(I) Chrome-plated body, chrome windows and plates, cast headlights, combination couplers, later Super motor, nickel spring and tank trim, chrome handrails, black frame, nickel flag stanchions, pendulum reverse, red lettering. One other example observed. Reportedly made as a salesman's sample.

TOP SHELF: orange 9U with high roof and early motor. The motor screwed into the frame. The later 9Us came with a motor mount and mounting clip. Uncatalogued dark green 9 with high roof, hand reverse, motor screws into frame. BOTTOM SHELF: gun-metal 9E with low roof, motor with motor mounting bars fastened by clips, extra leading, and trailing trucks. This locomotive usually came with two-tone green cars. Two-tone green 9E with low roof, later version of Bild-A-Loco motor, and leading and trailing trucks.

Gd Exc Rst

Some collectors do not regard this as a true Lionel product. Ten years ago, Choo-Choo Charlies, a train store owner on Route 202 north of Wilmington, had many junk Lionel engines: 8s, 10s, 253s, 402s, 254s, etc. chrome-plated and for sale in his store. C. Weber comment. However, we would like further comments from readers. **NRS**

9 ELECTRIC: Catalogued 1929, 0-4-0, NYC prototype. Motor held to frame by four machine screws rather than latches used in other 9s, dark green, hand-reversing knob, 14-1/2". Excellent reproductions have been made by Williams Reproductions and Mike's Train House. See next entry for details. **1200 2000 650**

9 ELECTRIC: 2-4-2, two-tone green, low roof tabbed in, brass trim, red wheels, "WRL" stamped into frame, "LIONEL" plates. Manufactured by Williams Reproductions and Mike's Train House. The following are reproductions.

(A) Two-tone green, brass trim, red wheels. **175 200 —**

(B) Gun-metal, nickel trim, black wheels. **175 200 —**

(C) 0-4-0, orange, high roof tabbed in, brass trim, red wheels, "WRL" stamped into frame, "LIONEL" plates. **175 200 —**

(D) 0-4-0, same as (C), but dark green. **175 200 —**

9E ELECTRIC: 1928-30, 0-4-0, NYC, 14-1/2". Excellent reproductions have been made by Williams Reproductions and Mike's Train House. Reproductions are valued at about $200.

(A) Motor fastened with two quick release levers, wiring does not require disconnection with motor removal, orange. **600 1200 600**

(B) Same as (A), but motor fastened with four machine screws, wires require disconnection with motor removal. Gray paint on headlight. Ely observation. **600 1200 600**

(C) 2-4-2, two-tone green, low clerestory roof, pony trucks, motor fastened with two quick release levers, wiring does not require disconnection for motor removal. Catalogued 1931-33 with Stephen Girard passenger car set: 424, 425, 426; (price for locomotive only). **750 1500 600**

(D) Same as (C), reversing lever under roof, but gun-metal, plate reads "No. 9E BILD-A-LOCO. LIONEL LINES". Catalogued 1934-35 with 309, 310, 312 in rare two-tone green; (price for locomotive only). **700 1250 600**

(E) 2-4-2 with E-unit slot, gun-metal, higher roof and pilot trucks, motor fastened with four machine screws, lettered "LIONEL LINES, 9E". Catalogued 1934-35 with 309, 310, 312 in rare two-tone green; (price for locomotive only). **700 1250 600**

9U ELECTRIC: Catalogued 1928-29, 0-4-0, NYC, higher roof, usually with motor fastened by quick release lever, orange. Came as kit with adapters for converting to three-speed reversible motor, reverse switch on side of locomotive, eight sections of curved track, locomotive is lettered "9U".

(A) 9U with motor adapter and original box. **1200 2000 1200**

(B) 9U without motor adapter and box. **700 1350 700**

(C) Same as 9U(A), but assembled, without motor adapter and weighted frame, lettered "9U". **700 1500 700**

10 ELECTRIC: Catalogued 1925-29, 0-4-0, Chicago, Milwaukee, St. Paul & Pacific Olympian prototype, (as with 380 and 381), hand-reversing lever. Early versions with large gear Super motor, combination latch couplers, strap headlights. Later, small gear Super motor, latch couplers, cast headlights. Combinations of these characteristics possible. One pantograph and one whistle, 11-1/2". Bowers comment.

(A) Mojave with brass inserts, black lettering, strap headlights, combination latch couplers, nickel pantograph and whistle. D. Ely comment. **75 160 95**

(B) Gray, brass inserts, black lettering, silver-painted cast headlights, combination latch couplers, nickel pantograph and whistle. P. Graves Collection. **75 160 95**

Four different Lionel 10s including three different peacock 10s with significant differences. TOP SHELF: mojave 10E with black frame, red lettering, combination couplers. Peacock 10 with black frame, black lettering, cast headlights, combination couplers, hand reverse, black frame, brass flag holders, nickel pantograph and whistle. BOTTOM SHELF: peacock with green frame, orange stripe, Bild-A-Loco motor, cast headlights, and regular couplers. This peacock 10E was a department store special and not offered in the Lionel catalogue. Peacock 10 with black frame, Ives plates, regular couplers, brass pantograph and whistle, regular motor, and brass flagholders. Lionel had acquired Ives with American Flyer in 1928, and in late 1929 purchased American Flyer's interest. Ives became a subsidiary of Lionel. In 1931 and 1932, Lionel utilized some of its regular equipment for its Ives line. R. Sullen and T. Riley Collections.

M. Feinstein photograph.

	Gd	Exc	Rst
(C) Peacock with brass inserts, red lettering, cast headlights, latch coupler.	75	160	95
(D) Peacock, brass inserts, black lettering, cast headlights, latch coupler, brass pantograph and whistle.	75	160	95
(E) Red with cream stripe along base of cab, cast headlights, brass pantograph, whistle, and flag stanchions, and black frame. Not catalogued by Lionel, but sold by Macy's Department Stores as part of a passenger set, including 337 and 338.	350	700	95
(F) Same as (B), but red lettering and dark green frame. D. Ely Collection.		NRS	
(G) Same as (C), but dark green frame and orange stripe. F. Reichenbach comment.		NRS	

10E ELECTRIC: Catalogued 1926-30, 0-4-0, similar to 10 above, but with E-unit reversing, usually with pendulum-type mechanism, with "10E" on plates. 10Es with drum reverse are the latest production. The 10E was not catalogued with the Bild-A-Loco motor.

	Gd	Exc	Rst
(A) Olive green, black frame, strap headlights, light red serif lettering on brass plates, large nickel pantograph, nickel whistle and flag holders, latch couplers. Came with 332, 337, and 338 cars in olive with red trim. D. Ely Collection.		NRS	
(B) Peacock, black frame, brass inserts, red lettering, cast headlights, latch coupler.	75	165	95
(C) Peacock, dark green frame, Bild-A-Loco motor (not Super motor), cast headlights and red lettering, orange stripe. D. Ely observation.	200	375	200
(D) State brown with dark green frame, Bild-A-Loco motor, cream stripe, red lettering, brass pantograph and whistle.	250	500	200
(E) Gray, black frame, latch couplers.	75	165	95
(F) Red with cream stripe, cast headlights, brass pantograph and whistle, black lettering. Not catalogued by Lionel, but sold by Macy's Department Stores.	350	700	95
(G) Same as (C), but no orange stripe. D. Ely Collection.	125	300	125

33 EARLY: Catalogued 1913, electric, 0-6-0, NYC S-type, was "1910" with U-frame, nickel bell, gold-painted side and door vents, red window outlines, six-spoke wheels and cowcatcher, pedestal headlight, gold rubber-stamped letters/numbers, 10-3/8".

	Gd	Exc	Rst
(A) "NEW YORK CENTRAL LINES" in oval, dark olive green, long crinkle hook couplers, turned stanchions for handrails. D. Ely Collection.	250	600	250
(B) Same as (A), but in black.	300	750	250
(C) "PENN R.R." in gold block letters. D. Ely Collection.	400	975	275
(D) Similar to (A), but block lettering, no oval. D. Ely Collection.	300	750	250

33 LATER: Catalogued 1913-24, electric, 0-4-0, NYC, round cab, with U-frame with end doors, vents, and turned stanchions,

Small, early electrics: 1911 and 33s. TOP SHELF: dark olive green 1911, maroon vents, end grills, short crinkle hook couplers, pedestal headlight with ridge, large brass bell. Dark olive green six-wheel 33 with pedestal headlight without top piece, end grills with larger holes than later grills, straight hook coupler at one end, and long crinkle hook coupler at other, only one powered axle, turned stanchions soldered to body. CENTER SHELF: black 33 with U-shaped frame, "THE LIONEL MFG CO." on end plates, pedestal headlight without top piece, turned stanchions, large crinkle hook couplers, no hand reverse, lighting post, and nickel small bell, both axles powered. Note that the U-shaped frame has a different side appearance than the six-rectangle frame on the next engine. Black 33 with "THE LIONEL MFG CO" on end plates, later frame with six punched-out rectangles on each side, strap headlight, small nickel bell, lighting post, "Y"-shaped stanchions, regular hook couplers, both axles powered. BOTTOM SHELF: maroon 33 with "THE LIONEL CORPORATION" on black end plates, last type frame with four punched-out rectangles on each side, strap headlight, small nickel bell, "Y"-shaped stanchions, regular hook couplers, both axles powered, no lighting post, but hole present on top of hood, hand-reverse side plate lettered "THE LIONEL CORPORATION". Dark olive green 33, lettered "THE LIONEL CORPORATION" on black end plates, last type frame with four rectangles on each side, strap headlights, small nickel bell, "Y"-shaped stanchions, combination couplers, both axles powered, no lighting post but hole present on top of hood, hand reverse lettered "THE LIONEL CORPORATION". R. Sullens and T. Riley Collections. M. Feinstein photograph.

(1916-23) or straight frame with end doors with plates and "Y"-shaped stanchions. All observed samples with plates read " . . . LIONEL CORPORATION . . .". All lettered "NEW YORK CENTRAL LINES" in oval except as noted. (1916-24), nickel bell, gold vents, red window outline, eight-spoke wheels, and cowcatcher, cast-iron wheels (1913-16) or die-cast wheels (1916-24), in 1916 added hand reversing and in 1924 a Super motor, combination latch couplers (1923-24). Came in sets with 100-series freight cars, and 35-series and 36-series passenger cars, 10-3/8". D. Ely and P. Graves comments.

	Gd	**Exc**	**Rst**
(A) Midnight blue body, made especially for Montgomery Ward in 1912 as part of set with 35 and 36 Passenger Cars, extremely rare. D. Ely observation.			**NRS**
(B) Dark olive green, in oval, pedestal headlight, early U-frame. D. Ely and M. Miles Collections.	**60**	**125**	**65**
(C) Black, "C & O".	**350**	**700**	**175**
(D) Black, in oval.	**60**	**125**	**65**
(E) Maroon.	**250**	**500**	**100**
(F) Red.	**300**	**600**	**125**
(G) Red with cream stripe.	**300**	**600**	**125**
(H) Peacock.	**300**	**600**	**100**

Lionel 38s, 50s, and 53s. TOP SHELF: black 38 with end plates "LIONEL CORPORATION", hook couplers, motor with only one powered axle, nickel bell, unpainted drivers, reverse unit lettered "LIONEL MFG...". Dark green 50 with early Super motor and two powered axles, nickel whistle and bell, combination couplers. CENTER SHELF: gray 50 with "LIONEL CORPORATION . . ." end plates, "LIONEL CORPORATION . . ." reversing unit, side plate, nickel bell and whistle, latch couplers, strap headlights, early Super motor with short wheelbase and two powered axles. Very early maroon 53 with two large nickel bells, pedestal headlight with raised area, lighting post, block-style, sans-serif lettering, hook couplers, one dummy motor, one powered motor, crinkle hook couplers. BOTTOM SHELF: later maroon-brown 53 with two small nickel bells, pedestal headlight without raised area, dark olive green trimmed ventilators, maroon-painted regular hook couplers, lighting post on hood top, end grills and side grills, no end plates, gold end stamping "LIONEL / LINES / N.Y. / MADE IN USA" on one end only. "THE LIONEL MFG CO." on reverse side plate. Latest 53 (which is similar to a 38) with maroon body, strap headlight, bell and lighting post, side rods, gold-painted three hole steps. R. Sullens and T. Riley Collections. M. Feinstein photograph.

	Gd	Exc	Rst
(I) Dark green, early large gear Super motor. D. Ely Collection.	100	200	65
(J) 1924, dark olive green, with early large gear Super motor, hand reverse. D. Ely Collection.	100	225	75
(K) Gray with early large gear Super motor.	75	150	65

34 ELECTRIC: Catalogued 1912, 0-6-0, NYC prototype, same as 33 0-6-0 in dark olive green with dark red-outlined windows. Rubber-stamped "NEW YORK CENTRAL LINES" in gold block letters or in script. Only the center axle is geared. Sliding shoe pickup, non-movable door, long crinkle hook couplers, fillister head screws hold pilot to frame. Large gold-painted stanchions support handrails atop hood. One nickeled bell, 10-3/8" long.

(A) Slide-on headlight, no lighting terminal. D. Ely Collection. **450 900 400**

(B) Same as (A), but with pedestal headlight. Probably included lighting terminal for lighting passenger cars. Came as part of set with 35 and 36 Passenger Cars, very rare. Baeuerle Collection. **450 900 400**

34 ELECTRIC: Catalogued 1913, 0-4-0, similar to 34 above, with U-frame, die-cast wheels, dark olive green, 10-3/8".
175 400 175

38 ELECTRIC: Catalogued 1913-24, 0-4-0, NYC prototype, slightly larger than 33, four thick-rimmed drivers and side rods, rubber-stamped "NEW YORK CENTRAL LINES" in oval or block letters, 11-1/8". Early 38s (Lionel Mfg. production) have turned handrail stanchions, vent holes in end doors, pedestal headlight, lighting terminal, long crinkle hook couplers. Middle Mfg. production has crimped handrail stanchions and door vents. Latest Mfg. production and Corporation production

TOP SHELF: 1912 Special Locomotive in brass with two large bells, pedestal headlight with top piece, passenger car lighting post, large crinkle hook couplers, sliding side door, plate for AC/DC switch on one side of the frame, but without mechanism and lettering "MADE BY / THE LIONEL MFG. CO. / NEW YORK". Second plate for hand reverse on other side with same lettering. CENTER SHELF: 1912 in dark olive with script lettering to the left of side door, short crinkle hook couplers, two large nickel bells, strap headlight, lighting post. 42 in gray with red trim, oval "NEW YORK CENTRAL LINES" logo, strap headlight, two small nickel bells, "THE LIONEL CORPORATION" end plate, AC/DC switch on one side, hand reverse on other, lighting post, switch, regular hook couplers, dual motors. BOTTOM SHELF: black 42 with strap headlight, two small nickel bells, lighting post, end grills, single motor, regular hook couplers, gold end stamping at one end: "LIONEL / LINES / N.Y. / MADE IN U.S.A." Hand reverse switch lettered "MADE BY / THE LIONEL MFG. CO / NEW YORK", second plate on other side with same lettering but no mechanism, Y-shaped stanchions, sliding doors. 42 in mojave with red trim, oval "NEW YORK CENTRAL LINES" logo, strap headlight, two small nickel bells, "THE LIONEL CORPORATION" end plate, plate for AC/DC switch on one side with no mechanism and lettering "MADE BY / THE LIONEL MFG. CO, / NEW YORK", second plate for hand reverse on other side with same lettering, lighting post, regular hook couplers, dual motors, doors do not slide. M. Feinstein photograph.

Gd Exc Rst

has crimped handrail stanchions and plates in doors. D. Ely comment.

(A) Black, early, pedestal headlight. D. Ely Collection. **70 125 65**

(B) Same as (A), but dark olive and "PENN R.R." lettering as in Early 33(C), red window trim and body edge trim, block gold lettering, pedestal headlight, small crinkle hook couplers, ventilator holes in inserts. P. Haidvogel Collection, C. Weber comment. **NRS**

(C) Red. **350 750 80**

(D) Mojave. **300 600 80**

(E) Dark green. **200 400 80**

(F) Brown, strap headlight. D. Ely Collection. **200 350 80**

(G) Pea green, strap headlight. D. Ely Collection. **300 600 80**

(H) Peacock. **300 600 80**

(I) Red with cream trim. **300 600 80**

(J) Olive green, strap headlight. D. Ely Collection. **100 200 80**

(K) Light olive green. **NRS**

(L) Maroon, strap headlight, Corp. production. D. Ely Collection. **125 300 80**

(M) Gray, strap headlight, Corp. production. D. Ely Collection. **80 140 80**

(N) Gray, celluloid insert headlight with switch, Corp. Production. D. Ely Collection. **NRS**

Gd Exc Rst

42 ELECTRIC: Catalogued 1912, 0-4-4-0, NYC prototype, square hood (same as 1912 Locomotive), dark green only, rare rubber-stamped "NEW YORK CENTRAL LINES" in oval or in block letters, 15-1/2". **900 1500 750**

42 ELECTRIC: Catalogued 1913-23, 0-4-4-0, the epitome of early Lionel electrics, a NYC prototype, round hood with NYC in the oval or in block letters. Early versions had a single motor (1913-21) and dummy second motor, three-tread steps (1913-18), sliding doors, and a coupler pocket soldered to the locomotive's outside end. Later versions have one-piece step and no sliding door; the coupler pocket was soldered to the inside of the body. In 1921, the 42 gained another motor and two switches, one for AC and DC operation, and one for hand reverse, 15-1/2" — 16".

	Gd	Exc	Rst
(A) Black.	200	450	275
(B) Maroon.	1000	2000	275
(C) Dark gray.	300	600	275
(D) Dark green.	400	800	275
(E) Mojave.	450	900	275
(F) Peacock.	900	1800	275
(G) Gray.	200	450	275
(H) Olive green.	600	1200	275
(I) Dark olive green.	600	1200	275

50 ELECTRIC: Catalogued 1924, 0-4-0, NYC S-prototype, round hood body, same as 38, red window trim and pilots, red trim along body base, four brass ventilator screens, two steel strap headlights, gold-painted handrails, nickel bell and whistle, gold rubber-stamped "NEW YORK CENTRAL LINES" in oval, hand reversing, three-hole steps.

(A) Dark green, Lionel Standard motor with only one geared wheel, same as 38, hook, couplers, side rods. **80 150 90**
(B) Same as (A), but dark gray. **80 150 90**
(C) Same as (A), but maroon. **200 400 90**
(D) Dark green, red trim along body base, Lionel early Super motor with large gears, no side rods, combination latch-hook couplers. **80 150 90**
(E) Same as (D), but mojave. **100 200 90**
(F) Same as (D), but dark gray. **80 150 90**

51 STEAM: Catalogued 1912-23, 5 Late, with eight-wheel double-truck tender, first catalogued in 1912, but previously called 5 Special, with single-rivet open truck and strap headlight.

(A) "N.Y.C. & H.R.R." tender. D. Ely comment. **750 1000 500**
(B) "PENNSYLVANIA" tender, base gold rubber-stamped "MADE IN U.S.A./THE LIONEL CORPORATION/NEW YORK". D. Ely Collection. **750 1000 500**

53 EARLY: Catalogued 1912-14, electric, 0-4-4-0, NYC prototype, maroon, square hood with eight "flap"-type ventilators and four gold-painted ventilator grills, one pedestal headlight, two large bells, auxiliary lighting post, long red-painted pilots, long crinkle hook couplers, side rods, three-tread brass steps, roof with later monitor section, 12".

(A) Gold rubber-stamped "NEW YORK CENTRAL LINES" in oval in either block or script lettering. **800 1700 750**
(B) Same as (A), but block lettering without oval. D. Ely Collection. **800 1700 750**

53 LATER: Electric, 0-4-0, NYC prototype, square hood, rubber-stamped "NEW YORK CENTRAL LINES" in oval in gold letters, 12-1/4". See 53 EARLY and 53 LATEST for other variations.

(A) Maroon with pedestal headlight, two small bells; short, crinkle hook couplers, reversing switch, long low pilot, split frame, fixed cab doors. **450 800 450**
(B) Mojave. **600 1200 450**
(C) Dark olive green. **500 1000 450**
(D) Same as (A), but strap headlight. D. Ely Collection. **NRS**
(E) Same as (D), but brown. D. Ely Collection. **NRS**

53 LATEST: Catalogued 1920-21, electric, 0-4-0, NYC prototype, similar to a 38, maroon, with gold rubber-stamped "NEW YORK CENTRAL LINES" in oval, gold-painted ventilators and handrails, strap headlight, bell and lighting post for cars, red pilot, side rods, gold-painted three-hole steps, 11-1/8". See 53 EARLY and 53 LATER for other variations. **150 400 200**

54 EARLY: Catalogued 1912, electric, 0-4-4-0, the top-of-the-line showpiece in brass, NYC prototype, square hood with eight "flap"-type ventilators and four red-painted ventilator grills located near ends on sides, no lettering on body sides although shown in catalogue, red-painted pilots and wheels. Single motor and dummy motor, sliding doors, thin-rimmed drivers, side rods. Two large nickeled bells, one pedestal or slide-on headlight and auxiliary lighting post. Reversing switch, 15-1/2". **2500 3500 2500**

NOTE: Reproduction 54s have been made from brass and extreme caution is required in purchasing an original piece. Square cab Early 42s have been brass-plated and may be misrepresented as 54s. A magnet test will distinguish brass from brass-plated steel locomotives. Expert advice is needed in purchasing an original. Also note that a Late 1912 is, in some cases, indistinguishable from an Early 54. Usually the 1912s can be distinguished by their thin rims, but it is believed that some 1912s came with thick rims.

54 LATE: Catalogued 1913-23, electric, 0-4-4-0, the top-of-the-line showpiece in brass, NYC prototype, round hoods without any lettering, red-painted pilots, ventilators and wheel spokes; similar to 42, but made from brass rather than steel.

(A) Single motor and dummy motor, sliding doors, pedestal headlight, two bells, auxiliary lighting post, long straight hook couplers, thick-rimmed wheels. **1650 2600 1650**
(B) Two motors, fixed doors, strap headlights, two small nickeled bells, auxiliary lighting post, regular hook couplers, thick-rimmed wheels, two switches: one for direction, one for changing from AC to DC operation. **1500 2400 1500**

NOTE: 42s have been brass-plated to appear as 54s. However, a magnet test will readily distinguish between the two since a 42 with a brass-plated steel cab will attract the magnet, while a true 54 will not. Reproduction 54s in brass have also been made. Extreme care is required in purchasing an original.

60 ELECTRIC: 0-4-0, NYC S-type, uncatalogued F.A.O. Schwarz Special, same as 33, but rubber-stamped "FAOS 60", black. **— 2000 —**

61 ELECTRIC: 0-4-4-0, NYC-type, uncatalogued F.A.O. Schwarz Special, same as 42, but rubber-stamped "FAOS 61", black. **— 2400 —**

62 ELECTRIC: 0-4-0, NYC-type, uncatalogued F.A.O. Schwarz Special, same as 38, rubber-stamped "FAOS 62", black. **— 2000 —**

318 ELECTRIC: Catalogued 1924-32, 0-4-0, New York Central S-type prototype. Originally a low-to-medium priced locomotive in the Lionel line. Brass name and number plates and inserts for windows, ventilators. One pantograph, one whistle.

Early Standard Sets

6 Locomotive and Tender

1911 SPECIAL

53 EARLY

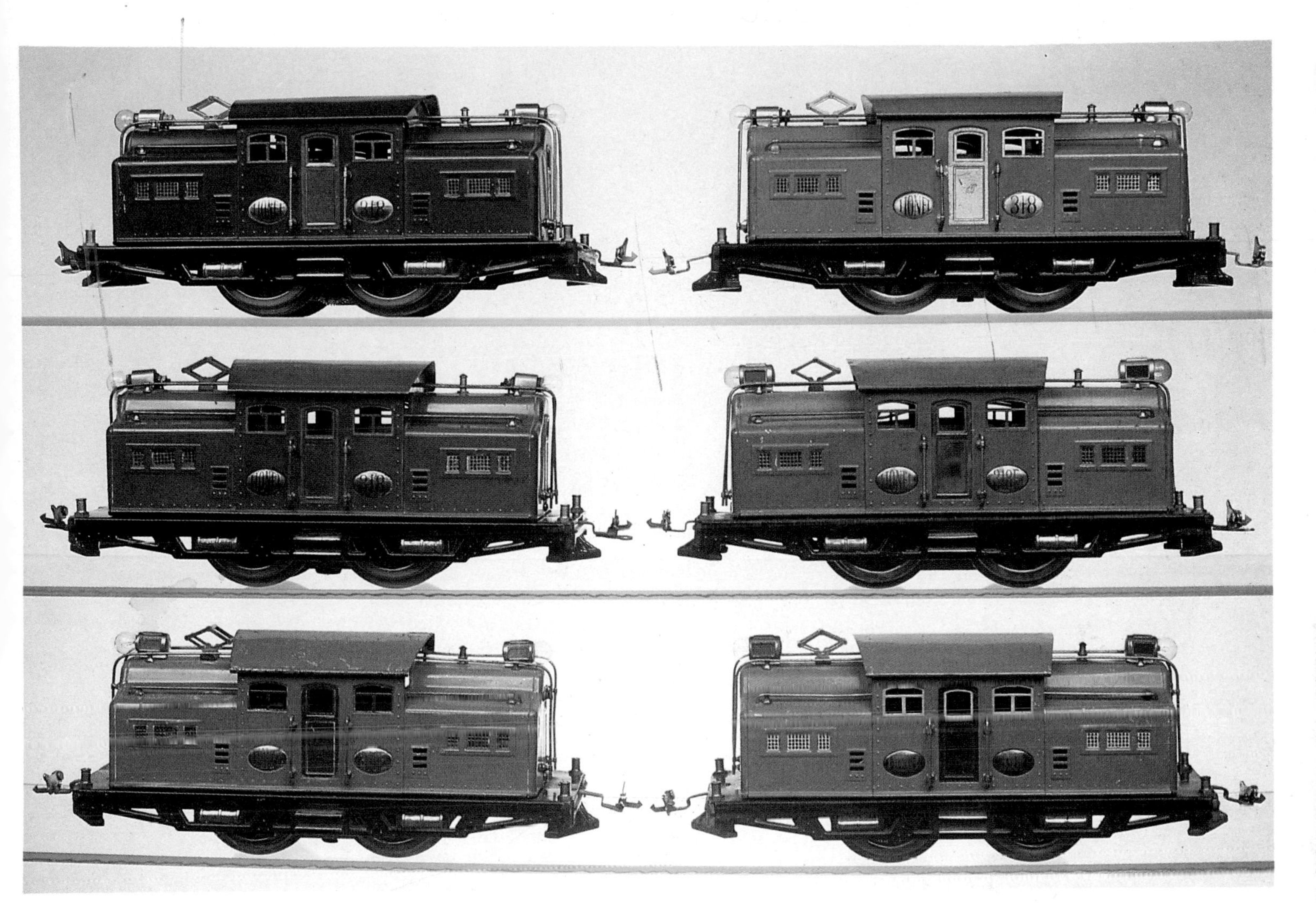

Six different 318s showing the development of the model. TOP SHELF: gray 318 with early motor with short wheelbase, all-nickel trim with strap headlights, combination couplers. Green 318 with late motor, strap headlights, and brass flag holders. CENTER SHELF: gray 318 with late motor, strap headlights, nickel flag holders, combination couplers. Mojave 318E with cast headlights, nickel flag holders, and red lettering. BOTTOM SHELF: pea green 318E, red lettering, brass flag holders and pantograph, and whistle. Tan 318 from "Baby State Set" with yellow-painted inserts and tan-painted pilots, Bild-a-Loco motor. The Bild-a-Loco motor features screwdriver assembly. R. Sullens and T. Riley Collections, M. Feinstein photograph.

Gd Exc Rst

Early versions with strap headlights, combination latch couplers, large gear Super motor. Later versions with cast headlights, latch couplers, small gear Super motor. Catalogued with 332, 337, 338, 339, 341, 309, 310, 312, as well as 100- and 500-series freight cars.

(A) Dark gray, black lettering, strap headlights, combination latch couplers, nickel pantograph and whistle. **110 225 110**

(B) Gray, black lettering, red pilots, brass handrails and trim. **100 225 110**

(C) Mojave, brass trim, red lettering, red pilots. **100 225 110**

(D) Pea green, cast headlights, red lettering, brass trim including ventilators, red pilots. **150 250 110**

(E) State brown with cream stripe, black lettering, cream ventilators, windows and door window frame, cast headlight, red or State brown pilot. **250 400 110**

(F) State brown without cream stripe, otherwise same as (E). **250 400 110**

318E ELECTRIC: Catalogued 1926-35, 0-4-0, similar to 318, but with either early pendulum-type or late drum-type reversing unit.

(A) Gray, black lettering, red pilots, brass handrails and trim. **110 225 110**

(B) Mojave, brass trim, red lettering, red pilots. **110 225 110**

(C) Pea green, cast headlights, red lettering, brass trim including ventilators. **110 225 110**

(D) State brown with cream stripe, black lettering, cream ventilators, windows, and door window frame, cast headlight, red or State brown pilots. **200 400 110**

(E) State brown without cream stripe, otherwise same as (D). **200 400 110**

(F) Black, red lettering, red pilots. **400 900 110**

380 ELECTRIC: Catalogued 1923-27, 0-4-0, Chicago, Milwaukee, St. Paul & Pacific, Olympian prototype. (Shares prototype with 10 and 381.) Introduced with 402 as first of new generation of electrics. Brass insert plates provide window, door, and letter boards. Early models with hook couplers, later

Four different 380s showing the development of the model. TOP SHELF: mojave 380 with early motor, short wheelbase, hook couplers, celluloid insert headlights, large nickel whistle, nickel bell, nickel flagholders. Maroon 380 with similar features, except later motor with longer wheelbase and combination couplers. BOTTOM SHELF: dark green 380E with combination couplers, red plate lettering, medium-sized nickel whistle, large nickel pantograph, brass flag holders. Dark green 380E with combination couplers, red lettering, medium brass whistles, brass pantograph, heavy weight fastened to frame, brass flag holders, cast headlights. R. Sullens and T. Riley Collections. M. Feinstein photograph.

Gd Exc Rst

combination latch, and finally latch couplers. Strap headlights first followed by large celluloid insert headlights, and cast headlights. Early ones with large gear Super motor, later small gear Super motor, with high coupler for 200-series cars, 13-1/2". Over the years, the 380 was catalogued with three different series of passenger cars: the 18, 19, and 190 set, the 319, 320, and 322 set, and the 428, 429, and 430 set. It also came with both the 10-series freights and later with 200-series freight cars. Bowes comment.

(A) Mojave, black lettering, extra large nickel bell and extra large nickel whistle, large celluloid insert headlights, hook couplers, large gear Super motor, red pilots. Early version with brass ends painted mojave. D. Ely Collection. **350 600 300**

(B) Mojave with black lettering, extra large nickel bell and extra large whistle, large celluloid insert headlights, hook couplers or combination latch couplers, large gear Super motor, red pilots. **300 550 175**

(C) Maroon with black lettering, large nickel bell, extra large nickel whistle, large celluloid insert headlights, combination latch couplers, red pilots, large gear Super motor. P. Graves comments. **200 350 150**

(D) Maroon, black lettering, nickel pantograph, extra large nickel whistle, cast headlights, regular latch couplers, small gear Super motor, red pilots. Sattler Collection. **200 350 150**

(E) Dark green with cast headlights, red lettering, large nickel whistle, brass pantograph, combination latch coupler, red pilots. Usually found with two weights added to frame for traction. C. Weber comment. **250 400 175**

(F) Terra-cotta. More information requested. **NRS**

380E ELECTRIC: Catalogued 1926-29, similar to 380, but with pendulum-type reversing unit. Some with two weights added to frame for traction, "E" stamped on door, or "380E" on number plate. Note that version with weights brings $25 more in excellent condition.

(A) Maroon, black lettering, large celluloid insert headlights, combination latch couplers, red pilots. **300 550 175**

(B) Maroon, red lettering, cast headlights, latch couplers, red pilots. **200 350 150**

(C) Mojave, black lettering, cast headlights, red pilots. **300 550 175**

(D) Dark green, black lettering, cast headlights, latch couplers, red pilots. **250 400 175**

381 ELECTRIC: Catalogued 1928-29, 4-4-4, Olympian prototype, largest and most elaborate locomotive ever constructed by Lionel. Bild-A-Loco motor. State green body, apple green sub-frame, and black frame, hand reversing with special brass plate numbered "381". Excellent reproductions have been made by Williams Reproductions and Mike's Train House. **1500 3500 1500**

381E ELECTRIC: Catalogued 1928-36, 4-4-4. Same as 381, but with reversing unit. Plate numbered "381E".

(A) State green body, apple green sub-frame. **1200 2250 900**

(B) State green body, red sub-frame. **1500 2800 900**

NOTE: ELECTRIC, 4-4-4, Chicago, Milwaukee & St. Paul Olympian prototype. Reproduction by Williams Reproductions and Mike's Train House. Comes with dummy motor, but many have been powered by their owners with original Lionel motors.

(A) Same as Lionel's, but without quick release strip from motor to lights, "WRL" stamped into frame, "LIONEL" plates. **— 300 —**

(B) Same as above, but with "Chicago, Milwaukee, St. Paul & Pacific" plates rather than "LIONEL". **— 275 —**

381U ELECTRIC: 1928-29, 4-4-4. Kit version of hand-reversing 381. Kit included parts for stationary motor and

TOP SHELF: 402E in mojave with red lettering and combination couplers, cast headlights, two small whistles, one small bell, and one small pantograph. BOTTOM SHELF: 381E with Bild-A-Loco plates. R. Sullens Collection.

	Gd	Exc	Rst

eight sections of track. "Excellent" price requires assembly tools and original box.

	Gd	Exc	Rst
(A) Plate numbered "381U".	1850	4000	1800
(B) Plate numbered "381".	1600	3800	1600

384 STEAM: Catalogued 1930-32, 2-4-0, with eight-wheel 384T Tender, Super motor, one-piece die-cast frame and pilot, black body with brass domes, handrails, bell, and stack, and copper piping. Brass plate on cab with black lettering: "No. 384 LIONEL LINES". Hand reversing, tender with copper or nickel journals.

	Gd	Exc	Rst
(A) Green stripe on frame edge, brass windows in cab.	300	400	300
(B) Green stripe on frame edge, green windows in cab.	300	400	300
(C) No stripe on frame edge, brass windows in cab.	300	400	300
(D) Green stripe on frame edge, 390T Tender with orange stripe.		NRS	
(E) Black crackle tender, uncatalogued.		NRS	

384E STEAM: Catalogued 1930-32, 2-4-0, similar to 384, but with E-unit reversing, red-lettered brass plate on cab reads "No. 384E LIONEL LINES".

	Gd	Exc	Rst
(A) Green stripe on frame edge, brass windows.	300	410	300
(B) Green stripe on frame edge, green windows.	300	410	300
(C) No stripe on frame edge, brass windows in cab.	300	410	300

385E STEAM: Catalogued 1933-39, 2-4-2, with 384T, 385TW, or 385W Tenders, Bild-A-Loco motor, die-cast frame, separate steel boiler and pilot, hinged boiler front for lamp access, Pennsylvania-style keystone plate on cab reads "LL", E-unit, 23-1/2", number board on boiler front reads "385E". Came with and without chugger, with and without whistle. For use with 500-series freights and passenger cars with lower coupler heights. Leip comment. Mike's Train House has made a reproduction of the 385E Locomotive with Tender. The current price of the reproduction is $495.

Classic Era Standard Steam

384 E

390 E

385 E

1835 E

392 E

Gd Exc Rst

The following is from the catalogue listings of locomotives and tenders:

1933: 385E with 384T Tender, chugger in locomotive
1934: 385E with 384T Tender, chugger in locomotive
1935: 385E with 385TW Tender, chugger in locomotive, whistle in tender
1936: 385E with 385W Tender, chugger in locomotive, whistle in tender
1937: 385E with 385W Tender, whistle in tender
1938: 385E with 385W Tender, whistle in tender
1939: 385E with 385W Tender, whistle in tender

(A) Dark gun-metal body with copper piping, domes, and brass whistle and bell, red-painted drivers, pilot, and trailing truck wheels, solid pilot truck wheels. Comes with 384T Tender with rectangular brass plate and "LIONEL LINES". **450 675 450**

(B) Gun-metal body with nickel piping, domes, stack, whistle, and bell, black-painted drivers, pilot, and trailing truck wheels, spoked pilot truck wheels, gun-metal boiler bands. Comes with 384T Tender with rectangular brass plate and "LIONEL LINES" in block lettering. **450 675 450**

(C) Gun-metal body with nickel piping, domes, whistle, bell, stack, black-painted drivers, pilot wheels, and trailing truck wheels, spoked pilot wheels, gun-metal boiler bands. Comes with 385T or 385W Tender with die-cast body often deteriorated, and long oval nickel and black plate that reads "THE LIONEL RAILWAY LINES". **450 675 450**

(D) Dark gun-metal body with copper piping, domes, and stack, brass whistle and bell, red-painted drivers, pilot, and trailing truck wheels, copper boiler bands. Comes with 384T Tender with gray crackle paint and rectangular brass plate with "LIONEL LINES" in serif block lettering. Chugger in locomotive. No whistle in tender, copper journals on tender. Locomotive box has black rubber-stamped "385E AND 81" on one side and tender box has black rubber stamped lettering "384T-G" on one end and inner flap is marked "390-T-15". Believed to be from 1934 set. D. Ely Collection. **NRS**

390 STEAM: Catalogued 1929 only; 2-4-2, Lionel reentered with steam in 1929 after a hiatus of six years as a response to the popular Ives steam engine line. Steel boiler and die-cast frame, separate headlight casting, hand reversing with Bild-A-Loco motor, 14". Less common than 390E. Black body and frame, orange stripe on frame. Some without orange stripe on frame edge. With 390T Tender, brass and copper trim only. **450 750 400**

390E STEAM: Catalogued 1929-31, 1933, 2-4-2, steel boiler and die-cast frame, pendulum-type E-unit with Bild-A-Loco motor, separate headlight casting, 14". With passenger car sets 309, 310, 312 or 424, 425, 426. Also came with 500-series freights unless it had 390X Tender with 200-series trucks. Then it pulled 200-series freights. Because of the relative scarcity of green and blue 390Es, and the availability of rough black 390Es, many green and blue restorations of black 390Es exist. Since some restorations are not marked, the buyer must exercise great care in purchasing original green or blue 390Es.

(A) Black body and frame, orange stripe on frame, brass domes. **450 650 450**

(B) Same as (A), but copper and brass trim. **450 650 450**

(C) Same as (B), but no orange stripe. **450 650 450**

(D) Two-tone blue, brass domes and smokestack, with copper trim, cream-orange stripe on locomotive frame and on tender. Came with three "Blue Comet" cars: 420, 421, 422, 1930 only. Leip comment. **600 1200 450**

(E) Two-tone green, copper domes, orange or apple green stripe on locomotive frame and tender. Rare. Never illustrated in the catalogue, it is found with matching green frame or lighter green frame, date unknown. **1000 2000 450**

(F) Two-tone green, brass domes and trim, copper pipe on side of engine, orange stripe on frame and tender, 390X Tender for 200-series cars. R. Flanagan Collection. **2000 1500 450**

392E STEAM: Catalogued 1932-39, 4-4-2, stamped-steel boiler, hinged boiler front for lamp access, die-cast frame, Bild-A-Loco motor, 16-1/2". Next to the top-of-the-line model. Keystone plate on cab with red background, lettered "LL". Excellent reproductions have been made by Mike's Train House. The current price of the reproduction is $695.

(A) 1932, black body, copper and brass trim, red wheels, nickel motor sides. With 384 Tender with green stripe, "384T" on bottom, nickeled leading truck. **650 1000 600**

(B) 1932, same as (A), but with chugger and cab switch, tender not striped. **700 1100 600**

(C) Black body, copper trim, some with blackened domes, blackened leading trucks, black wheels. With large 12-wheel tender, "LIONEL LINES", brass plate with black background. **1200 1700 800**

(D) 1935-39, gun-metal body, nickel trim, black wheels, blackened leading truck, 12-wheel large tender. Tender plates read "LIONEL LINES" on red background. **1000 1500 800**

(E) Same as (C), but red wheels. **1000 1800 800**

400E STEAM: Catalogued 1931-39, 4-4-4, with 12-wheel 400T Oil Tender, Bild-a-Loco motor, whistle in tender; 1935-39, steel boiler, die-cast frame, hinged boiler front. Leip comment. Nickel-trimmed 400s are very rare and hard to find with a good original frame. Excellent reproductions have been made by Mike's Train House. For details see next entry.

(A) 1931-33, black with copper and brass trim handrails held by brass clips, red and white number boards, red wheels. Tender has brass and copper trim, brass plates with black lettering and brass journals. Narrow Bild-a-Loco motor. Leip comment. **1200 2000 1200**

(B) 1931-33, medium blue boiler, dark blue frame, with/without cream stripe on frame. Copper trim, brass boiler bands, handrails held by brass clips, red and white number boards, red wheels. Matching 400T Tender with brass trim and nameplates with black lettering, brass journal boxes. **1200 2600 1200**

(C) 1933-34, same as (A), but handrails held by turned brass posts. **1200 2000 1200**

(D) 1933-34, same as (C), but black number boards with white lettering, chugger with switch on firewall. **1200 2000 1200**

(E) 1934, same as (C), but black number boards with white lettering. **1200 2000 1200**

(F) 1934-35, medium blue boiler, dark blue frame, copper and brass trim, copper boiler bands, handrails held by turned brass posts, black number boards with white letters, 400T Tender with brass trim and nameplates with black lettering, brass journal boxes. **1200 2400 1200**

(G) 1934-35, gray (dark gun-metal), copper trim and brass boiler bands, handrails held by turned brass posts, black and white number boards, red wheels with solid pony wheels, tender has brass trim and plates, chugger mechanism. **1200 2000 1200**

(H) 1935, medium blue boiler, dark blue frame, with/without cream stripe on frame. Copper trim, blue-painted boiler bands, handrails held by turned brass posts, black and white number boards, black wheels, matching tender with brass journals and trim, red-painted brass plates. **1200 2600 1200**

(I) 1935, crackle black locomotive and tender, locomotive with

The Dual Motored Giant

The Top of the Line 400 E

Gd Exc Rst

copper trim and boiler bands, handrails held by turned brass posts, black number boards with white lettering, red wheels, solid leading truck wheels, nickeled motor side plates and leading and trailing truck frames with chugger. Many restorations and fakes. Few originals are known to exist. **2500 6000 1200**

(J) 1936-39, gun-metal with nickel trim, gray-painted number boards, handrails held by turned nickel posts, black number boards with white letters, black wheels, motor side plates and leading and trailing truck frames, no chugger, with matching gray whistle with nickel trim and plate with red paint. **1200 2500 1200**

(K) 1936-39, light blue with dark blue frame, with/without cream stripe on frame. Nickel trim, blue-painted boiler bands, handrails held by turned nickel posts, black and white number boards, black wheels. Matching 400T Tender with brass trim and aluminum plates with red paint. **1400 2800 1200**

(L) Black with nickel trim. Very rare. **2500 6000 1200**

(M) Dark blue with purplish dark blue frame, copper trim and brass boiler bands, with/without red stripe on frame. Very rare. **2500 4000 1200**

(N) Black with red stripe on frame and tender. Very rare. **2500 3750 1200**

NOTE: In 1985 Mike's Train House of Columbia, Maryland reproduced the 400E Locomotive. It was offered in light blue color with nickel trim, medium blue color with brass trim, black color with brass trim, gun-metal gray color with brass trim, gray color with nickel trim, and crackle black color with brass trim. A total of 500 units were produced and rapidly sold out. The engines were offered for a retail price of $750. These may be distinguished from the original locomotives by the following features:

1. Under the paint is a zinc plating, which is gold in color.
2. They are marked with "MTH" on the frame, inside firebox, and in inner halves of the tender.
3. They had "NYC" plates on them when offered, but Lionel plates are available through other sources, and consequently some will be replated.

In early 1986 Mike's Train House offered a second run of the 400E. These were available in two-tone blue with nickel trim, two-tone blue with brass trim, black with brass trim, gray with nickel trim, gray with brass trim, crackle black with brass trim, and three new finishes: black with nickel trim, two-tone brown with brass trim, and State green with brass trim. These engines sold for $795. At the same time, Mikes's Train House also offered the Blue Comet cars in nickel or brass. In addition, a fourth car marked "HALLEY" was offered in either nickel or brass trim. Note: 1985-86 marked the return of the Halley Comet to the vicinity of our planet after an absence of 76 years.

The second run of the 400Es was identical to the first run. M. Wolf comment.

402 ELECTRIC: Catalogued 1923-27, 0-4-4-0, NYC S-prototype, two Super motors, 17-1/2". Nearly always found in mojave, hole punched in frame near end for auxiliary lighting post, two different sized holes. Catalogued with 418, 419, and 490 Passenger Cars as well as with either 10-series freight (Early) or 200-series freight cars (Later). Numerous 402 variations exist. A listing of some follows. We would appreciate reader reports on other 402 variations.

(A) Strap headlights, hook couplers, two large gear Super motors, two nickel bells, two extra large nickel whistles. **300 450 275**

(B) Celluloid insert headlights with on-off switch, combination latch couplers, two large gear Super motors, two nickel bells and two extra large nickel whistles, black lettering on plates. Leip comments. D. Ely Collection. **300 450 275**

(C) Same as (B), but latch couplers, regular large-sized whistles. **300 450 275**

(D) Cast headlights, latch coupler, small gear Super motors, two medium-sized nickel pantographs, two large nickel whistles, red lettering on plates. **300 450 275**

(E) Cast headlights, latch couplers, small gear Super motors, two brass pantographs, one nickel whistle, one brass bell, 3/16" hole for lighting post. **300 450 275**

402E ELECTRIC: Catalogued 1926-29, 0-4-4-0, same as 402, but with pendulum-type reversing unit and small gear Super motors, mojave. Some with plates lettered "402E", others with plates numbered "402" with "E" stamped on cab door. Some variations listed, more believed to exist:

(A) Celluloid insert headlights, combination couplers, two bells, two whistles, black lettering. **325 475 275**

(B) Cast headlights, combination couplers, red lettering, one pantograph, two whistles, one bell. **325 450 275**

(C) Cast headlights, latch couplers, red lettering, two pantographs, two whistles. **325 450 275**

408E ELECTRIC: Catalogued 1927-36, 0-4-4-0, NYC S-prototype, two motors. More elaborate version of 402 with added roof, side, and end trim, as well as two additional lights on each end. Two large folding pantographs, two whistles, 17-1/2". Excellent reproductions have been made by Williams Reproductions and Mike's Train House. See next entry for details.

(A) Apple green, most common color, red pilots. **600 1200 500**

(B) Mojave, combination or latch couplers, red pilots. **600 1200 500**

(C) Two-tone brown body (known as State brown paint scheme) and roof, with two Bild-A-Loco motors, or two Super motors, brown pilots. **1800 2700 700**

(D) State brown body, dark brown roof with two Bild-A-Loco motors, brown pilots. **1600 3500 675**

(E) State car dark green, uncatalogued. Rare. Usually a factory repaint to match the State Cars, red pilots. **1600 3500 600**

NOTE: Williams Reproductions' 408E Electric, 0-4-4-0, NYC S-type prototype, dual dummy electric motors, most with "NYC" plates, some with "LIONEL" plates. "WRL" stamped on frame. Many have been powered by their owners with original Lionel motors.

(A) Apple green. **— 450 —**
(B) Dark green. **— 450 —**
(C) Two-tone brown. **— 500 —**
(D) Mojave. **— 450 —**

In addition, in 1979 Williams produced a 408E set in silver and black to commemorate the 25th Anniversary of the Train Collector's Association. The set consisted of a 408E numbered "1954" and "1979" and lettered "TWENTY FIFTH ANNIVERSARY" with the TCA logo, a 418 Parlor Car named "J. LIONEL COWEN", a 419 Combine named "HARRY C. IVES" and "TRAIN COLLECTORS ASSOCIATION", and a 490 Observation named "A. C. GILBERT". All cars are lettered "TWENTY FIFTH ANNIVERSARY SPECIAL" and numbered "1954" and "1979". Current value of the set in mint condition is $1600. H. Turner comment.

1835E STEAM: Catalogued 1934-39, 2-4-2, with 384T, 1835T, 1835TW, or 1835W Tenders, chassis and motor identical to

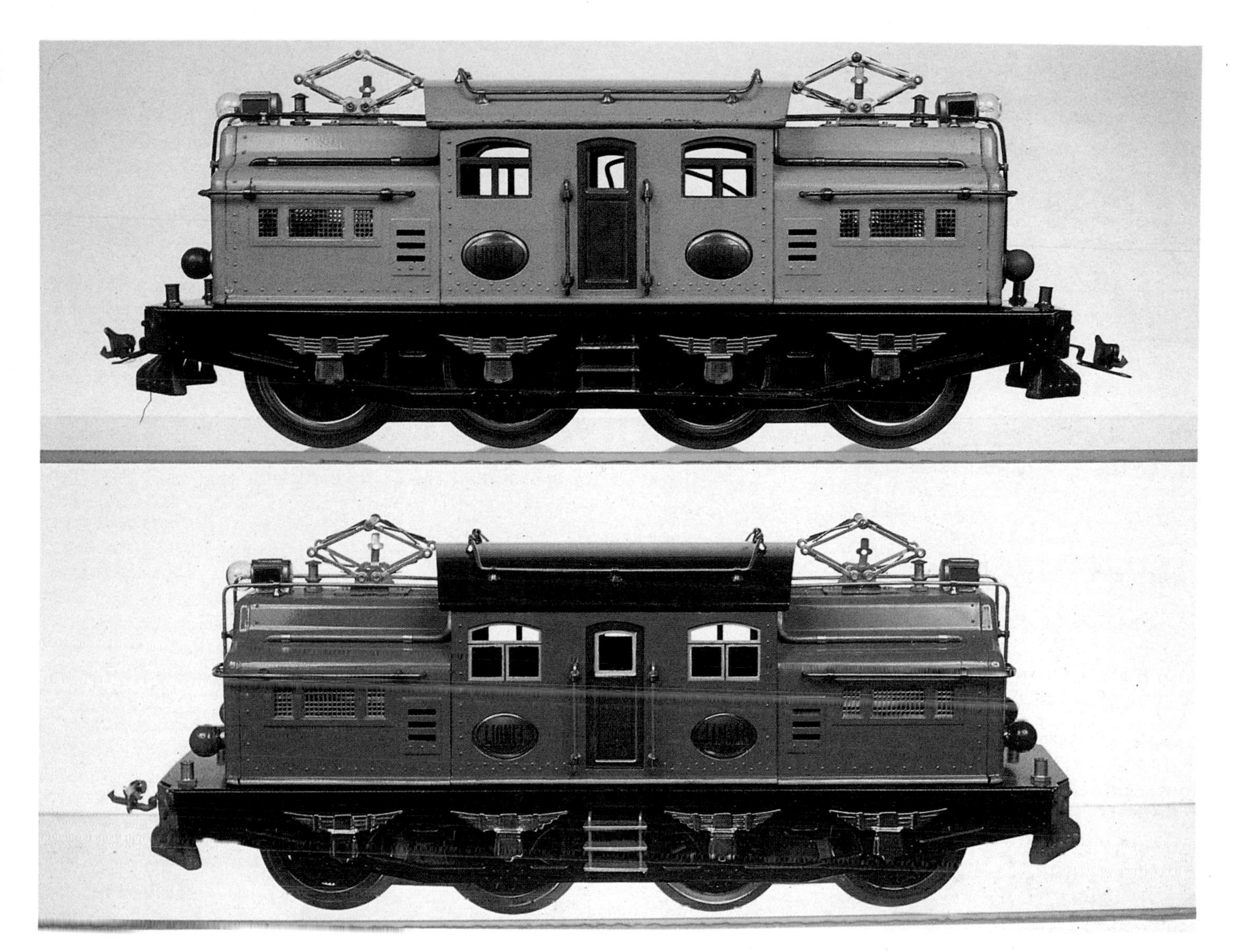

Two Lionel 408E double-motor locomotives. TOP SHELF: apple green locomotive with combination latch couplers. BOTTOM SHELF: reproduction of two-tone brown 408E by Williams. The owner, T. Riley, has added cream striping along edge of frame and windows to more accurately copy the original paint scheme. The original 408E also has cream trim on its pilot.

Gd Exc Rst

385E, but different paint and trim scheme. See 385E for details. The 1835E was less expensive than the 385E and did not have a chugger, although in later years it did come with a whistle. Black boiler, cab, and frame, black domes, stack, and boiler bands, one nickel pipe on each side, black-spoked drivers, pilot and trailing wheels. Pennsylvania-style keystone plate on cab reads "LL". The 1835 Tender is die-cast and frequently deteriorated. Reproduction tops are available and many tenders offered for sale have reproduction tops. The following is a listing taken from the catalogues:

1934: 1835E with 1835T Tender. (Illustration shows 384T Tender.)

1935: 1835E with 1835TW Tender. Tender with whistle.

1936-39: 1835E with 1835W Tender. Tender with whistle.

(A) 1835E with 384T Tender. **450 750 425**

(B) 1835E with 1835T, 1835TW, or 1835W Tender (die-cast tender with long oval plate that reads "THE LIONEL RAILWAY LINES"). **450 850 475**

1910 EARLY: Catalogued 1910-11, electric, 0-6-0, NYC S-prototype, dark olive green body with square hood, "New York, New Haven and Hartford" in fancy gold script, large nickel bell, red trim on eight ventilator flaps, four ventilator grills and long pilots, raised monitor roof. Operated in only one direction. The two center wheels are cast-iron and are powered, while the other four wheels are stamped-steel and not powered, 9-3/4". Came with two short (7-1/2") gondolas.

(A) Soldered handrails by door, slide-on headlight, short crinkle hook couplers. D. Ely Collection. **750 1600 600**

(B) Embossed handrails by door, slide-on headlight, short crinkle hook couplers, maroon primer inside body. D. Ely Collection **750 1600 600**

1910 LATE: Catalogued 1912 only, electric, 0-6-0, NYC S-prototype, dark olive green body with round hood, same body as 33, large nickel bell, pedestal headlight, one direction only, red pilots and window trim. Came with two short (7-1/2") gondolas. Price for locomotive only.

(A) "NEW YORK CENTRAL LINES" gold-stamped in oval, gold-painted ventilator grills. **450 1000 450**

Gd Exc Rst

(B) Same as (A), but lettered "New York, New Haven and Hartford" in fancy gold script, brass ventilators. C. Weber Collection. **450 1000 450**

1911 EARLY: Catalogued 1910-12 electric, 0-4-0, NYC S-prototype, square hoods, nickeled bell, slide-on or pedestal headlight, auxiliary lighting post, eight ventilator flaps, four ventilator grills, long red pilots, cast-iron wheels, long straight hook couplers.

(A) Dark olive green body with "New York, New Haven and Hartford" in fancy gold script, slide-on headlight, thin-rimmed drivers, reverse, short crinkle hook couplers. D. Ely Collection. **1000 2000 450**

(B) Maroon body with "NEW YORK CENTRAL LINES" gold rubber-stamped inside oval. **1000 2000 350**

(C) Dark olive green body with "NEW YORK CENTRAL LINES" in gold block lettering. **1000 2000 350**

1911 LATE: Catalogued 1913, electric, 0-4-0, NYC S-prototype, round hood, same body as early 38, "NEW YORK CENTRAL LINES" in gold-stamped block lettering, gold-painted ventilators and handrails, nickeled bell and slide-on or pedestal headlight, iron wheels, long crinkle hook couplers, short red pilots, red window trim and side rods. **700 1200 350**

1911 SPECIAL: Catalogued 1911-12, electric, 0-4-4-0, NYC S-prototype, maroon body with square hood, and eight ventilator flaps, larger body than regular 1911. Large nickel bell, pedestal headlight, auxiliary lighting post, gold-painted handrails, long red-painted pilots, side rods, long straight hook couplers, gold-stamped "1911 SPECIAL".

(A) Gold rubber-stamped in fancy script "New York, New Haven and Hartford". **1000 2000 400**

(B) Gold rubber-stamped in block lettering "NEW YORK CENTRAL LINES". **1000 2000 400**

1912 ELECTRIC: Catalogued 1910-12, 0-4-4-0, NYC S-prototype, dark olive green body with square hood, eight red ventilator flaps, four red ventilator grills, gold-painted handrails, red-painted pilot, one motor, one dummy motor, side rods, two large bells, auxiliary lighting post, raised monitor section on roof, "1912" rubber-stamped in gold on side, reversing switch, sliding cab doors.

(A) Circa 1910-11, thin rims, slide-on headlights, gold-stamped "New York, New Haven and Hartford" in fancy script, short straight hook couplers. **1800 3200 1700**

(B) Same as (A), but short crinkle hook couplers. Coupler is painted same color as body, the front of the coupler is painted the same color as the pilot. D. Ely Collection. **1800 3200 1700**

(C) Circa 1912, thin rims, pedestal headlights, gold-stamped "NEW YORK CENTRAL LINES" in block lettering. **1750 3000 1600**

(D) Circa 1912, thick rims, pedestal headlights, gold-stamped "NEW YORK CENTRAL LINES" in block lettering. **1500 2700 1450**

1912 SPECIAL: Catalogued 1911, electric, 0-4-4-0, NYC S-prototype. Same as 1912, but polished brass body with red-painted ventilator flaps and grills, pilots and drivers. Two large brass bells, auxiliary lighting post, long straight hook couplers, sliding cab doors, no lettering on sides, soldered-on headlight, thin rims. This locomotive and the early Lionel 7 in brass are the most prized of the early Lionel series. As with the Lionel 7, great care must be exercised by buyers searching for originals since fine, unmarked reproductions have been made. **2000 5000 1700**

Trolleys, Interurbans, And Trailers

1 TROLLEY: Catalogued 1906-14, four wheels, open platform.

(A) Circa 1906, cream body, orange band and roof, with cream solid clerestory, rubber-stamped "No. 1 Electric-Rapid Transit No. 1", five windows without embossed frames on each side, L-shaped solid steps, early New Departure motor with friction drive, short frame, 5-1/8", roof 8-1/2" long. **1300 3000 1000**

(B) Circa 1907, white body, blue band and roof, with solid white clerestory, rubber-stamped "No. 1 Electric Rapid Transit No. 1", five windows without embossed frames on each side, L-shaped solid steps, New Departure motor with gear drive, short frame, 5-5/8", roof 8-1/2" long. **1200 3000 1000**

(B-1) Matching non-powered trailer. **1000 2800 900**

(C) 1908, cream body, blue band and roof with solid cream clerestory, rubber-stamped "No. 1 Electric Rapid Transit No. 1", six windows with embossed frames, L-shaped solid steps, Standard motor, frame 5-7/8", roof 9-9/16" long. **900 2000 900**

(C-1) Matching non-powered trailer. **800 2000 800**

(D) Same as (C), but lettered "No. 1 CURTIS BAY No. 1". "Curtis Bay" was a Baltimore streetcar line. Specially lettered for a Baltimore area retailer. **1500 3500 1100**

(E) Circa 1910, blue body, cream window band, blue roof with cream clerestory, rubber-stamped "No. 1 Electric Rapid Transit No. 1", six windows with embossed frames, open rung steps, Standard motor, frame 5-7/8" long, roof 10-15/16" long, platform with maroon posts, light. **1000 2000 800**

2 TROLLEY: Catalogued 1906-16, rubber-stamped "No. 2 ELECTRIC RAPID TRANSIT No. 2", four wheels, six windows, Standard motor, frame 5-7/8" long.

(A) 1906, yellow body, red band, light blue squared roof with yellow open clerestory, windows without embossed frames, open rung steps, open platform with light blue posts, short straight hook couplers. **900 2000 900**

(A-1) Matching non-powered trailer. **800 2000 800**

(B) 1908-09, yellow body, red band, yellow rounded end roof with yellow clerestory with partial openings, windows with embossed frames, wire suspended L-shaped steps, closed platform, long straight hook couplers or long crinkle hook couplers. **1000 2000 900**

(B-1) Matching non-powered trailer. **800 1800 800**

(C) 1910-12, red body, yellow window bands, doors, rounded end roof, and clerestory with partial openings, yellow clerestory with light red window bands, closed platform with offset window, long crinkle hook couplers, one light on platform end, hand reversing. D. Ely Collection. **1000 2000 900**

(C-1) Matching non-powered trailer. **1000 2000 900**

(D) 1910-12, same as (E), but platform window offset from lower platform panel. **1000 1800 800**

(E) 1913-16, red body, yellow window bands and doors, rounded end yellow roof and clerestory with partial openings, windows with embossed frames, wire suspended L-shaped steps, closed platform, long straight hook or crinkle hook coupler, one light, flush platform window and lower panel. **1000 2000 900**

(E-1) Matching non-powered trailer. **1000 1800 1000**

(F) Lettered "No. 2 EDMONDSON AVE. No. 2" for a Baltimore streetcar line. Not confirmed. **NRS**

3 TROLLEY: Catalogued 1906-13, eight wheels, nine windows, Standard motor.

(A) 1906-07, cream body, orange band and roof with straight ends, open clerestory, rubber-stamped "No. 3 ELECTRIC

Trolleys, Trailers and Interurbans

8 Reproduction

1 (B)

1(B-1)

2 (D)

2 (D-1)

1 (A)

3 (A)

1010 (B-1)

3300 (A)

Gd Exc Rst

RAPID TRANSIT No. 3", solid three-rivet trucks, windows without embossed frames, roof 13-7/8" long, open platform with posts, short straight hook couplers. **1400 3000 1400**

(B) 1908-09, cream body, light orange band, orange roof with straight ends, open clerestory, rubber-stamped "No. 3 ELECTRIC RAPID TRANSIT No. 3", solid three-rivet trucks, windows with embossed frames, roof 13-7/8", open platform with posts, short straight hook couplers. **1400 3000 1400**

(C) Same as (B), but cream body, dark olive green band and roof. **1400 3000 1400**

(D) Same as (B), but cream sides, dark olive green band and roof, and open three-rivet trucks. **1400 3000 1400**

(D-1) Matching non-powered trailer. **1300 2700 1300**

(E) Same as (A), but orange sides, dark olive green band and roof, and solid three-rivet trucks. **1400 3000 1400**

(F) Dark green body, roof and lower platform ends, cream windows, doors, and clerestory roof, maroon suspended L-shaped steps and coupler supports, rubber-stamped "No. 3 ELECTRIC RAPID TRANSIT No. 3", open three-rivet trucks, windows with embossed frames, roof 15-1/4" long, closed platform with offset windows. **1400 3000 1400**

(G) Green body, roof, and lower platform end, cream windows, door, and clerestory roof, maroon suspended L-shaped steps and coupler supports, rubber-stamped "No. 3 BAY SHORE No. 3", open single-rivet trucks, windows with embossed frame, roof 15-1/4" long, closed platforms with flush ends, one headlight, long straight hook couplers. Bay Shore was a Baltimore streetcar line. **1650 3500 1650**

(H) Same as (G), but lettered "No. 3 ELECTRIC RAPID TRANSIT No. 3". **1400 3000 1400**

(I) Same as (F), but green coupler supports and steps. **1450 3200 1400**

4 TROLLEY: Catalogued 1906-12, rubber-stamped "No. 4 ELECTRIC RAPID TRANSIT No. 4", eight wheels, three-rivet trucks, nine windows with embossed frames, two Standard motors.

(A) Cream body, windows, and clerestory roof, dark olive green band and roof, closed trucks, open steps, 13-7/8" long roof, open platform with posts, no headlights, short straight hook couplers. **3000 5000 2000**

(B) Same as (A), but with interior light and headlight. **3000 5000 2200**

(C) Dark olive green body, roof, and platform ends, cream windows and clerestory roof, open trucks, open steps, roof 13-7/8" long, open platform with posts, no headlights, short straight hook couplers. **3000 5000 2200**

(D) Green body, roof, and platform ends, cream windows, doors and clerestory roof, maroon steps and coupler supports, open trucks, suspended L-shaped steps, 15-1/4" long roof, closed platform, flush ends, headlight, long straight couplers. **3000 5000 2200**

8 TROLLEY: Catalogued 1908-14, eight wheels, open trucks, embossed window frames, Standard motor, offset windows on platforms. Excellent reproductions were made by Williams Reproductions. See next entry for details.

(A) 1908-09, cream body, doors, clerestory roof, and platform ends, orange roof and band, rubber-stamped "No. 8 PAY AS YOU ENTER No. 8", three-rivet trucks, nine windows, 17-3/4" long roof, large closed platform. Based on No. 3 body with long vestibules adapted for No. 8. **3000 5000 1500**

(B) Largest Lionel trolley: dark green sides, roof, platform, and lower panels, cream windows, door, clerestory roof, maroon steps and coupler supports, rubber-stamped "No. 8 PAY AS YOU ENTER No. 8", single-rivet trucks, eleven windows, large perforated steps, 20-1/4" long roof, one headlight, no couplers, large vestibule. D. Ely Collection. **3000 5000 1500**

(C) Same as (B), but rubber-stamped "8 PAY AS YOU ENTER 8". **3000 5000 1500**

(D) Same as (B), but green steps and coupler supports. **3000 5000 1500**

(E) Lettered "No. 8 Gilmor Street P-A-Y-E No. 8" for a Baltimore streetcar line. Not confirmed. **NRS**

(F) Williams Reproduction No. 8 Trolley is the same as Lionel's 8(C), but has tab-and-slot construction, rather than soldered joints, and a can-type motor with two diodes rather than the original type of motor; dark olive and cream; came with redwood box; stamped "Made by Williams Reproductions Limited, Laurel, Md." on trolley floor. **175 400 —**

9 MOTOR CAR: Catalogued 1909-12, rubber-stamped "No. 9 PAY AS YOU ENTER No. 9".

(A) 1909, matches 8(A), two Standard motors. Based on No. 3 body with long vestibules adapted for Nos. 8 and 9. **3000 5000 3000**

(B) Matches 8(B), except two motors. **3000 5000 2750**

10 INTERURBAN: Catalogued 1910-16, gold rubber-stamped "NEW YORK CENTRAL LINES" on sides, open trucks, two large, black wooden air tanks.

(A) Maroon body and roof, high black knobs soldered to roof, solid clerestory and gold-painted steps with many small holes, gold windows and coupler supports, gold rubber-stamped "INTERURBAN", gold-painted wire handrails, three-rivet trucks, ring and disc reverse, short crinkle hook couplers, slide-on headlight with bracket, two doors. For matching unpowered trailer, 1010(A). **2000 4000 700**

(B) Dark olive green body and roof, high black knobs soldered to roof, solid clerestory, gold-painted steps with many small holes, gold and maroon window trim and gold-painted coupler supports, gold rubber-stamped "10 INTERURBAN 10" on sides, three-rivet trucks, removable floor, maroon doors, short crinkle hooks, slide-on headlight with bracket. For matching trailer, see 1010(B). **800 1500 700**

(B-1) Same as (B), but low black knobs. **800 1500 700**

(C) Maroon body and roof, seven windows, closed vestibules, high black knobs soldered to roof, solid clerestory, gold-painted steps with many small holes, green and gold window trim, gold-painted coupler supports, gold rubber-stamped "10 INTERURBAN 10" on sides, three-rivet trucks, removable floor, green doors, short crinkle hooks, slide-on headlight with bracket, matching trailer, see 1010(C). **2000 4000 700**

(D) Dark olive green body and roof, seven windows, closed vestibules, no knobs, removable roof with one thumb screw and pierced clerestory with blue-painted celluloid, gold-painted steps punched with many small holes, maroon and gold trim, red-painted celluloid window material for upper window section, gold-painted coupler supports, gold rubber-stamped "10 INTERURBAN 10" on sides, three-rivet trucks, maroon doors, long straight hook couplers, slide-on headlight with bracket, single motor, ring and disc reverse, matching trailer, see 1010(D). D. Ely Collection. **800 1500 700**

(E) Same as 10(D), but single-rivet truck, simple tabs for headlight. D. Ely Collection. **800 1500 700**

(F) Same as 10(D), but single-rivet truck and gold rubber-stamped "10 W. B. & A. 10" on lower side and "INTERURBAN" above window. Special markings for Baltimore area retailer. **1750 2750 700**

101 Summer Trolley marked "THE LIONEL LINES" and a second 101 Summer Trolley marked "101 WILKENS AVENUE 101". Note the fender on the left trolley. Sullens Collection, M. Feinstein photograph.

Gd Exc Rst

(G) Same as 10(D), but elaborately pierced clerestory with tabs, single-rivet trucks, gold-painted stamped steps with three holes, matching trailer, see 1010(G). **800 1500 700**

(H) Similar to 10(D), but elaborately pierced clerestory with tabs, single-rivet trucks, gold-painted stamped steps with three holes, pedestal headlight, lighting post for trailer on vestibule, matching trailer, see 1010(H). **800 1500 700**

100 TROLLEY. Catalogued, 1910-16, 5-7/8" long frame.

(A) 1910, blue body, roof, and ends, white windows, doors, clerestory, five windows, offset windows on closed end platforms, maroon steps and coupler supports, one headlight, short crinkle hook couplers, turned door knobs, gold rubber-stamped "100 ELECTRIC RAPID TRANSIT 100", 10-7/8" long roof. **1000 2000 1000**

(A-1) Matching non-powered trailer, see 1000(A). **1000 2000 1000**

(B) 1912-14, blue body, roof, and ends, cream windows, doors, clerestory, five windows, embossed window frame, flush windows on closed end platforms, maroon couplers, steps, and coupler supports, one headlight, short straight hook couplers, stamped door knobs, gold rubber-stamped "100 ELECTRIC RAPID TRANSIT 100", 10-7/16" long roof. **1000 2000 1000**

(B-1) Matching unpowered trailer, see 1000(B). **700 1500 700**

(C) Same as 100(B), but red sides, roof, and ends, cream windows, doors and clerestory. **700 1500 700**

(D) Same as 100(B), but rubber-stamped "100 LINDEN AVE. 100" for a Baltimore streetcar line for sale by Baltimore area retailer. **2000 4000 700**

(E) 1914-15, red body, roof, and ends, cream windows, doors, clerestory, six windows, embossed window frames, flush windows on end platforms, black couplers, coupler supports, and steps, one headlight, long straight hook couplers, stamped door knobs, rubber-stamped "100 ELECTRIC RAPID TRANSIT 100", 11-1/2" long roof. **700 1500 700**

(F) 1915, blue body, roof, and ends, cream windows, doors, clerestory, six windows, embossed frames, flush windows on end platforms, nickel-plated couplers, maroon coupler supports and suspended L-shaped steps, two headlights, long crinkle hook couplers, rubber-stamped "100 Electric Rapid Transit 100", 11-1/2" long roof. **700 1500 1000**

101 SUMMER TROLLEY: 1910-13, smallest Lionel summer car with five benches, yellow clerestory, gold rubber-stamped "101 ELECTRIC RAPID TRANSIT 101", Standard motor, 5-7/8" long frame, 10-3/8" long roof.

(A) Benches with blue ends, blue roof and ends, maroon posts and base side, maroon-painted short crinkle hook couplers, maroon coupler supports. Matching non-powered trailer, see 1100(A). **800 1800 800**

(B) Same as (A), but blue base side, cream posts. **800 1800 800**

(C) Same as (A), but red roof and ends, yellow posts, black side, black-painted short hook couplers, black coupler supports. **800 1800 800**

(D) Same as (A), but lettered "101 WILKENS AVENUE 101" for a Baltimore streetcar line. Sullens Collection. **1500 3500 800**

200 TRAILER: Catalogued 1910-13, matches 2(C) Trolley, but non-powered and rubber-stamped "No. 200 ELECTRIC RAPID TRANSIT No. 200". **— 3000 —**

202 SUMMER TROLLEY: Catalogued 1910-13, medium-sized, summer car with six benches with red ends, red roof and ends, yellow clerestory, and posts, black base, sides, black-painted long straight hook coupler, Standard motor, manual reverse, matching non-powered trailer, see 2200.

(A) Gold rubber-stamped "202 ELECTRIC RAPID TRANSIT 202". **800 2400 1000**

(B) Gold rubber-stamped "202 PRESTON ST. 202" for a Baltimore streetcar line. L. Battley Collection. **2000 4000 —**

303 SUMMER TROLLEY: Catalogued 1910-13, largest Lionel summer car with eight cream benches, and dark olive ends, dark olive green roof and ends, yellow clerestory and posts, maroon base and side, one Standard motor, two four-wheel trucks, 15" long roof, one headlight, matching non-powered trailer, see 3300.

(A) Gold rubber-stamped "303 ELECTRIC RAPID TRANSIT 303". **1500 3000 1400**

(B) Gold rubber-stamped "303 MADISON AVE 303" for a Baltimore streetcar line. Not confirmed. **NRS**

1000 TRAILER: Catalogued 1910-13, not powered, gold rubber-stamped "1000 ELECTRIC RAPID TRANSIT 1000".

(A) Matches 100(A). **NRS**

(B) Matches 100(B). **NRS**

1010 TRAILER: Catalogued 1910-14, interurban, but no motor.

(A) Matches 10(A). **600 1400 600**

(B) Matches 10(B). **600 1400 600**

(B-1) Matches 10(B-1). **600 1400 600**

(C) Matches 10(C). **600 1400 600**

The No. 202 Summer Trolley

(D) Matches 10(D). **600 1400 600**

(E) Matches 10(E). **NRS**

(F) Matches 10(F). **NRS**

(G) Matches 10(G). **NRS**

(H) Matches 10(H). **NRS**

(I) Rubber-stamped "No. 1010 W. B. & A. No. 1010" for Baltimore area retailer. **NRS**

1100 TRAILER: Catalogued 1910-13, matches 101(A), but not powered, gold rubber-stamped "1100 ELECTRIC RAPID TRANSIT 1100". **NRS**

2200 TRAILER: Catalogued 1910-13, matches 202, but not powered, gold rubber-stamped "2200 RAPID TRANSIT 2200". **1100 2500 1100**

3300 TRAILER: Catalogued 1910-13, matches 303, but not powered, gold rubber-stamped "3300 ELECTRIC RAPID TRANSIT 3300". **1400 3000 1400**

10 Series Freights

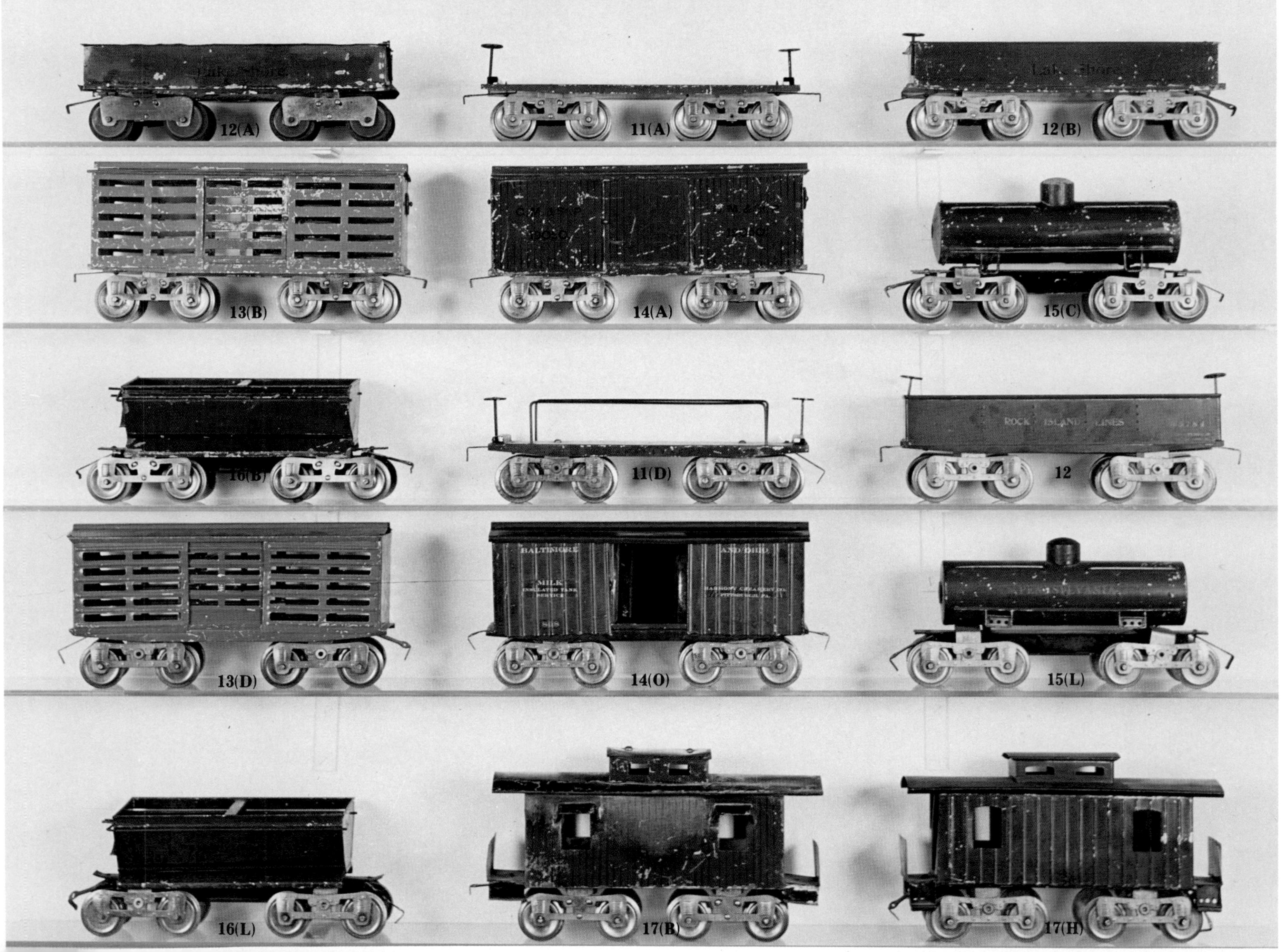

12(A) 11(A) 12(B)

13(B) 14(A) 15(C)

16(B) 11(D) 12

13(D) 14(O) 15(L)

16(L) 17(B) 17(H)

Chapter II
Standard Gauge Freight Cars

By Henry Edmunds, Dave Ely, Jim Flynn,
Roland E. LaVoie, and William Schilling

During the years from 1906 to 1940, Lionel produced four basic series of Standard Gauge freight cars: the 10 Series, 100 Series, 200 Series, and 500 Series. Very early in its history, Lionel instituted the practice of a "deluxe" series and a "regular" series of freight cars. The 10 Series, produced from 1906 to 1926, became the "deluxe" series when the 100 Series was introduced in 1910. When a major production shift occurred in the mid-1920s, the 200 Series replaced the 10 Series and the 500 Series replaced the 100 Series. The 100- and 500-series freight cars are significantly smaller than their 10 and 200 counterparts. However, most of the construction techniques between a deluxe series and its regular counterpart are very similar and, in a great many cases, are identical except for size.

Construction of the 200 and 500 freights was fairly uniform. Most of the differences found in the variations concern the use of nickel or brass trim or combinations of paint colors. For that reason, the variations of the later cars are easy for the collector to spot. However, such is not the case with the 10 and 100 freights.

To the beginning enthusiast the earlier freight cars present a bewildering variety of configurations. However, Marx and prewar American Flyer enthusiasts claim that their favorites produced even more varieties. Some American Flyer enthusiasts have been known to wonder aloud if their Chicago Flyer ever produced two or three pieces which are exactly the same. With experience, however, these varieties become more familiar and patterns become visible. The usual question is why a particular change was made. Unfortunately, the 60 to 80 years separating us from the men and women who made the trains means that first-hand information is usually lost. However, a more general explanation is available. Lionel was a small scale manufacturing company with annual production in the high hundreds or low thousands. Management consequently made manufacturing and design changes readily to control or reduce costs. Sometimes this involved taking advantage of special material purchases and substituting the new for the old. Other times, a change was intended to solve the problem of worn or broken tooling. Finally, changes were sometimes made to make a better product.

Another reason for the variety of the 10 and 100 cars is simply their great age. Examples of old and flaking paint have been found where the car was repainted outside the factory very soon after it was made. Over the years, many cars have had trucks, couplers, brakewheels, and other parts replaced outside the factory. Truly excellent examples of these cars have helped clarify the situation, but such cars are very hard to find. When an unusual variation turns up for sale which is presented as original, the purchaser is urged to exercise extreme caution.

Up to this time, manufacturing variations of 10- and 100-series cars have been given little attention. Consequently, the market does not usually differentiate value, cash-wise, among varieties. With increased study and interest, we expect increased price differentiation between the harder and easier to find varieties.

We recognize that the astonishing number of varieties which have turned up, especially among the older cars, will lead to some confusion because most collectors will have no certain way to make judgments about scarcity. That is where you, the readers, come in. For the next edition of this book, we would like inventories of collections from as many collectors as possible. We would then be able to establish the relative scarcity or commonness of the varieties listed.

A great many people assisted the writers of this chapter in its preparation. Rev. Robert E. (Bob) Pauli and George Koff graciously allowed us to examine their extensive collections, and they shared with us their expertise developed over many years of collecting these cars. Numerous dealers allowed us to look over the pieces on their tables. Al Weaver sent in beautiful slides of his extensive collection. James Sattler shared photos with us and gave us a long list of variations in his collection. Charles Weber carefully recorded variations from his collection. Philip Graves dramatically expanded our manuscript with new information on production variations in the 200 and 500-series cars. These two gentlemen caught a number of errors and made this a much more accurate chapter. Also making significant contributions were Roger Bartelt, Birk Leip, and Woody Hoffman.

THE 10-SERIES FREIGHT CARS

These freight cars were introduced by Lionel in 1906 as the first Standard Gauge freight cars made by the company. Between their introduction and the cessation of their production in 1926, many changes in their construction occurred with frequent overlapping. These changes somewhat obscure the dating of the cars, but in general there are four readily identifiable phases of construction. Chronologically, they are:

PHASE I. EARLY "LIONEL MANUFACTURING CO."

The earliest cars of the 10 Series show a lemon-yellow undercoat, and the bottom is neither stamped nor embossed. The color of the undercoating was changed to flat red a few years afterward, possibly when the early closed-side truck was replaced by the three-rivet open-side truck. In later production during this period, the underside was painted the same as the base color of the car.

PHASE II. LATER "LIONEL MANUFACTURING CO."

These cars, definitely manufactured prior to 1918, usually have their undersides painted the same color as the car. However, the bottom of the car is boldly embossed in large block letters, "LIONEL MFG. CO." In 1918, Lionel changed its corporate name to the "Lionel Corporation".

PHASE III. EARLY "LIONEL CORPORATION"

These cars are essentially the same as Phase II, but their undersides carry neither an embossing, nor rubber-stamped black lettering. Great care must be used in dating cars from this phase. They may indeed belong to a transitional period between the embossing and rubber-stamping. On the other hand, the undersides may have once been rubber-stamped but repainted outside or even within the factory. They may also be cars which missed either the embossing or the rubber-stamping process. Examples of these cars with original paint are readily observable. However, more research is needed to determine whether they represent a legitimate phase of construction. Other clues from couplers and trucks can help date these cars — assuming the couplers and trucks have never been replaced.

PHASE IV. LATER "LIONEL CORPORATION"

These cars, representing the last period of construction, are rubber-stamped with the car's number in black on the underside. Also rubber-stamped in black (sometimes gold) is the legend "MADE IN U.S.A. THE LIONEL CORPORATION NEW YORK" in three lines below the number.

Trucks and couplers are often helpful in assigning a 10-series car to a particular phase of construction. The earliest cars (1906-1908) have closed-side three-rivet trucks. From 1908-1910, another three-rivet truck was used which has open slots and embossed springs. In these cases — and no others — the wheels and axles turn as one unit. All later trucks feature wheels which turn individually. In 1911, a single-rivet open-side truck was introduced. It has a large eyelet or rivet fastening the bolster to the side frame. There are at least three major varieties of the 10-series truck with one rivet on each side holding the side frame and bolster together. We believe the earliest version had two crimps on each side where the bolster was bent to form vertical sections. The bolster's vertical section was stamped out such that it matched the side frame, and was not visible through it. A later version eliminated the crimping at the bend-over area. The third version did not have the crimping at the bend-over area. The vertical section was rectangular and readily visible behind the side frame. We believe that several different kinds of rivets were used to join the side frames and bolster, but we do not know which type of rivet went with which truck version.

The 1911 version of the 10-series truck has two crimps where the bolster is bent and the bolster is stamped out to match the side frame. The vertical sections of the bolster were stamped out so that they are not visible through the side frame. R. Bartelt photograph.

The couplers show similar variety. The early cars from 1906 to 1914 use a straight L-shaped hook which can be short (5/16") or long (1/2"). About 1910, Lionel began to install these hooks with a crinkle at the bent end, presumably to keep them from popping out of the coupler slots. As before, there were short and long versions of these couplers, which were used until 1918. In 1917, Lionel began to install by far the most common coupler used on the 10 Series. It replaced the crinkle with two projecting nibs or ears on the bottom of the bent end. This coupler was used until production ended in 1926.

LEFT: hook coupler with ears. RIGHT: long crinkle hook coupler. The crinkle hook coupler is the earlier style. R. Bartelt photograph.

An unusual fate befell the 10 Series in its last year of production. In 1926, Lionel began manufacturing its 200 Series to replace the 10 Series. American Flyer, then beginning its manufacture of Standard Gauge trains in Chicago, purchased an unknown quantity of Lionel 10-series bodies. They then stamped the cars, with yellow ink "American Flyer Lines" underneath the body and mounted them on American Flyer trucks. These cars are now very rare and highly prized. For further information, refer to the short article on these cars by Bob Robinson and Ed Pinsky in the Autumn 1978 issue of the **Atlantic Division Express.** The 12 Lionel Gondola became the 4007 Sand Car, the 13 Cattle Car became the 4005 Cattle Car, the 14 Boxcar became the 4008 Automobile Car, and the 17 Caboose became the 4011 Caboose. In 1927 American Flyer introduced its own Wide Gauge freight cars.

Gd Exc Rst

11 FLATCAR: 1906-26. Some of the earliest production models have handrails running the length of the car; most models were without handrails; end bolsters or stops were usually painted black.

I. Early "Lionel Manufacturing Co." Production: Yellow or maroon underframe, no embossing, Type I or II 10-series trucks.

(A) Maroon body, two brakewheels, three-rivet Type II open-side trucks, no handrails, short hook couplers. **150 300 50**

(B) Same as A, but handrails and Type I three-rivet closed-side trucks, short straight hook coupler. D. Ely comment. **200 400 50**

II. Later "Lionel Manufacturing Co." Production: Embossed "LIONEL MFG. CO." on car underside.

(C) Brown body, two brakewheels, handrails, single-rivet flex trucks, long hook couplers, rubber-stamped "PENNSYLVANIA" in sans-serif lettering. D. Ely comment. **40 60 25**

Gd Exc Rst

(D) Maroon body, two brakewheels, handrails, single-rivet flex trucks, long hook couplers. 32 50 25

(E) Orange body, two brakewheels, no handrails, single-rivet flex trucks, long hook couplers, black rubber-stamped "PENNSYLVANIA R.R." on side. 75 125 50

(F) Red body, two brakewheels, no handrails, hook couplers with ears, single-rivet flex trucks. 45 65 25

III. Early "Lionel Corporation" Production: No embossing or stamping on car floor.

(G) Brown body, two large 1" brakewheels on same side of car, Type V trucks, "PENNSYLVANIA R.R." rubber-stamped in black sans-serif lettering. D. Ely Collection. 40 60 25

IV. Later "Lionel Corporation" Production: Rubber-stamped "MADE IN U.S.A. / THE LIONEL CORPORATION / NEW YORK" on underframe in black or gold in three lines, either with or without car number.

(H) Brown body, two brakewheels, no handrails, hook couplers with ears, single-rivet flex trucks. 32 50 25

(I) Same as (H), except rubber-stamped "PENNSYLVANIA R.R." in black on car side. Kotil comment. 45 65 25

(J) Gray body, two brakewheels, no handrails, hook couplers with ears, single-rivet flex trucks. 45 65 25

(K) Maroon body, two brass brakewheels, no handrails, hook couplers with ears, single-rivet flex trucks with embossed screw slot on bottom bolster. The brass brakewheels have the same construction and application techniques as their black counterparts. Koff Collection. 32 50 25

(L) Same as (K), but has coupler brackets and two black brakewheels, black lettering on underside. Koff, Weaver, and D. Ely Collections. 32 50 25

(M) Same as (K), but only one brakewheel, open-side flex trucks and wheels keyed to axles. Edmunds observation. 32 50 25

(N) Maroon body, black-painted handrails (possibly not original), Type V trucks, coupler slots in frame, lettered "PENNSYLVANIA" in black serif letters. D. Ely Collection. 45 65 25

12 GONDOLA: 1906-26, earliest construction has either yellow or flat red undercoating, but some with these colors are also embossed. Many variations are found in trim colors. Most examples are lettered "LAKE SHORE". In Phase I and II cars, only the "L" and the "S" in "LAKE SHORE" are capitalized. All the letters are in capitals on the later cars.

I. Early "Lionel Manufacturing Co." Production: Yellow or red undercoating, no embossing or rubber-stamping.

(A) Red body, black rubber-stamped "Lake Shore" and "CAPACITY 80000 LBS. WEIGHT 35000 LBS.", three-rivet trucks with solid sides embossed "PAT. PENDING", black-painted short hook couplers held on by escutcheon pins, yellow undercoat. The top of the body edge is bent over to form a rim which is painted black. There are soldered corner braces on the rim. Two black-painted brakewheels have shafts which go through the body rim. Sullens Collection. 175 350 25

(B) Red body, body edges not rolled, soldered corner braces, black rubber-stamped "Lake Shore", early Type I three-rivet trucks with solid sides, short hook couplers, yellow undercoat, brakewheel soldered to outside of body. D. Ely Collection. 150 300 25

(C) Same as (B), but no yellow undercoating. 100 200 25

(D) Same as (A), but Type II open-side three-rivet flex trucks, one brakewheel mounted on top lip of body. D. Ely comment. 150 300 25

II. Later "Lionel Manufacturing Co." Production: Embossed "LIONEL MFG. CO." on underside. The earliest examples from this period retained yellow or flat red undercoating.

(E) Red body, dark olive green lower stripe, yellow undercoating, black rubber-stamped "LAKE SHORE", Type II three-rivet open-side flex trucks, short crinkle hook couplers, two green-painted brakewheels. D. Ely comment. 45 80 25

(F) Red body, dark green lower body edge, flat red undercoat, black rubber-stamped "Lake Shore" 2-3/4" long, "Capacity" on left, Type II three-rivet open-side flex trucks, long crinkle-hook couplers, black brakewheels with red-painted shaft. D. Ely Collection. 45 80 25

(G) Like (F), but dark olive lower body edge and body rim, no undercoating. C. Weber Collection. 45 80 25

III. Early "Lionel Corporation" Production: No embossing or rubber-stamping.

(H) Brown body, black-painted body rim, single-rivet flex trucks, Type II data lines and "LAKE SHORE 65784" rubber-stamped in black, two gold-painted brakewheels, hook couplers with ears, no coupler brackets, no underside stamping. Koff Collection. 45 80 25

(I) Gray body, gold rubber-stamped lettering "ROCK ISLAND LINES", two brakewheels, hook couplers with ears, single-rivet flex trucks. 32 50 25

(J) Brown body, black rubber-stamped "LAKE SHORE 65784", dark olive green-painted body edge, four lines of data rubber-stamped in black, "CAPACITY 60000 LBS / WEIGHT 34500 LBS / LENGTH INSIDE 38 FT / M.C.B. COUPLERS AIR BRAKE", hook couplers with ears, brakewheels do not reach floor. D. Ely Collection. 45 90 25

(K) Light brown body, light brown lower body edge, rubber-stamped "LAKE SHORE 65784" in black, two lines of data on right: "Capacity 20,000 LBS / Weight 80,000 LBS", large one-inch brakewheels. D. Ely Collection. 45 90 25

(L) Similar to (F), but 3-1/8" lettering, brakewheels reversed. D. Ely Collection. **NRS**

IV. Later "Lionel Corporation" Production: Data lines on sides vary as follows:

Type I: two lines, "CAPACITY 20000 LBS / WEIGHT 10000 LBS"

Type II: two lines, "CAPACITY 60000 LBS / WEIGHT 36500 LBS"

Type III: two lines, "CAPACITY 60000 LBS / WEIGHT 34500 LBS"

Type IV: four lines, "CAPACITY 60000 WEIGHT 34500 / LENGTH INSIDE 36 FT / M.C.B. COUPLERS / AIR BRAKE" rubber-stamped in black or gold on bottom, "MADE IN U.S.A. / THE LIONEL CORPORATION / NEW YORK" in three lines, most often with car number.

(M) Dark gray body, olive green-painted upper rim and lower body edge, single-rivet flex trucks (some blackened), two brakewheels, Type IV data lines and "LAKE SHORE 65784" rubber-stamped in black, hook couplers with ears, coupler brackets. Pickard, Koff, Weaver, and D. Ely Collections. 32 50 25

(N) Gray body and lower body edge, pea green-painted body rim, Type I data lines and "LAKE SHORE" rubber-stamped in black, hook couplers with ears, coupler brackets, two brakewheels. 32 50 25

(O) Same as (N), except no data lines and dark green-painted rim, gold "Corp." stamp on bottom. D. Ely Collection. 35 55 25

(P) Gray body, pea green-painted body rim and lower body

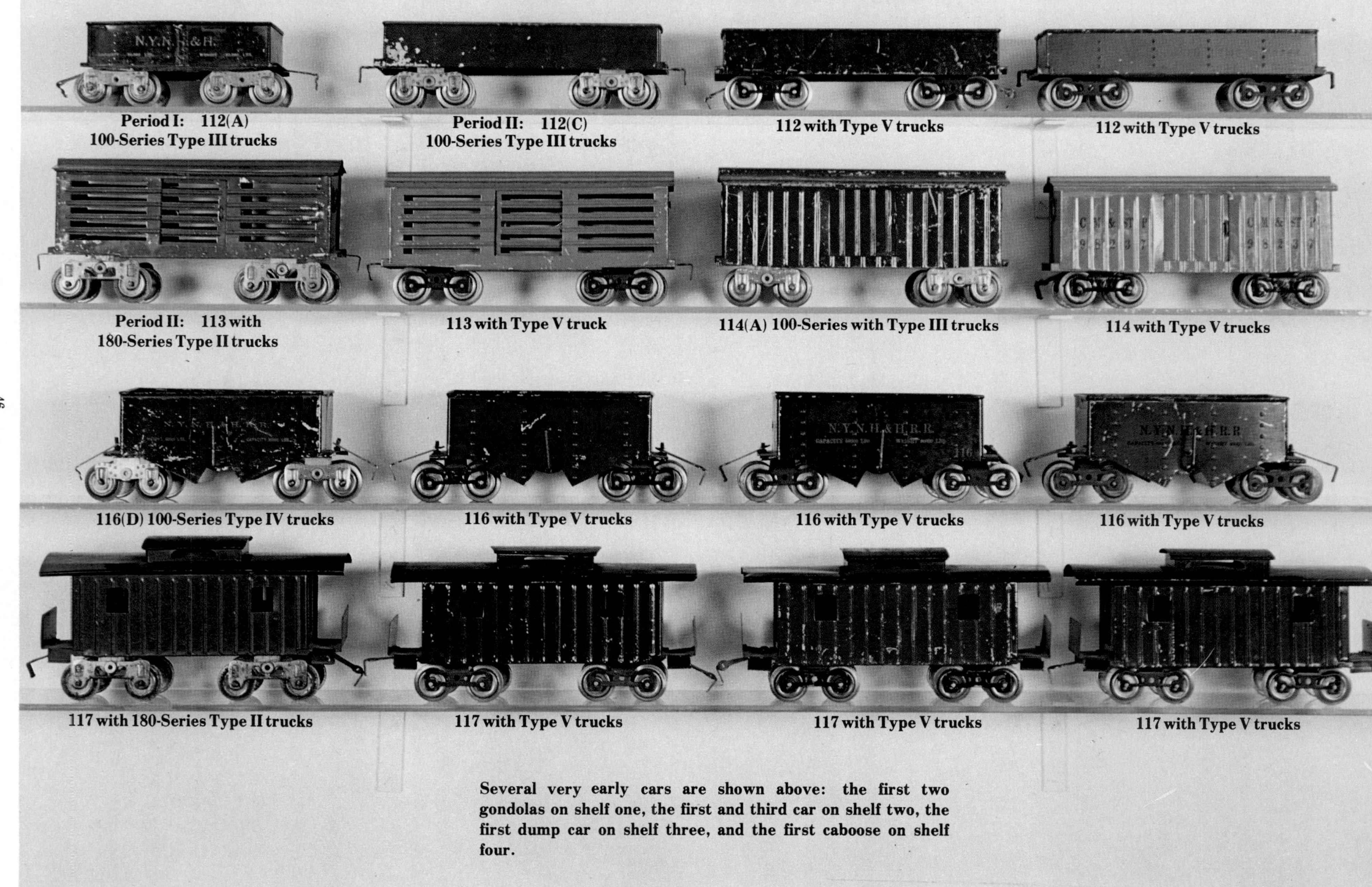

100 Series Freights

Period I: 112(A)
100-Series Type III trucks

Period II: 112(C)
100-Series Type III trucks

112 with Type V trucks

112 with Type V trucks

Period II: 113 with
180-Series Type II trucks

113 with Type V truck

114(A) 100-Series with Type III trucks

114 with Type V trucks

116(D) 100-Series Type IV trucks

116 with Type V trucks

116 with Type V trucks

116 with Type V trucks

117 with 180-Series Type II trucks

117 with Type V trucks

117 with Type V trucks

117 with Type V trucks

Several very early cars are shown above: the first two gondolas on shelf one, the first and third car on shelf two, the first dump car on shelf three, and the first caboose on shelf four.

Gd Exc Rst

edge, gold-lettered "ROCK ISLAND LINES", Type I data lines, hook couplers with ears, coupler brackets, two brakewheels, understamping in gold. D. Ely Collection. **35 55 25**

(Q) Same as (K), except black rubber-stamped "LAKE SHORE" only with no data lines. **32 50 25**

(R) Gray body, pea green-painted body rim, Type II data lines and "LAKE SHORE" rubber-stamped in black, hook couplers with ears, no coupler brackets, two brakewheels. Kotil comment. **32 50 25**

(S) Same as (R), but dark green body rim and coupler brackets. Kotil comment. **32 50 25**

(T) Gray body, green body rim, "LAKE SHORE 65784" rubber-stamped in gold, Type I data lines at upper left, single-rivet flex trucks, hook couplers with ears, two brakewheels. D. Ely Collection. **32 50 25**

(U) Red-brown body, dark green body rim, Type III data lines and "LAKE SHORE 65784" rubber-stamped in black, blackened single-rivet non-flex trucks, hook couplers with ears, no coupler brackets, two brakewheels. Kotil comment. **50 85 25**

(V) Same as (U), but Type IV data lines and single-rivet Type V flex trucks. D. Pickard Collection. **NRS**

(W) Dark gray body, dark green upper rim and lower body edge, single-rivet flex trucks, "LAKE SHORE 65784" rubber-stamped in black, Type IV data lines, black underframe lettering, hook couplers with ears, coupler brackets, two brake-wheels, latest 10-series truck variation with bubbles and slots. C. Weber Collection. **35 55 25**

13 CATTLE CAR: 1906-26, usually made with either four or five slats on door and five open slots on side, usually found in either pea green or apple green. On some samples, one of the vertical dividing lines for the side slats of the body may be stamped out of line on the last two rows of slats.

I. Early "Lionel Manufacturing Co." Production: Yellow underframe and usually two-piece roof construction.

(A) Yellow underframe, flat sides, five slats on both doors and sides, two brakewheels, each on left, two-piece roof with second piece forming walkway, green body, Type I three-rivet solid-side trucks, short hook couplers. D. Ely Collection. **200 400 25**

II. Later "Lionel Manufacturing Co." Production: Embossed "LIONEL MFG. CO." on underside.

(B) Same as (A), except three-rivet Type II open-side trucks, brakewheels on right, embossed "MFG." on underside. D. Ely Collection. **200 400 25**

(C) Green body, three-rivet Type II open-side trucks, long crinkle hook couplers, five slats in doors and sides, two brakewheels, one-piece roof, embossed "LIONEL MFG. CO." on underside. **150 300 25**

III. Early "Lionel Corporation" Production: No embossing or rubber-stamping.

(D) Dark green body, embossed sides, hook couplers with ears, no brakewheels, Type V trucks, four door slots. D. Ely Collection. **50 80 25**

IV. Later "Lionel Corporation" Production: Rubber-stamped with car number and "MADE IN U.S.A. / THE LIONEL CORPORATION / NEW YORK" in three lines on car bottom below number. Horizontally embossed stiffeners are present on the slats of these late production cars. Graves observation.

(E) Pea green body, five slots in doors and sides, one horizontal dividing bar uneven on last two rows of slats near base of body, single-rivet flex trucks, hook couplers with ears, no coupler brackets, no brakewheels, one-piece roof. Koff Collection. **50 80 25**

(F) Same as (E), except horizontal dividing bars evenly stamped, apple green body, and coupler brackets. Weaver Collection. **50 80 25**

(G) Same as (F), but no number on bottom (other lettering is crisp), has coupler brackets. D. Pickard Collection. **50 80 25**

(H) Same as (G), but pea green. C. Weber Collection. **50 80 25**

14 BOXCAR: 1906-26, most samples are lettered for "C. M. & ST. P." in rubber-stamped black lettering, usually painted red, yellow-orange, or orange. Early production shows considerable variations.

I. Early "Lionel Manufacturing Co." Production: Yellow-painted underframe and body interior, no embossing or stamping, usually two-piece roof.

(A) Red body, thin black vertical stripes, no embossing on frame or body, yellow-painted frame and body interior, two-piece red-painted roof, black-painted brakewheel at each end held by escutcheon pins, black-lettered "C. M. & ST. P. / 19050" to both left and right of doors in two lines, door handles made from escutcheon pins, short hook couplers held in place by escutcheon pins, closed-side Type I three-rivet trucks. Sullens Collection. **175 350 50**

(B) Same as (A), but Type II three-rivet open-side trucks, red-painted brakewheel on right, short crinkle hook couplers. D. Ely Collection. **175 350 50**

(C) Red body with thin black striping, yellow underframe, embossed sides, two-piece roof, one brakewheel, Type I closed-side three-rivet trucks, short hook couplers, lettered "NYC & H.R.R.R. 5906" on sides. **175 350 50**

(D) Yellow-orange body, embossed sides, Type I three-rivet closed-side trucks, long crinkle hook couplers, black rubber-stamped lettering "NYC & H. R. R.R. 4351". Sattler Collection. **175 350 50**

(E) Dark red body, no primer, embossed slats painted black, lettered "C.M. & ST.P. / 54087", frame embossed "LIONEL MFG. CO. / N.Y.", long straight hook couplers, no coupler brackets, couplers painted same as car, doors open left to right, one Type IV and one Type V single-rivet flex truck. C. Weber Collection. **175 350 50**

(F) Same as (C), but numbered "54087", no black lines or embossing on sides, brakewheel on left, long crinkle hook couplers. **175 350 50**

(G) Same as (F), but yellow-orange body. **175 350 50**

II. Later "Lionel Manufacturing Co." Production: Embossed "LIONEL MFG. CO." on underside.

(H) Same as (A), but body and door sides are embossed, short hook couplers, Type III trucks, unpainted brakewheel on left. D. Ely Collection. **50 80 25**

(I) Red body, one-piece roof, black-painted embossed vertical slats and door handles. Unpainted brakewheels at each end, red-painted long straight couplers fastened by rail type fastener. Flex trucks with T bolsters and no crimps, black lettering in simple block style: "CM & ST P / 54087". One letter is fitted between each slat except for "ST" which was made thinner to fit space. C. Weber Collection. **75 150 25**

(J) Yellow-orange body, embossed sides, single-rivet flex trucks, numbered "98237", hook couplers with ears. **40 70 25**

Gd Exc Rst

III. Early "Lionel Corporation" Production: No embossing or rubber stamping on underside.

(K) Orange body, embossed sides, no black stripes, rubber-stamped "C. M. & ST. P 98237" twice on both sides in black, single-rivet flex trucks, hook couplers with ears, no coupler brackets, no brakewheels, one-piece roof, no underside markings. Koff Collection. **40 70 25**

IV. Later "Lionel Corporation" Production: Rubber-stamped on car frame with car number and "MADE IN U.S.A. / THE LIONEL CORPORATION / NEW YORK" in three lines.

(L) Same as (K), but with coupler brackets and lettering shown immediately above. C. Weber Collection. **50 100 25**

(M) Same as (K), but red rubber-stamped "Made and Guaranteed By / The Lionel Corporation / New York, U.S.A." on underside of frame. Rubber-stamped lettering on bottom is similar to the type of lettering produced by a typewriter. Hook couplers with ears painted same color as car. (Unusual for a late car to have painted couplers. Car probably made for export.) J. Flynn Collection. **55 100 25**

(N) Same as (K), but rubber-stamped frame, doors are a brown-orange color clearly different from car body color, door handles stamped from door itself rather than separately attached. Weaver Collection. **40 70 25**

(O) Circa 1920. Special "Harmony Creamery" issue, dark green embossed sides, gold rubber-stamped "BALTIMORE & OHIO" high on sides, railroad name separated by door, rubber-stamped gold "MILK INSULATED TANK SERVICE" in three lines at left of door and "HARMONY CREAMERY PITTSBURGH PA" in two lines at right of door, single-rivet flex trucks, hook couplers with ears, coupler brackets, number "8118" on lower left of car sides. Very rare, produced for promotional purposes only. P. Graves comment. **NRS**

15 OIL CAR: 1906-26. All varieties of this car have a black girder supporting the tank and attaching the couplers; early versions had wooden painted domes and tank ends; all had gold-painted handrails. Later production features metal domes and ends; steps are found on the sides of the tank near the ends and are of three types: simple, U-shaped steps on earliest production; four-piece gold-painted soldered steps later on; and one-piece gold-painted steps with three holes on the last versions of the car. Early cars have long slots for couplers with stops soldered in. The listings below are grouped by body colors for the user's convenience.

I. Red Tank Bodies

—Early "MFG." Production

(A) Rubber-stamped "PENNSYLVANIA RR 416" in black, Type I three-rivet closed-side trucks, short hook couplers, red dome, U-shaped steps, wooden ends and dome. **200 400 50**

—Later "MFG." Production

(B) Same as (A), except Type II three-rivet open-side trucks. **175 350 50**

(C) Rubber-stamped "PENNSYLVANIA RR" in black without number, single-rivet flex trucks, hook couplers with ears, two gold handrails, black wooden dome, three-hole steps, black metal ends. **35 65 25**

II. Maroon Tank Bodies

—Early "MFG." Production

(D) Rubber-stamped "PENNSYLVANIA RR 416" in black, Type I three-rivet closed-side trucks, long crinkle hook couplers, maroon dome, four-piece steps, wooden ends. **32 50 25**

(E) Rubber-stamped "PENNSYLVANIA RR 416" in black, Type II three-rivet open-side trucks, short hook couplers, maroon dome, U-shaped steps, wooden ends. **75 150 25**

(F) Rubber-stamped "PENNSYLVANIA RR" in sans-serif gold letters without number, three-rivet open Type II trucks, long straight couplers, coupler stops near end of girder, black dome, four-piece steps, wooden ends. D. Ely Collection. **75 150 25**

—Later "Lionel Manufacturing Co." Production

(G) Rubber-stamped "PENNSYLVANIA RR" in gold serif letters without number, three-rivet open Type II trucks, long straight hook couplers, higher dome. D. Ely Collection. **32 50 25**

(H) Rubber-stamped "PENNSYLVANIA RR" in gold sans-serif letters without number; black ends, dome, frame, and couplers; gold handrails and steps, wooden dome, metal ends, one side of frame stamped in gold "LIONEL / LINES / N.Y. / MADE IN U.S.A.", long crinkle hook couplers, Type IV trucks. C. Weber Collection. **32 50 25**

(I) Rubber-stamped "PENNSYLVANIA" in gold sans-serif lettering, single-rivet flex trucks, hook couplers with ears, two gold-painted handrails on each side, black metal dome, four-piece soldered steps, black metal ends. Kotil comment. **32 50 25**

—Early "Lionel Corporation" Production

(J) Same as (H), but long crinkle hook couplers and "PENNSYLVANIA RR" in gold serif rubber-stamped lettering. Sattler Collection. **32 50 25**

(K) Rubber-stamped "PENNSYLVANIA RR" in black, single-rivet flex trucks, hook couplers with ears, two gold handrails, black wooden dome, three-hole steps, black metal ends. **32 50 25**

—Later "Lionel Corporation" Production

(L) Same as (I), but three-hole steps and "PENNSYLVANIA" in gold serif lettering. Weaver Collection. **32 50 25**

(M) Same as (I), but three-hole steps. Koff and Sullens Collections. **32 50 25**

III. Brown Tank Bodies

—Later "Manufacturing Co." Production

(N) Rubber-stamped "PENNSYLVANIA" in gold sans-serif lettering, single-rivet flex trucks, hook couplers with ears, long coupler slots, wooden dome, two gold handrails on each side and black metal ends. D. Ely Collection. **35 55 25**

—Early "Lionel Corporation" Production

(O) Same as (N), but three-hole gold steps, short coupler slot, metal dome. D. Ely Collection. **35 55 25**

(P) Same as (N), but three-hole gold steps, short coupler slot, gold lettering with serifs. C. Weber Collection. **45 65 25**

(Q) Same as (N), but brown wooden dome and sans-serif gold lettering. Lotstein Collection. **35 55 25**

16 BALLAST (DUMP): 1906-26, a popular operating car with levers at the ends to dump the load by opening the car sides, measures 10-3/4", found in red, maroon, brown, and dark green colors with a variety of trim and girder colors as well as variations in trucks and couplers. Listed by body colors for user's convenience. The prototype for this car can still be observed on the Strasburg Railroad near the TCA Museum in Strasburg, Pennsylvania.

I. Brown Bodies

—Early "Lionel Manufacturing Co." Production

(A) Black trim, three-rivet trucks, short hook couplers, and yellow girder. Confirmation requested as to whether girder has long cut and strap. **225 450 40**

Gd Exc Rst

—Later "Lionel Manufacturing Co." Production

(B) Black trim, black girder, rubber-stamped "PENNSYLVANIA 65784", "CAPACITY 20000 LBS, WEIGHT 10000 LBS" in sans-serif gold lettering. Confirmation requested. **150 300 25**

(C) Black trim, black frame, rubber-stamped as in (B), except weight is "34500 LBS". Kotil Collection. **150 300 25**

II. Maroon Bodies

—Early "Lionel Manufacturing Co." Production

(D) Dark green trim, yellow girder, Type II three-rivet open-side trucks, short straight hook couplers, lettered "PENNSYLVANIA 65784" in serif black letters, two lines of data. **200 400 40**

—Later "Lionel Manufacturing Co." Production

(E) Same as (D), but black girder and short crinkle hook couplers. **85 175 40**

(F) Black trim, frame and couplers, lettered "PENNSYLVANIA R.R." in gold san-serif lettering, long crinkle hook couplers, Type IV single-rivet flex trucks, girder with long cut and strap. C. Weber Collection. **85 175 40**

—Early "Lionel Corporation" Production

(G) Same as (E), but single-rivet flex trucks and hook couplers with ears. **85 175 40**

III. Red Bodies

—Early "Lionel Corporation" Production

(H) Black trim, black girder, single-rivet flex trucks, hook couplers with ears, rubber-stamped "PENNSYLVANIA 76399" in sans-serif gold lettering. Confirmation requested. **85 175 40**

(I) Same as (H), but brown-maroon, small "PENNSYLVANIA" in black block letters, "65784", four lines of data, matte finish. D. Ely Collection. **85 175 40**

(J) Same as (H), but brown-maroon, large "PENNSYLVANIA" in black serif letters, "65784", two lines of data, gloss finish. D. Ely Collection. **85 175 40**

IV. Dark Green Bodies

—Early "Lionel Manufacturing Co." Production

(K) 1911-12, dark green with maroon trim and girder, lettered "PENNSYLVANIA R.R." in 3/16" gold-stamped sans-serif lettering, long crinkle hook couplers, Type IV single-rivet flex trucks with large hole eyelet, open side frames, and embossed springs and rivets. R. Kirchner Collection. **85 175 40**

—Later "Lionel Corporation" Production

(L) Maroon trim, green girder, single-rivet flex trucks, hook couplers with ears, "PENNSYLVANIA 65784" in black 1/4" block lettering, "16" stamped on end opposite dump mechanism, two lines of data on right, Type V truck. Weaver and D. Ely Collections. **85 175 40**

(M) Same as (L), but 3/8" serif lettering, and couplers painted green with frame, Type V truck. D. Ely comment and C. Weber Collection. **85 175 40**

17 CABOOSE: 1906-26. This car occurs in early, middle, and late construction styles and comes in red, maroon, and brown body colors. Cupola sides are found in both smooth and embossed sides, and the cupola roof can be found with rounded or squared ends. Nearly all examples are rubber-stamped "NYC & H.R.R.R." in black, and there are different numbers below that stamping, the most common being "4351". All listings are stamped "NYC & H.R.R.R. 4351" unless otherwise noted.

I. Early "Lionel Manufacturing Co." Production: Yellow underframe, no embossing or rubber-stamping.

(A) Red body, black-lettered "NYC & H.R.RR. / 51906." (Note that "H. R.R R." is correct. There is no period after the second "R".) Yellow undercoat on both sides of frame, black stripes on body side, sides not embossed, black steps. Platform end plate is a separate piece of metal soldered to the frame. Car ends each have a large door flanked by large window cutouts. Black main window awnings, black-painted main roof and cupola roof. Red-painted smooth-sided cupola with two rectangular windows on each side. Inside the car, there is a bench along part of each side in front of the window. Each bench has a pin to hold a figure of a train crewman. (This is somewhat similar to the arrangement found on early Standard Gauge trolleys.) Three-rivet closed-side trucks embossed "PAT. PENDING", short straight hook couplers held by escutcheon pins. R. Sullens and D. Ely Collections. **175 350 45**

(B) Same as (A), but Type II three-rivet open-side trucks. D. Ely comment. **175 350 40**

(C) Red body, black-lettered "NYC & H.R.R.R. / 5906", embossed sides with painted black lines, three-rivet open-side trucks, long straight hook couplers. D. Ely Collection. **NRS**

(D) Red body, no undercoat or stamping on underside, single-rivet flex trucks, black main roof, integral black steps, awnings on cupola windows, but not on main windows (reverse of A), squared black cupola roof, number 342715, long crinkle hook couplers. D. Ely Collection. **150 300 40**

(E) Same as (D), but no pins for figure. D. Ely Collection. **NRS**

(F) Same as (E), but later arched cupola windows, rolled edge cupola roof, no awnings, long crinkle hook couplers. D. Ely Collection. **150 300 40**

(G) Brown body, no undercoat or stamping on underside, hook couplers with ears, rubber-stamped "NYC & HRR 4351" (note one "R" not present), brown platform, black main roof, soldered black steps, black cupola roof, cupola windows smaller than usual. Kotil Collection. **150 300 40**

II. Later "Lionel Manufacturing Co." Production: Embossed "LIONEL MFG. CO." on underside. All sides have smooth body sides without awnings unless otherwise stated.

(H) Brown body and underside, single-rivet flex trucks, hook couplers with ears, no coupler brackets, brown end platform with integral black-painted steps, black main roof, smooth cupola sides, square brown cupola roof. Koff Collection. **60 120 30**

(I) Same as (H), but no embossing on bottom. D. Pickard Collection. **60 120 40**

(J) Brown body, hook couplers with ears, rubber-stamped "NYC & HRR 4351" (note absence of one "R"), brown platform, black main roof, soldered black steps with two risers, smaller windows, brown cupola roof. Kotil Collection. **60 120 35**

(K) Maroon body, number 5906, single-rivet flex trucks, black main roof, integral black steps, embossed cupola sides, awnings on cupola but not on main windows, square black cupola roof. D. Ely comment. **75 150 35**

(L) Red body, number 342715, single-rivet Type V flex trucks, long crinkle hook couplers, black main roof, integral red steps, embossed cupola sides, cupola has stamped awnings, square black cupola roof. D. Ely comment. **75 150 35**

(M) Same as (L), but no awnings and maroon body. D. Ely comment. **60 120 35**

Gd Exc Rst

(N) Dark red body, lettered "NYC & HRRR", number 342715, integral black steps, black main roof, black square cupola roof, embossed sides, smooth cupola sides, cupola windows with stamped awnings, long crinkle hook couplers, single-rivet flex trucks. C. Weber Collection. **75 150 35**

III. Early "Lionel Corporation" Production: No embossing or rubber-stamping.

(O) Same as (G), but three "R"s in "NYC & H.R.R.R." lettering, three-hole steps and normal cupola window size, brown cupola and roof. D. Ely Collection. **75 150 40**

IV. Later "Lionel Corporation" Production: Rubber-stamped "17" and "MADE IN U.S.A. / THE LIONEL CORPORATION / NEW YORK" in three lines on car bottom.

(P) Maroon body, number 4351, single-rivet flex trucks, hook couplers with ears, no coupler brackets, black main roof, soldered black steps with three punched holes (similar to 15 Oil Car), smooth cupola sides, maroon cupola ends, no awnings, square black cupola roof. Koff and Weaver Collections. **32 50 25**

(Q) Same as (M), except cupola is embossed and has rounded roof. **32 50 25**

(R) Brown body, rubber-stamped lettering differs in height and thickness from earlier samples, number 4351, single-rivet flex trucks, hook couplers with ears, black main roof, soldered three-hole steps, embossed cupola sides, no awnings, rounded black cupola roof. D. Ely Collection. **35 60 25**

(S) Same as (O), except rounded maroon cupola roof. D. Ely Collection. **35 60 25**

(T) Brown body, embossed sides, square black cupola roof, black main roof, three-hole black steps, number 4351, hook couplers with ears. D. Ely Collection. **35 60 25**

THE 100-SERIES FREIGHT CARS

By David Ely, Jim Flynn, and William Schilling
With the assistance of Chris Rohlfing

The 100 Series of freight cars began in 1910, with the introduction of the 112 Gondola and 116 Ballast cars. Two years later, Lionel began sales of the 113 Cattle Car, 114 Boxcar, and 117 Caboose. No other types of cars were introduced between these years and the cessation of production in 1927, when the 500 Series replaced these cars.

This section has been completely rewritten thanks to the research efforts of William Schilling, David Ely, and Jim Flynn. This work is the result of observation and comparison of over 150 cars. Their efforts clearly indicate the kind of intensive research work that is needed to establish a construction chronology in other car series.

Bill Schilling began the project by acquiring as many 100-series cars as he could and noting the observable characteristics of each car. Bill's conclusions were based on data from 85 cars. Prior to this research, the only chronology we knew for certain was that cars with embossed floors were clearly from the "Lionel Manufacturing Co." production, and cars with rubber-stamped floors were clearly from later "Lionel Corporation" production. Cars with plain floors were from the transition period of either very late "Lionel Manufacturing" production or very early "Lionel Corporation" production. Trucks and couplers were not a very good determiner because they are easily replaced. The same is also true of roof styles and colors since roofs are easily changed from one car to another.

The Type I crimp of side to floor is very tight. Note that this early car does not have a coupler support bar and that the coupler is fastened to the body by a nail-type fastener soldered on to the car floor. W. Schilling Collection, M. Feinstein photograph.

The top photo shows the Type II crimp where the inner lip is folded loosely and vertically. The lower photo shows the Type III crimp where the inner lip is folded at approximately a 45 degree angle. Type III crimps are usually found on late cars with the "Corporation" stamping on the frame underside. The discovery of these crimping differences gave us a very important tool in dating cars.

Bill's observations led to the discovery of construction techniques that clearly point to the chronology of the cars.

These are details that cannot be altered and therefore can be verified as original, and when combined with the above mentioned floor information further delineate the time frame. The first clue is the body to frame crimping on the underside of the car. The earliest or Type I crimp is a very tight crimp with no visible spaces. The Type II crimp has the inner lip folded up to vertical, but loosely. We call this open crimping. The last or Type III crimp has the inner lip folded to approximately a 45 degree angle. It is called very open crimping. As in most construction techniques, there is some overlapping of types, but the body to frame crimping is the first clue to the age of the cars. Since the tight crimp is most common on cars with embossed floors and almost never found with cars with rubber-stamped Corporation floors, cars with tight body to frame crimping are clearly the earliest production. Likewise, very open crimping is most common on rubber-stamped Corporation frames.

A comparison of two 112 Gondolas. The later car with a Type II crimp is on the left, while the earlier car with a Type I crimp is on the right. The earlier car has an embossed floor and a long crinkle hook coupler. W. Schilling Collection, M. Feinstein photograph.

The end construction of the cars is not as helpful in determining chronology since all three types seem to be used throughout. Logic would seem to indicate that the earliest Type I end had the two pieces of metal loosely rolled over and interlocking. The second or Type II end had the side bent around the end and then the lip folded back tightly 180 degrees and spot-soldered to the end. The Type III end had the side bent around the end and soldered to the end. The folded back lip is eliminated entirely. The logical chronology from a construction standpoint would be for Type I to be early and Type III to be late, but this is not the case. Type I rolled ends are found on both ends of production and therefore do not help with dating.

The next characteristic that Bill discovered was the roof style on the 113 Cattle Car and the 114 Boxcar. The earliest cars had the corners of the roof nipped off at a 45 degree angle. All later cars have roofs with square corners. These cars also give us another clue as to their dating. Bill found that the earliest cars have door guides that are round on one side and flat on the other. We call these flat door guides. The later cars have full round wire door guides. The change in both the roof corner and the door guides takes place near the end of the Manufacturing period.

The last variables to be entered are paint color, trucks, and couplers. Trucks and couplers really give very little help as there is considerable overlapping. Bill did define several variations of the 100-series truck types, however. (See descriptions of 100-series Trucks in the Appendix.) The Type I truck is a solid-side truck with embossed springs and rivets, straight single-bend bolster with dimples in the bend, and pointed-end bolster. It was used in 1910-1912. The Type II truck (1912-1914) had a double-bend, round-end bolster. Both Types I and II attached the bolster to the side frame with a small hole eyelet. Type III (1912-1924) is similar to Type II but is 1/8" taller and the bolster is attached with a large flat-end "eyelet" rivet. This is the common "flex truck". Type IV (1912-1913) is a plain, open-side frame nickel-plated truck. This is commonly reported as a passenger car truck for the 35 and 36 Passenger Cars. However, it is frequently found on earlier 100-series freight cars. There are three variations of the Type IV truck. Type IV-A has a smooth top bolster. Type IV-B has two round bumps on the top of the bolster. Type IV-C has two bumps with a slot in each bump. The Type V truck (1912-1926) is the same as the Type IV, but is black. It is commonly called the "100-series Truck". There are three variations painted black, and three that are chemically blackened. Type V-A, V-B, and V-C are all painted black. V-A has a smooth bolster, V-B has two round bumps on the bolster, V-C has slotted bumps. Type V-D, V-E, and V-F are chemically blackened. V-D has smooth bolsters, V-E has bumps, and V-F has slotted bumps. Most of the later cars have Type V trucks.

There are five coupler types that can be found on 100-series cars. We have no reports of cars with short straight hook couplers except the early 7" gondolas, although they were in use between 1906 and 1914. All other early Manufacturing cars have either long straight hook couplers, short crinkle hook, or long crinkle hook couplers. The end of the Manufacturing period as well as the transition and Corporation period cars have couplers referred to as Hook with Ears. The earliest couplers were riveted on with a round-head rivet. Next a flat-head rivet with a stepped end was used. Finally, a number of cars had couplers attached with cotter pins, but this method has not been verified as factory original.

On the gondolas and ballast cars, Bill identified two types of rim rolls. Type I has a round cross section. Type II has an inverted teardrop cross-section. This characteristic is very difficult to see, however. Also, there does not seem to be a clear cut pattern to its use. Therefore, it is not an important variable. Likewise, caboose cupola roofs have either round ends or square ends, but there is no pattern. Brakewheels are all six-spoked unpainted cast metal and are either 3/4" or 1" in diameter. Again there is no pattern.

Finally, Bill identified four types of road name lettering styles. First is the 10-series style used on the early gondolas. 10-series lettering uses upper and lower case letters. Lionel also used "sans-serif" block lettering and "serif" block lettering. Most significantly, Bill identified the lettering used on most of the later cars as Times New Roman, referred to as "Roman Block". This style uses all capitals with very small serifs.

Bill's preliminary list was then turned over to David Ely to compare with his large collection of 100-series cars. The number of observed variations now approached 150. Dave had a number of cars that were produced earlier than Bill's cars. He verified many of Bill's variations as well. Dave believed that Bill's identification of construction techniques was an important contribution to the research on these cars. He put all of the data on computer and arranged the characteristics in the following order: (1) construction characteristics of the body of the car, (2) trucks, and (3) color, trim, lettering, and lettering type characteristics which may vary. Dave spent considerable time sorting through the data and creating as accurate a chronological list as possible.

We then took Dave Ely's expanded list to Jim Flynn who compared it to his collection. We found thirteen more variations. In addition, we discovered two more construction variables and one lettering variable which were confirmed by Dave Ely when he revised his list to include Jim's cars. First, all early brakewheels were attached with a round-faced eyelet rivet. All later brakewheels were attached with a flat-faced eyelet rivet. Second, on all cabooses, while the distance between the windows varies, the spacing from the bottom of the window to the bottom of the car is a constant. All observed windows are 1-7/16" from the bottom. This would indicate that the windows were punched out one at a time rather than two at a time. This also explains one of Jim's cabooses that has one window considerably lower than the other three. Thirdly, on most cabooses until well into the Corporation period, the bottom of the lettering is nearly even with the bottom of the window. Then it gradually drops to 1/2" below the window bottom. The brakewheel rivet and the caboose lettering placement also give us clues to chronology.

While this research is significant and has greatly expanded our knowledge of these cars, all of us who worked on this project would agree that there are still variations to uncover. This list is far from complete. We invite anyone who has a 100-series car that does not fit the listings that follow to let us know so that we can correct and expand our listings. We have not listed variations that are identical except for truck types as separate variations since trucks are so easily exchanged. We note only the trucks found on the variations.

NOTE: The 100-series listings have been completely rewritten based on the research outlined above. While some previously listed legitimate variations may inadvertantly have been omitted, it is hoped that those collectors having those variations will resubmit them to us. Also, a maroon gondola lettered "PENNSYLVANIA" is known to exist. We need details of its construction and other characteristics.

Gd Exc Rst

112 GONDOLA: 1910-26. Over the 16 years of production of this car, a great number of variations were produced. Most of them are rubber-stamped "LAKE SHORE 65784" in black; exceptions are noted below. There are six main types of data lines rubber-stamped in black on the car sides.

Type I: two lines, "CAPACITY 80000 LBS / WEIGHT 30000 LBS"

Type II: two lines, "CAPACITY 80000 LBS / WEIGHT 35000 LBS"

Type III: one line, "WEIGHT 35000 LBS" on lower left car side, "CAPACITY 60000 LBS" on lower right side.

Type IV: same as Type III, but reversed.

Type V: four lines, "CAPACITY 60000 WEIGHT 34500 / LENGTH INSIDE 36 FT / M.C.B. COUPLERS / AIR BRAKE"

Type VI: two lines, "CAPACITY 20000 LBS / WEIGHT 10000 LBS"

I. Early "Lionel Manufacturing Co." Production: 7" cars, some versions embossed "LIONEL MFG. CO." Trim color refers to the body rim.

(A) Dark olive green body only 7" long, red body rim, rubber-stamped "LAKE SHORE" only in gold, Type II flex trucks, Type I data lines, short crinkle hook couplers, embossed "LIONEL MFG. CO." on car floor. **150 300 75**

(B) Dark olive green body only 7" long, red body rim and bottom edge, rubber-stamped "N.Y.N.H. & H." in gold, Type I flex trucks, Type I data lines, long crinkle hook couplers, unmarked body floor. Weaver Collection. **150 300 75**

(C) Same as (B), but embossed body floor and long straight hook couplers. D. Ely Collection. **150 300 75**

(D) Same as (C), but short crinkle hook couplers attached outside body. D. Ely Collection. **150 300 75**

(E) Same as (C), but olive interior, red lower body edge, and long crinkle hook couplers, Type II trucks. D. Ely Collection. **150 300 75**

(F) Same as (E), but red body rim, no primer, floor embossing end to end instead of side to side, Type I data but larger, higher, and farther from ends than normal. C. Weber Collection. **150 300 75**

II. Later "Lionel Manufacturing Co." Production: Embossed "LIONEL MFG. CO." on car floor, 9" bodies, no coupler bracket, car number does not appear on car.

(A) Red body, dark olive rim, rubber-stamped "LAKE SHORE" in black 5/16" 10-series lettering, Type I tight bottom crimp, long crinkle hook couplers, Type II data lines, Type I trucks. D. Ely Collection. **35 55 30**

(B) Same as (A), but long crinkle hook couplers painted to match car and frame, and 3/8" black 10-series lettering. J. Flynn Collection. **35 55 30**

(C) Same as (A), but long straight hook couplers. **35 55 30**

(D) Same as (A), but Type II open bottom crimp, couplers not present, Type V-A trucks. D. Ely Collection. **35 55 30**

(E) Same as (D), but unusual data lines "CAPACITY 20000 LBS / WEIGHT 30000 LBS". D. Ely Collection. **NRS**

(F) Same as (D), but Type I tight bottom crimp, teardrop rim roll, and Type III data lines. W. Schilling Collection. **35 55 30**

(G) Same as (F), but short crinkle hook couplers, Type IV-A trucks. W. Schilling Collection. **35 55 30**

(H) Same as (B), but unpainted long crinkle hook couplers, round rim roll, Type IV data lines, Type II trucks. W. Schilling Collection. **35 55 30**

(I) Brown body, rubber-stamped "LAKE SHORE / 65784" in 5/16" black 10-series lettering, Type II open bottom crimp, hook with ears couplers, Type V data lines, Type V-A trucks. D. Ely Collection. **35 55 30**

(J) Same as (I), but dark olive rim, 3/8" lettering, Type IV-A trucks. D. Ely Collection. **35 55 30**

(K) Dark brown body, dark olive rim, rubber-stamped "NYC & HRRR / 65784" in 3/8" black 10-series lettering, Type II open bottom crimp, Type VI data lines, Type V-A trucks. D. Ely Collection. **35 55 30**

(L) Same as (K), but lettered "N.Y.C. & H.R.R. / 76399" in 1/4" black 10-series lettering, Type V data lines. One example reported with Type III trucks and one with Type V-D trucks. D. Ely and J. Flynn Collections. **35 55 30**

III. "Transition Period" Production: No embossing or stamping on car undersides, no coupler bracket, car number does not appear on car.

(A) Red-brown body, dark olive rim, rubber-stamped "LAKE SHORE / 65784" in 9/32" black Roman block lettering, Type I tight bottom crimp, teardrop rim roll, hook with ears couplers, Type VI data lines, Type V-A trucks. W. Schilling Collection. **35 55 30**

(B) Same as (A), but brown body with dark olive rim, 5/16" lettering, Type II open bottom crimp, Type III couplers. D. Ely Collection. **35 55 30**

	Gd	Exc	Rst

IV. Later "Lionel Corporation" Production: Rubber-stamped "MADE IN U.S.A. / THE LIONEL CORPORATION / NEW YORK" in black in three lines. All reported examples have coupler brackets, hook with ears couplers, Type III very open bottom crimp, round rim roll type, and Type VI data lines.

(A) Dark gray body, dark green rim, rubber-stamped "LAKE SHORE / 65784" in black 9/32" Roman block lettering, car number on bottom, Type V-E trucks. W. Schilling Collection. **30 50 25**

(B) Same as (A), but green rim, no number on bottom, Type V-A trucks. W. Schilling Collection. **30 50 25**

(C) Dark gray body, dark olive rim, rubber-stamped "LAKE SHORE / 65784" in black 9/32" Roman block lettering, no number on bottom, Type V-A trucks. W. Schilling Collection. **30 50 25**

(D) Dark gray body, green rim, rubber-stamped "LAKE SHORE / 65784" in black 9/32" Roman block lettering, number on bottom. Reported with both V-A and V-B trucks. D. Ely and W. Schilling Collections. **30 50 25**

(E) Gray body, dark green rim, rubber-stamped "LAKE SHORE / 65784" in gold 9/32" Roman block lettering, data lines also gold, number on bottom, Type V-F trucks. W. Schilling Collection. **30 50 25**

(F) Gray body, green trim, rubber-stamped "ROCK ISLAND / 65784" in gold 1/4" Roman block lettering, data lines also gold, number on bottom, Type V-E trucks. D. Ely and W. Schilling Collections. **30 50 25**

(G) Same as (F), but rubber-stamped "LAKE SHORE / 65784". W. Schilling Collection. **30 50 25**

(H) Bright red body, pea green rim, rubber-stamped "LAKE SHORE / 65784" in black 9/32" Roman block lettering, no number on bottom, Type V-E trucks. D. Ely Collection. **30 50 25**

(I) Same as (H), but green rim. D. Ely Collection. **30 50 25**

113 CATTLE CAR: 1912-26. Previous editions listed this car as having either four or five slats. However, there are no known verifiable reports of five-slat cars. All known verifiable examples have four slats with five holes. Confusion may well have developed over whether the top of the car should be counted as a slat.

I. and II. "Lionel Manufacturing Co." Production: Embossed "LIONEL MFG. CO." on car floor; no examples have been reported which can be assigned to the earliest production. Reader contributions are requested. No lettering on car, number does not appear on car, no coupler brackets. Note that roofs can easily be switched to create square corner and nipped corner variations. Please make a special effort in reporting on the roof to determine its originality. Please note if roof is original.

(A) Medium green body, Type I tight bottom crimp, Type I rolled end, nipped roof corners, flat door guides, 3/4" brakewheel on left side of end, long crinkle hook couplers, Type II trucks inset further from end than all other variations. D. Ely Collection. **40 60 30**

(B) Same as (A), but brakewheel on right side of end, Type II trucks in regular position. W. Schilling Collection. **40 60 30**

(C) Flat green, Type III very open bottom crimp, Type I rolled end construction, square roof corners, round door guides, 3/4" brakewheel on right side of end, hook with ears couplers, Type V-A trucks. W. Schilling Collection. **40 60 30**

(D) Medium green, bottom is reverse embossed (embossed in instead of out), Type II open bottom crimp, Type I ends, nipped roof corners, flat door guides, 3/4" brakewheel on left side of end, hook with ears couplers, Type V-A trucks. W. Schilling Collection. **40 60 30**

(E) Gloss green, Type I tight bottom crimp, Type I ends, nipped roof corners, flat door guides, 3/4" brakewheel on left side of end, long crinkle hook couplers, Type V-A trucks. D. Ely and W. Schilling Collections. **40 60 30**

(F) Pea green, Type III very open bottom crimp, Type I ends, nipped roof corners, round door guides, 3/4" brakewheel on right side of end, couplers not present on example, Type V-A trucks. W. Schilling Collection. **40 60 30**

(G) Gloss green, reverse embossed bottom lettering, Type II open bottom crimp, Type I ends, square roof corners, flat door guides, brakewheel missing on example but located on right side of end, hook with ears couplers, Type V-A trucks. W. Schilling Collection. **40 60 30**

(H) Gloss green, Type I tight bottom crimp, Type I ends, nipped roof corners, flat door guides, 3/4" brakewheel on left side of end, hook with ears couplers, Type IV trucks. D. Ely Collection. **40 60 30**

(I) Same as (H), but Type III bottom crimp, square roof corners, 1" brakewheel on right side of end, and Type V-A trucks. D. Ely Collection. **40 60 30**

III. Transition or Early "Lionel Corporation" Production: No embossing or rubber-stamping on car floor. Light pea green, Type III very open bottom crimp, Type III soldered end construction, square roof corners, round door guides, 3/4" brakewheel on left side of end, hook with ears couplers, no coupler bracket, Type V-A trucks. D. Ely, J. Flynn, and W. Schilling Collections. **40 60 30**

IV. Later "Lionel Corporation" Production: Rubber-stamped on car floor in black with car number and "MADE IN U.S.A. / THE LIONEL CORPORATION / NEW YORK" in three lines below number. All reported examples have Type III very open bottom crimp, square roof corners, round door guides, 3/4" brakewheels on the left side of the end except where noted, hook with ears couplers, and coupler brackets.

(A) Light pea green, Type III soldered end construction, brakewheel on right side of end, car number not on car, Type V-A trucks. W. Schilling Collection. **35 55 25**

(B) Light pea green, Type III ends, brakewheel on left, number on bottom, Type V-E trucks. W. Schilling Collection. **35 55 25**

(C) Same as (B), but Type II end construction, Type V-A trucks. **35 55 25**

(D) Same as (C), but no lettering on bottom (number is present), and no coupler brackets. W. Schilling Collection. **35 55 25**

(E) Same as (C), but Type I ends. W. Schilling Collection. **35 55 25**

(F) Same as (D), but Type I ends, and no number on bottom. W. Schilling Collection. **35 55 25**

(G) Pea Green, Type III ends, number on bottom. Examples reported with V-C and V-E trucks. D. Ely, J. Flynn, and W. Schilling Collections. **35 55 25**

(H) Same as (F), but pea green. W. Schilling Collection. **35 55 25**

(I) Pea green, Type I ends, no coupler bracket, no number on bottom, bottom rubber-stamped in white, Type V-F trucks. D. Ely Collection. **35 55 25**

Four different 114 Boxcars. The top left car, numbered "62976" was a very exciting discovery. It had not been previously reported. Note that it has the early Type II trucks. The lower right car has coupler guides as its couplers are not sagging. W. Schilling Collection, M. Feinstein photograph.

Gd Exc Rst

114 BOXCAR: 1912-26. Early versions of this car came in red, but most were finished in orange or yellow-orange. All known examples are rubber-stamped "CM & ST P" in black on both sides of the door, but the car numbers vary. All versions feature vertical embossed ribs on the sides.

I. and II. "Lionel Manufacturing Co." Production: All reported versions from this period have embossed car floors. No examples have been reported which reflect the earliest period of production. Reader comments are requested. No cars from this period have coupler brackets and the car number (114) does not appear on the car.

(A) Red body, black door handle, number "54087", Type I tight bottom crimp, Type I rolled end construction, nipped roof corners, 3/4" brakewheel on left side of end, flat door guides, 3/16" black sans-serif lettering, couplers not present on reported example, Type III trucks. D. Ely Collection. **100 150 35**

(B) Yellow-orange body, dark red door handle, number "62976", Type I bottom crimp, Type I ends, nipped roof corners, 3/4" brakewheel on left side of end, flat door guides, 3/16" black sans-serif lettering, long crinkle hook couplers, Type II trucks. D. Ely and W. Schilling Collections. **75 125 30**

(C) Same as (B), but number "54087" and Type V-A trucks. D. Ely Collection. **75 125 30**

(D) Same as (C), but hook with ears couplers. W. Schilling Collection. **75 125 30**

(E) Yellow-orange body, dark red door handle, number "54087", Type III very open bottom crimp, Type I ends, nipped roof corners, 3/4" brakewheel on right side of end, round door guides, 9/32" black Roman block lettering, hook with ears couplers, Type V-A trucks. W. Schilling Collection. **25 45 25**

(F) Yellow-orange body, dark red door handle, number "98237", Type II bottom crimp, Type II ends, square roof corners, 3/4" brakewheel on left side of end, round door guides, 9/32" black Roman block lettering, hook with ears couplers, Type V-A trucks. D. Ely Collection. **25 45 25**

(G) Same as (F), but 1" brakewheel on right side of end. D. Ely Collection. **25 45 25**

(H) Same as (D), but small rubber-stamped lettering on one end "LIONEL / LINES / N.Y. / MADE IN USA", and Type IV trucks. D. Ely Collection. **25 45 25**

(I) Same as (H), but Type II ends, 3/16" black Roman block lettering, long crinkle hook couplers, and Type V-A trucks. J. Flynn Collection. **25 45 25**

III. Transition or Early "Lionel Corporation" Production: No embossing or rubber-stamping on car floor. All reported examples are yellow-orange with dark red door handles, round door guides, no coupler brackets, no number (114) on car.

(A) Number "54087", Type II bottom crimp, Type I ends, nipped roof corners, 3/16" brakewheel on right side of end, 3/16" black sans-serif lettering, hook with ears couplers, Type V-A trucks. W. Schilling Collection. **25 45 25**

(B) Same as (A), but Type I bottom crimp, square roof corners, and 1" brakewheel on right side of end. Large rubber-stamping on one end "LIONEL LINES / NEW YORK / MADE IN USA". D. Ely Collection. **25 45 25**

(C) Same as (B), but 3/4" brakewheel on left side of end, 9/32" black Roman block lettering, no lettering on end. D. Ely Collection. **25 45 25**

(D) Same as (C), but number "98237", Type II bottom crimp, 3/16" black sans-serif lettering. D. Ely Collection. **25 45 25**

(E) Same as (D), but 1" brakewheel on right side of end. Lettering information not known as reported example has been painted over. W. Schilling Collection. **25 45 25**

Gd Exc Rst

(F) Same as (E), but Type III bottom crimp, 3/4" brakewheel on left side of end. W. Schilling Collection. 25 45 25

IV. Later "Lionel Corporation" Production: Rubber-stamped black lettering on car floor; "MADE IN U.S.A. / THE LIONEL CORPORATION / NEW YORK" in three lines below car number. All reported examples are orange, numbered "98237", with dark red door handles except where noted. All have Type III bottom crimps, square roof corners, 3/4" brakewheels on the left side of the end, round door guides, hook with ears couplers, coupler brackets.

(A) Type II ends, 5/16" black Roman block lettering, number (114) on bottom of frame, Type V-A trucks. W. Schilling Collection. 40 60 30

(B) Orange door handles, Type III ends, 5/16" black serif lettering, number on bottom, Type V-E trucks. J. Flynn Collection. 40 60 30

(C) Same as (A), but Type III ends. Examples reported with V-A and V-E trucks. D. Ely and W. Schilling Collections. 40 60 30

(D) Same as (A), but number on end. D. Ely and W. Schilling Collections. 40 60 30

116 BALLAST CAR: 1910-26. This smaller version of the 16 Operating car works differently from its "big brother". Instead of a lever on the end, the operating lever is on the side of the 116 car. It releases two flaps so that the load dumps out the car bottom, not its side. Both of these features are more prototypical than on the 16. It had been thought that all examples were stamped "N.Y.N.H. & H.R.R." in black or gold, but several exceptions have been found. There are four main types of data lines.

Type I: "CAPACITY 80,000 LBS" on left side, "WEIGHT 35,000 LBS" on right side.

Type II: "CAPACITY 80,000 LBS" on left side, "WEIGHT 30,000 LBS" on right side.

Type III: "CAPACITY 50,000 LBS" on left side, "WEIGHT 30,000 LBS" on right side.

Type IV: same as Type III, but left and right reversed. Data numbers are found with or without commas.

I. and II. "Lionel Manufacturing Co." Production: Floor embossed "LIONEL MFG. CO." All examples are lettered "N.Y.N.H. & H.R.R." unless otherwise noted. Car number does not appear on car. All road name lettering is serif style unless noted.

(A) Maroon body, black end piece, black rim, reverse embossed yellow underframe, lettered "N.Y.N.H. & H.", gold 5/16" lettering, 2-3/4" road name width, Type I data lines, short crinkle hook couplers, Type I trucks. D. Ely Collection. 40 60 30

(B) Maroon body, black end piece, black teardrop rim, regular embossed frame, lettered "N.Y.N.H. & H.", gold 5/16" Roman block lettering, Type II data lines, long straight hook (LS) couplers, Type III trucks. W. Schilling Collection. 40 60 30

(C) Same as (B), but serif lettering, road name width 2-7/8", long crinkle hook couplers painted to match car frame and body, Type II trucks. D. Ely and J. Flynn Collections. 40 60 30

(D) Same as (C), but 1/4" lettering, road name width 2-3/4", Type III data lines, unpainted long crinkle hook couplers, Type III trucks. D. Ely Collection. 40 60 30

(E) Maroon body, black end piece, black rim, lettered "N.Y.N.H.&H.R.R.", gold 3/16" lettering, 2-1/2" road name width, Type III data lines, long crinkle hook couplers, Type III trucks. D. Ely Collection. 40 60 30

(F) Same as (E), but 1/4" lettering, 3-1/2" road name width. Right end is stamped "LIONEL / LINES / N.Y. / MADE IN USA". D. Ely Collection. 40 60 30

(G) Same as (F), but maroon end piece, 3/16" lettering, 3-3/8" road name width, Type IV data lines. D. Ely and J. Flynn Collection. 40 60 30

(H) Same as (F), but maroon end piece, 3-1/4" road name width, hook with ears couplers, no lettering on end. J. Flynn Collection. 40 60 30

(I) Brown body, end piece and rim, gold 9/32" sans-serif lettering, 3-7/8" road name width, Type III data lines, hook with ears couplers, Type III trucks. D. Ely and W. Schilling Collections. 40 60 30

(J) Same as (I), but black 1/4" serif lettering, 3-13/16" road name width. D. Ely Collection. 40 60 30

(K) Same as (J), but 5/16" lettering, 3-1/2" road name width. 40 60 30

(L) Same as (J), but red-brown body, end piece, and teardrop rim, 7/32" lettering. W. Schilling Collection. 40 60 30

(M) Same as (L), but black round rim, 9/32" lettering. W. Schilling Collection. 40 60 30

III. and IV. "Lionel Corporation" Production: No embossing or rubber-stamping on floor. All reported examples are lettered "N.Y.N.H. & H.R.R." and have black 9/32" Roman block lettering except where noted, Type III data lines, and hook with ears couplers.

(A) Red-brown body and end piece, dark olive round rim, serif lettering, no number on car, Type III trucks. D. Ely Collection. 40 60 30

(B) Same as (A), but teardrop rim roll, 3-3/8" road name width, number on end, Type V-A trucks. J. Flynn Collection. 40 60 30

(C) Same as (B), but Roman block lettering, no number on car. W. Schilling Collection. 40 60 30

(D) Maroon body and end piece, dark olive teardrop rim, no number on car, Type III trucks. W. Schilling Collection. 40 60 30

(E) Same as (D), but number on end. W. Schilling Collection. 40 60 30

(F) Same as (D), but round rim roll. W. Schilling Collection. 40 60 30

(G) Same as (D), but V-A trucks. W. Schilling Collection. 40 60 30

(H) Brown body and end piece, dark olive teardrop rim, 3-1/2" road name width, no number on car, Type III trucks. D. Ely, J. Flynn, and W. Schilling Collections. 40 60 30

(I) Dark green body and end piece, red teardrop rim, gold lettering, no number on car, Type V-E trucks. W. Schilling Collection. 40 60 30

(J) Same as (I), but black lettering, number on end, 3-3/8" road name width. Examples reported with Type III and Type V-C trucks. D. Ely, J. Flynn, and W. Schilling Collections. 40 60 30

(K) Same as (I), but number on side. D. Ely and W. Schilling Collections. 50 75 35

(L) Dark gray body and end piece, green teardrop rim, 3-3/8" road name width, number on end. Examples reported with Type V-A and V-E trucks. 40 60 30

117 CABOOSE: 1912-26. All known examples of this car have fifteen embossed vertical ribs and are rubber-stamped "NYC & HRRR 4351" in black or gold. The lettering varies in size and

Gd Exc Rst

thickness. "4351" is 5/32" in all cases except one. Cupola roofs can be rounded or squared. All windows are 1-7/16" from the bottom of the car. The distance between the windows varies. No cabooses have been found with coupler brackets. All have black steps.

I. Early "Lionel Manufacturing Co." Production: All cars listed here have no embossing or rubber-stamping on the bottom. Lettering is 3/16" black serif lettering, number does not appear on car.

(A) Dark red body, (roof, cupola, and cupola roof are homemade replacements on reported example), Type I tight bottom crimp, Type II end construction, 4" between windows, short crinkle hook couplers, Type IV-A trucks. W. Schilling Collection. **30 50 25**

(B) Dark red body, cupola, and cupola roof, black main roof, Type I bottom crimp, Type I ends, 3-15/16" between windows, square cupola end shape, long crinkle hook couplers, Type III trucks. D. Ely Collection. **30 50 25**

II. Later "Lionel Manufacturing Co." Production: All floors are embossed "LIONEL MFG. CO.". All have square cupola roof ends. Car number does not appear on car.

(A) Dark brown body and cupola, black cupola roof and main roof, Type I bottom crimp, Type I ends, 3-31/32" between windows, 3/16" black serif lettering, long crinkle hook couplers, Type V-A trucks. One end black rubber-stamped "LIONEL LINES / N.Y. / MADE IN USA". D. Ely and W. Schilling Collections. **30 50 25**

(B) Dark brown body, cupola, and cupola roof, black main roof, frame reverse embossed, Type I bottom crimp, Type I ends, 4" between windows, 9/32" black Roman block lettering, hook with ears couplers, Type V-A trucks. W. Schilling Collection. **30 50 25**

(C) Same as (A), but frame is reverse embossed, Type II ends, and Roman block lettering. J. Flynn Collection. **30 50 25**

(D) Brown body, cupola, and cupola roof, black main roof, Type I bottom crimp, Type II ends, 3-31/32" between windows, 9/32" black serif lettering, long crinkle hook couplers, Type II trucks. D. Ely Collection. **330 50 25**

(E) Same as (D), but black cupola roof, 4" between windows, hook with ears couplers, and Type IV trucks. W. Schilling Collection. **30 50 25**

III. Transition or Early "Lionel Corporation" Production: No embossing or rubber-stamping on car floor. All have black lettering and the number does not appear on the car except where noted.

(A) Dark brown body and cupola, black cupola roof and main roof, Type I bottom crimp, Type II ends, 4" between windows, 9/32" Roman block lettering, square cupola roof ends, one car end black rubber-stamped "LIONEL LINES / N.Y. / MADE IN USA", car number on end, Type V-A trucks. W. Schilling Collection. **30 50 25**

(B) Same as (A), but Type II bottom crimp, 3/16" Roman block lettering, logo on end. D. Ely Collection. **30 50 25**

(C) Same as (B), but Type I bottom crimp and Type IV-A trucks. Logo on end. J. Flynn Collection. **30 50 25**

(D) Dark brown body, maroon cupola, black cupola and main roofs, "MFG." embossed frame, Type III bottom crimp, Type I ends, 3-3/4" between windows, 9/32" Roman block lettering, round cupola roof ends, Type V-A trucks. W. Schilling Collection. **30 50 25**

(E) Dark brown body, cupola, and cupola roof, black main roof, Type III bottom crimp, Type II ends, 3-13/16" between windows, 9/32" Roman block lettering, square cupola roof ends, Type V-A trucks. D. Ely and W. Schilling Collections. **30 50 25**

(F) Red-brown body and cupola, black roof and cupola roof, Type III bottom crimp, Type III ends, 9/32" Roman block lettering, round cupola roof ends, Type V-C trucks. W. Schilling Collection. **30 50 25**

(G) Tuscan body, cupola, and cupola roof, black main roof, Type III bottom crimp, Type I ends, 3-13/16" between windows, 9/32" Roman block lettering, Type V-A trucks. W. Schilling Collection. **30 50 25**

(H) Same as (G), but 4" between windows, 9/32" serif lettering, "4351" is 7/32" instead of the normal 5/32", logo and number are on the car end. On this example, three of the windows are the usual 1-7/16" from the bottom, and one window is 9/16" from the bottom. J. Flynn Collection. **30 50 25**

(I) Same as (G), but Type III ends, 4" between windows, and serif lettering. W. Schilling Collection. **30 50 25**

(J) Same as (G), but brown instead of tuscan, Type II bottom crimp, and 4" between windows. D. Ely Collection. **30 50 25**

IV. Later "Lionel Corporation" Production: Rubber-stamped lettering in black "MADE IN U.S.A. / THE LIONEL CORPORATION / NEW YORK" in three lines below rubber-stamped car number. All reported examples have Type III bottom crimps except where noted. All Type III ends except where noted. All have 9/32" Roman block lettering. Lettering is black except where noted. All have hook with ears couplers.

(A) Dark red body and cupola, black cupola and main roofs, Type III ends, 3-3/4" between windows, round cupola roof ends, Type V-A trucks. W. Schilling Collection. **30 50 25**

(B) Same as (A), but red-brown body, cupola, and cupola roof. One example reported with V-C trucks, and one reported with V-E trucks. W. Schilling Collection. **30 50 25**

(C) Same as (B), but black cupola roof, Type V-A trucks. W. Schilling Collection. **30 50 25**

(D) Red body, cupola, and cupola roof, black main roof, Type I ends, 3-13/16" between windows, square cupola roof ends, Type V-A trucks, no number on bottom. W. Schilling Collection. **30 50 25**

(E) Maroon body, cupola, and cupola roof, black main roof, Type III ends, 3-3/4" between windows, gold lettering, round cupola roof ends, one Type V-E and one V-F trucks. W. Schilling Collection. **30 50 25**

(F) Same as (E), but black cupola roof, Type V-A trucks. Bottom lettering is gold. W. Schilling Collection. **30 50 25**

(G) Same as (F), but side lettering is black, Type V-E trucks. J. Flynn Collection. **30 50 25**

(H) Same as (F), but road name lettering line is shifted 1/2" below bottom of window line. (Cars after this follow this pattern.) Type V-E trucks. D. Ely and J. Flynn Collections. **30 50 25**

(I) Same as (H), but both bottom lettering and side lettering is black instead of gold, Type V-A trucks. D. Ely Collection. **30 50 25**

(J) Red body, cupola, and cupola roof, black main roof, Type I ends, 3-13/16" between windows, square cupola roof ends, no number on bottom, examples reported with Type V-A and V-B trucks. W. Schilling Collection. **30 50 25**

(K) Same as (J), but black cupola roof, Type V-A trucks. D. Ely Collection. **30 50 25**

	Gd	Exc	Rst
(L) Same as (K), but Type I bottom crimp, number on bottom. D. Ely Collection.	30	50	25
(M) Same as (K), but number on end. D. Ely Collection.	30	50	25
(N) Same as (J), but cherry red instead of red, no number on bottom, Type V-A trucks. W. Schilling Collection.	40	60	30

OIL LABEL TYPES ON LIONEL STANDARD AND O GAUGE FREIGHT CARS

During the early to middle production run of the 200 and 500 Series, Lionel pasted a label with oiling instructions on the car's underside. (The practice was apparently discontinued some time in 1933; we invite reader comments.) Reverend Robert Pauli has identified three different oil labels used on Lionel cars. They are as follows:

Type I: Picture of an 800-series small O Gauge car frame viewed from its left side; label has no red border outline and red-lettered instructions with block printing style. We do not know for sure if this O Gauge label has in fact been seen on very many 200- and 500-series trucks. We invite reader comments.

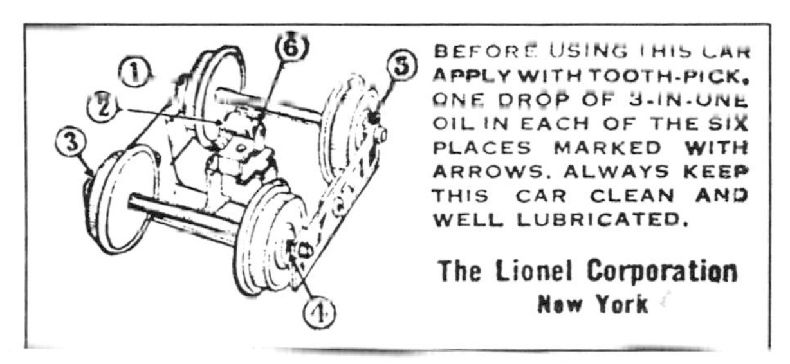

Type II Oil Label with 10-series trucks. R. Bartelt photograph.

Type II: Picture of a 10-series four-wheel truck with electric roller pickup as viewed from its right side, no border on label, red-lettered instructions in block printing style.

Type III: Picture of a 200-series four-wheel truck with electric roller pickup as viewed from its left side, red border outline on label, and red-lettered instructions in serif printing style.

200- AND 500-SERIES FREIGHT CARS DETAILING DEVELOPMENTS

By Philip Graves

PART I: BRAKEWHEELS

The nickel and brass brakewheels used on the 200- and 500-series freight cars are very useful in assigning a particular car to its date of manufacture. In addition, the examination of these brakewheels, together with an analysis of other variables such as plates, trucks, and couplers, can help the collector determine whether or not the car was altered after it left the factory.

As with all the variables on these cars, Lionel's production changed according to a regular, predictable pattern. There are four types of brakewheels which can be found:

TYPE I: EARLY PRODUCTION

Three-piece construction consisting of a hub, a wheel, and an L-shaped brake shaft. The brakewheel is inserted from the bottom of the shaft up to the point where the shaft bends. A hub with a slot to fit over the bent shaft is then crimped around the wheel hub. The assembly is mechanical. The soldered wheel is 5/8" in diameter, and all material used is brass. See Figure 1 below.

TYPE I: Brakewheel with wheel spokes flaring outward towards rim. R. Bartelt photograph.

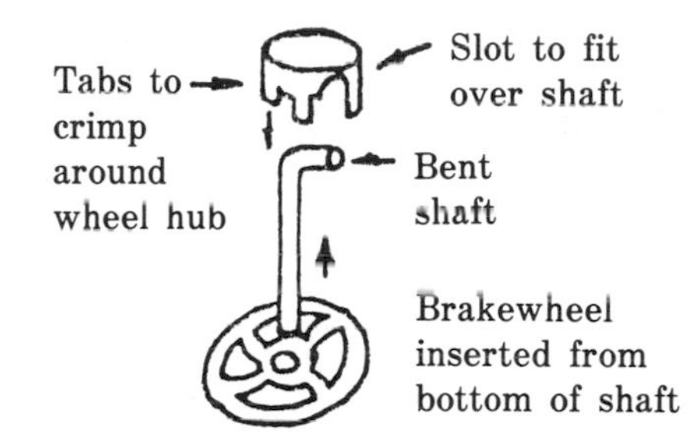

FIGURE 1: Type I and Type II. Drawing by Ralph E. Graves.

TYPE II: Brakewheel with uniform size wheel spokes. R. Bartelt photograph.

TYPE II: MIDDLE PRODUCTION

Same materials and assembly as Type I, but the brakewheel is larger, measuring 3/4" in diameter.

Note: The Type I and Type II brakewheels differ in other ways besides size. In the larger Type II brakewheel, the wheel spokes are of uniform diameter from hub to rim, and the hub is flush with the rim surface. In the smaller Type I brakewheel, the wheel spokes flare outward where they meet the rim, and the hub is recessed below the rim surface. See Figures 3 and 4.

EARLY 200-SERIES FREIGHT CARS
212(A)
219(E)
211(A)
214(A)
213(A)
214R(B)
215(B)
216(A)
217(A)
212
218(A)

LATER 200-SERIES FREIGHT CARS

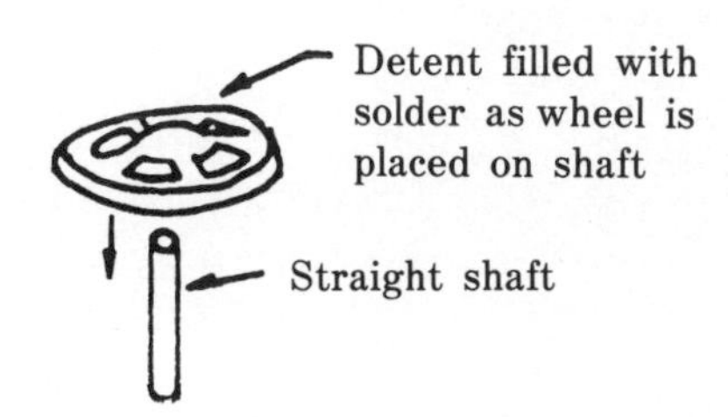

FIGURE 2: Type III and Type IV. Drawing by Ralph E. Graves.

TYPE III: LATER PRODUCTION

Two-piece construction consisting of a 3/4" brass brakewheel soldered directly to the brass brake shaft, which is straight instead of L-shaped. As the wheel is placed on the shaft, a detent in the wheel is filled with solder. See Figure 2 below.

TYPE IV: LATEST PRODUCTION

Same as Type III, but all material is nickel-plated instead of brass.

PART II: COUPLERS

Another way of dating the production of the 200- and 500-series freight cars is to examine the latch couplers on the cars. The latch coupler was introduced in 1923. Its first version included a horizontal tab with a slot so that the car could be coupled to the earlier hook couplers. This early latch coupler, known more commonly as the "combination" coupler, is not found on the 200- and 500-series cars. There are two clearly different later types of latch couplers which are used:

TYPE I: EARLY TO MIDDLE PRODUCTION

This coupler was of five-piece construction. The shank, latch, and rivet were nickeled, and there was a brass spring retainer and a wire spring. A tang on the latch was bent towards the shank end of the coupler. There was no flange on the lower surface of the latch. The wire spring was shaped to fit its retainer. The rivet was perfectly round. See Figure 3.

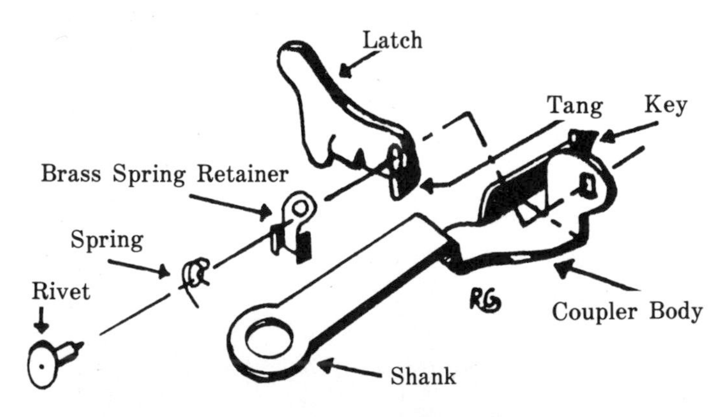

FIGURE 3: Type I. Drawing by Ralph E. Graves.

TYPE II: MIDDLE TO LATE PRODUCTION

This coupler was of four-piece construction because Lionel's engineers were able to modify it so that the brass spring retainer was omitted. As before, the three main parts were nickeled and the spring was made of wire. The tang on the latch was bent outward towards the key end of the coupler, rather than inward towards the shank. A flange was added to the lower surface of the latch to retain one end of the spring. The other end of the spring (shaped differently from its Type I predecessor) was held by a detent cut out of the rivet head. Note that the end of the rivet and the hole in the coupler are now square. See Figure 4.

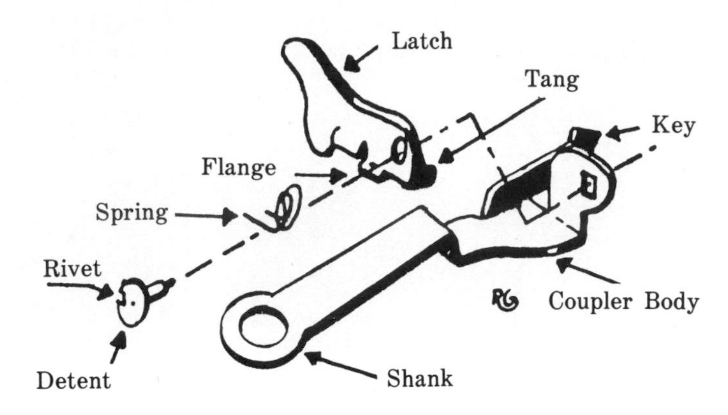

FIGURE 4: Type II. Drawing by Ralph E. Graves.

THE 200-SERIES FREIGHT CARS

These very large cars, introduced in 1926, represent a magnificent achievement in toy train construction. All of the varieties, regardless of scarcity, are highly prized by collectors today. The 200 Series, intended to replace the 10 Series, all had black frames. However, the colors on the cars showed far more variety and were much brighter (if less realistic). Lionel paid a great deal of attention to play value in these cars. The 218 Dump Cars operate manually, as do the magnificent 219 Crane Cars, which are among the most highly prized of this series. The 217 Caboose was the first Lionel caboose to be lighted.

As far as is known, the 200 Series only had one major type of truck. It has a small squared cutout at the center of the side frame, embossed springs, and black paint. The wheel journal boxes are mounted separately and are either copper or nickel. There are, however, six variations of this truck.

Type I has two dimples on the bolster bar, slots in the dimples, and attaches to the car with a cotter pin.

Type II is the same as Type I, but without slots.

Type III is the same as Type I, but attaches with a retaining washer.

Type IV has no dimples, two slots, and attaches with a cotter pin.

Type V is the same as Type IV, but without slots.

Type VI is the same as Type IV, but attaches with a retaining washer.

Most of these cars possess nickel or brass trim in profusion. Plates on the sides of the cars have red or black lettering; sometimes they possess an oval border in red or black. Even small pieces of trim such as boxcar door handles are always brass. The 218 and 219 cars feature knurled operating knobs of solid brass, and on the dump car even the entire end bolsters are made of solid brass in a few versions.

All of the 200-series freight cars are 12-1/2" long (although the huge boom on the crane car doubles its total length). They all possess latch couplers.

NOTE: Since we have recently identified at least six variations of the 200-series truck, we would like reader comments on truck types so that we can more accurately date the chronological order of both the trucks and the cars.

NOTE: Some letter designations of the 200-series cars have changed to place new variations in their proper chronological order. Some 200-series cars have been reproduced. See discussion at end of series lists (page 65).

Gd Exc Rst

211 FLATCAR: 1926-40, originally sold with lumber loads, all have latch couplers, black bodies, and "211 THE LIONEL LINES 211" rubber-stamped on the sides of the car in gold. These cars, as well as the floodlight and oil cars, may have the brake stands in reversed positions due to the car frame being placed in the punch press upside down. Bohn comment.

(A) Nickel journals, brass Type I brakewheels, nickel stakes, Type I couplers, and Type II oil label. Graves and Hoffman Collections. **60 80 40**

(B) Copper journals, brass Type II brakewheels, nickel stakes, Type II oil label, and Type II couplers. Koff and Weaver Collections. **60 80 40**

(C) Nickel journals, nickel Type IV brakewheels, nickel stakes, Type II couplers, no oil label, trucks mounted with retaining washer instead of cotter pin. Graves Collection. **60 80 40**

212 GONDOLA: 1926-40, originally sold with barrel loads, all have latch couplers and two plates, one of which reads "LIONEL LINES" and the other "NO. 212 CAPACITY 80000 WEIGHT 30000".

(A) 1926 only, gray body (earliest color), nickel journals, brass black-lettered plates, brass Type I brakewheels, Type I couplers and Type II oil label. Koff and Graves Collections. **100 150 45**

(B) Maroon body, copper journals, black-lettered brass plates, brass Type II brakewheels, Type II couplers, Type II oil label. Graves Collection. **75 100 40**

(C) Same as (B), but no oil label. Koff Collection. **75 100 40**

(D) Same as (B), but nickel journals. Graves, Hoffman, and Weaver Collections. **75 100 40**

(E) Same as (B), but Type III brakewheels, no oil label, Type II couplers. C. Weber Collection. **75 100 40**

(F) Medium green body, nickel journals, black-lettered nickel plates, nickel Type IV brakewheels, no oil label, trucks secured by horseshoe clip, Type II couplers. Graves Collection. **100 150 50**

(G) Dark green body, nickel journals, brass plates, brass Type II brakewheels, Type II oil label, very rare. Weaver Collection. **125 200 50**

213 CATTLE CAR: 1926-40, all have latch couplers and black frames.

(A) Mojave body, maroon roof and door guides, nickel journals, black-lettered brass plates, brass trim, Type II oil label, brass Type I brakewheels, Type I couplers. C. Weber Collection. **175 250 80**

(B) Terra-cotta body, pea green roof and door guides, nickel journals, brass plates and trim, Type II oil label, brass Type I brakewheels, Type I couplers. Koff and Graves Collections. **125 175 80**

(C) Same as (B), except no oil label, Type II brass brakewheels, Type II couplers. D. Witman Collection. **125 175 80**

(D) Same as (B), except Type III brakewheels, copper journals, Type II couplers. **125 175 80**

(E) Same as (D), except no oil label, one Type II and one Type III brass brakewheel, Type III trucks with copper journals. C. Rohlfing Collection. **125 175 80**

(F) Same as (B), but maroon roof and door guides. Made as department store special. Graves observation. **125 175 80**

(G) Cream body, maroon roof and door guides, nickel Type IV brakewheels, Type II couplers, nickel journals, no oil label, trucks secured with horseshoe clip. **300 600 80**

NOTE: The 1979 edition listed two 213 varieties as having orange bodies. We have concluded that these are terra-cotta varieties. Reader comments are requested.

214 BOXCAR: 1926-40, all have latch couplers, black frames, and large double doors. Left side plate reads "LIONEL LINES"; right side plate reads "NO. 214 / AUTOMOBILE / FURNITURE". Hoffman observation.

(A) Terra-cotta body, dark green roof and door guides, nickel journals, brass trim, brass Type I brakewheels, brass plates with borders, Type II oil label, Type I couplers. **225 300 120**

(B) Cream body, orange roof and door guides, nickel journals, brass plates and trim, brass Type II brakewheels, Type III oil label, Type II couplers. Graves, Weaver, and Hoffman Collections. **150 250 100**

(C) Same as (B), but cream-yellow body clearly different from (B). Koff Collection. **170 270 120**

(D) Yellow body, brown roof and door guides, nickel journals, nickel trim, nickel Type IV brakewheels, Type II couplers, no oil label, trucks secured with horseshoe clips. **350 500 100**

(E) Same as (D), but brass trim and brakewheels. **375 550 120**

214R REFRIGERATOR CAR: 1929-40, two small doors, plate across top reads "LIONEL VENTILATED REFRIGERATOR", harder to find than most 200-series freight cars, did not come with sets, black frame, and latch couplers.

(A) Ivory body, peacock roof, nickel journals, brass plates, brass trim, and brass Type II brakewheels, Type II couplers, Type II oil label. Koff Collection. **375 550 200**

(B) Same as (A), but white body, clearly a different color from (A). Weaver Collection. **375 550 200**

(C) White body, light blue roof, nickel journals, nickel plates, nickel trim and nickel Type IV brakewheels, Type I couplers, no oil label, trucks secured by horseshoe clip. **500 800 300**

(D) Same as (E), but brass plates. Sattler Collection. **525 825 325**

215 TANK CAR: 1926-40, black frame and latch couplers. Reportedly, the small domes used on these and the 500-series cars are of two types. The first type was a smooth top; this variety had a very short production period compared to the second type, which had a fine mesh grid across the top of the dome. Sattler comments. Which cars are found with the smooth-top small domes? Are there similar differences in the large domes? Reader comments are requested.

(A) Pea green tank, brass trim and domes, red-lettered brass plates, nickel journals, brass Type I brakewheels, Type I couplers, oil label missing. The center dome has a series of step-up ridges, small domes with smooth tops are solid brass turnings force-fitted (not screwed) into the top of the tank, trucks are mounted by means of a cotter pin and brass washer. A. Thomson Collection. **120 150 70**

(B) Pea green tank, brass trim and domes, red-lettered brass plates, nickel journals, brass Type I brakewheel, Type I couplers, Type II oil label, smooth domes. C. Weber Collection. **120 150 70**

(C) Same as (B), but Type II couplers. D. Witman Collection. **120 150 70**

(D) Same as (B), but Type II brakewheels, Type II couplers. **120 150 70**

(E) Same as (D), but smaller turned brass domes are screwed into tank, top of the largest dome flat or ridged, small domes are smooth-surfaced. D. Ely Collection. **130 175 75**

LATE 200-SERIES FREIGHT CARS
219(I)
212(F)
219(G)
LIONEL VENTILATED REFRIGERATOR
214(D)
214R(C)
213(G)
SUNOCO
THE LIONEL LINES
211(C)
215(H)
216(G)
LIONEL
217
217
217(J)
THE LIONEL LINES
220(C)
218
218(D)

380
218(C)
219
220(A)
214R(A)
215(B)
216(A)
217
LIONEL
217
437
217(C)
208 Toolbox
214(D)
213(A)
212(D)
211(A)
Contents of 208 Box

Gd Exc Rst

(F) Ivory tank, brass trim and domes, brass plates, red-lettered "SUNOCO" decal, copper journals, brass Type III brakewheels, Type II couplers, Type III oil label. **200 300 70**
(G) Same as (F), but no "SUNOCO" decal. **175 250 70**
(H) Silver tank, black-lettered "SUNOCO" decal, nickel journals, black-lettered nickel plates, nickel trim, nickel Type IV brakewheels, Type II couplers, no oil label. **250 500 75**
(I) Same as (H), but brass trim. **250 500 80**
(J) Light tan tank, black-lettered "SUNOCO" decal, copper journals, brass trim, brass plates with varied lettering (one has black "LIONEL LINES" lettering, the other red "NO. 215" lettering), no oil label. Probable factory error concerning color of tank and plates. D. Ely and Koff Collections. **130 175 75**

216 HOPPER CAR: 1926-38, all known varieties are dark green, all have black frames and latch couplers.
(A) Nickel journals, red-lettered brass oval plates, one plate has "LIONEL / LINES" in two lines separated by a double horizontal line (see illustration), the other plate reads "NO. 216 / CAPACITY / 20,000 CU. FT. / 110,000 LBS" in four lines, brass Type I brakewheel, no oil label, Type I couplers. Graves and Hoffman Collections. **175 250 120**

"LIONEL LINES" brass plate. R. Bartelt photograph.

(B) Same as (A), but copper journals. Weaver Collection. **175 250 120**
(C) Same as (A), but early 200-series trucks with larger rectangular cutout in middle of truck frame between embossed springs, rather than small cutout in more common later 200 trucks. Koff Collection. **180 275 130**
(D) Same as (A), but Type II brakewheels, Type II couplers. D. Witman Collection. **175 250 120**
(E) Copper journals, red-lettered brass plates, brass Type III brakewheels, Type II couplers. C. Weber Collection. **175 250 120**
(F) Copper journals, black-lettered brass plates, brass Type III brakewheels, Type II couplers. **175 250 120**
(G) Nickel journals, black-lettered nickel plates, nickel Type IV brakewheels, Type II couplers, trucks secured with horseshoe washer. **400 800 150**

217 CABOOSE: 1926-40, black frame, latch couplers, rear illumination.
(A) Orange body, maroon main roof, maroon plates rubber-stamped in gold lettering, nickel journals, dark green platform railing, no window inserts, maroon doors, all-maroon cupola, Type I couplers, Type II oil label. However, most early versions came with window material. P. Graves comment. C. Weber Collection. **300 400 150**
(B) Same as (A), but black platform railing. Edmunds observation. **250 325 125**
(C) Red body, peacock main roof, peacock doors, nickel journals, black-lettered brass plates, brass platform railings, brass window inserts, red cupola with peacock front and rear, Type II oil label, Type II couplers. Graves Collection. **120 150 70**
(D) Same as (C), but no oil label, one Type I and one Type IV truck. C. Rohlfing Collection. **120 150 70**
(E) Same as (C), but no oil label, one Type I and one Type II coupler. C. Weber Collection. **120 150 70.**
(F) Same as (C), but copper journals and no oil label. Weaver Collection. **135 175 75**
(G) Same as (C), but all-peacock cupola. **135 175 75**
(H) Same as (C), but cream doors with peacock inserts. Koff Collection. **150 190 80**
(I) Red body, white door, copper journals on oxide-treated truck frames, red main roof, black-lettered aluminum plates, nickel platform railings, aluminum window inserts, all-red cupola. Visnick observation. **150 200 75**
(J) Light red body, light red main roof, nickel journals, black-lettered aluminum plates, aluminum platform railings and window inserts, light red cupola, Type II couplers, no oil label. **150 200 70**

218 DUMP CAR: 1926-38, operating bin controlled by one knob (sometimes two) on a geared rod. When bin tilts, the side of the car opens and the load empties. All samples have black-lettered brass plates, black frames, nickel journals, and Type II latch couplers. Replacement gears are available for decayed gears.
(A) Mojave body, die-cast gears, two brass knobs, brass ends, Type II oil label. Koff Collection. **175 225 100**
(B) Same as (A), but no oil label. G. Thomson Collection. **175 225 100**
(C) Same as (A), except one brass knob, Type V trucks. C. Rohlfing and Weaver Collections. **160 200 100**
(D) Mojave body, die-cast gears, one brass knob, mojave-painted metal ends, Type III oil label. Koff Collection. **175 225 100**
(E) Circa 1926 early production, green body, maroon-painted metal ends; probably a special promotion for a department store. Graves observation. **NRS**
(F) Gray body, brass ends; probably a department store special. Graves observation. **NRS**

219 CRANE CAR: 1926-40, a very popular car then and now because of its immense play potential and sheer size. Lionel described it, quite rightly, as "an accessory that has won the admiration of every boy". One knob rotates the cab, another raises or lowers the boom, and a third controls the hook. The car has a nickel clamping device to attach it to the rails to keep it from toppling when it lifts loads. All have black frames and latch couplers. One plate reads "LIFTING CAPACITY 20 TONS" on rear of cab. Paper label on top of boom reads "Read directions / before operat- / ing this derrick."
(A) Peacock cab, dark red boom, dark green cab roof, nickel journals, steel-cut working gears (probably replacements), red windows, brass handrails, plates, and knobs, dark green toolboxes, brass pulleys, Type I oil label. Koff and Hoffman Collections. **120 175 75**
(B) Same as (A), but red boom, Type V Trucks, oil label missing. C. Rohlfing Collection. **120 175 75**
(C) Same as (A), except copper journals and black die-cast

Gd Exc Rst

gears, Type II oil label, Type II couplers. Pauli, Weaver, and Graves Collections. **140 190 80**

(D) Same as (C), except no oil label. C Weber Collection. **120 175 75**

(E) Same as (A), except peacock windows and black die-cast gears, Type II oil label. Koff, Weaver, and Graves Collections. **100 150 70**

(F) Same as (A), except green boom and red cab roof. Edmunds observation, reader comments requested. **NRS**

(G) Yellow cab, light green boom, red roof, nickel journals, nickel handrails and nickel knobs, red windows and toolboxes, Type II couplers, no oil label, trucks secured with horseshoe clips. Graves Collection. **250 300 100**

(H) Same as (G), but copper journals. Weaver and Cirillo Collections. **250 300 120**

(I) Ivory cab, red windows, roof, and toolboxes, light green boom, black knobs, nickel handrails. **250 325 150**

(J) Cream body, red boom, red roof, nickel journals, red windows, aluminum plates, black knobs, nickel pulleys. Kent Collection. **120 230 100**

(K) White body, green boom, red roof, nickel journals, red windows, steel-cut gear wheels (probably replacements), brass knobs and plates, red toolboxes, brass pulleys, no oil label. LaVoie observation. **275 350 150**

(L) Same as (K), but black die-cast gears and knobs. Weaver Collection. **220 290 130**

(M) Dark blue cab body with doors at rear of cab sides rather than front. Young and Ely observations. Further details and confirmation are needed; this is a very unusual piece. **NRS**

220 FLOODLIGHT CAR: 1931-40, the last 200-series car introduced, it shares its base and lights with 820 O Gauge cars. All have on-off switch, Type II latch couplers, and are rubber-stamped in sans-serif gold lettering "220 THE LIONEL LINES 220" on frame sides, have black frames, and no oil labels on any varieties.

(A) Terra-cotta base, copper journals, brass light housings, brass handrails, Type III brakewheels. C. Weber, Koff, Graves, and Weaver Collections. **200 275 120**

(B) Same as (A), except nickel journals. **200 275 120**

(C) Green base, nickel journals, nickel light housings and nickel Type IV handrails. **300 350 120**

NOTE: Excellent reproductions of the 213 Cattle, 214 Boxcar and the 214R Refrigerator cars were made in 1985 by Mike's Train House. They produced 500 refrigerators, 350 of which were painted blue and white with nickel trim, and the remaining 150 were painted ivory and peacock with brass trim.

The boxcar was painted in yellow and brown with nickel trim, cream and orange with brass trim, terra-cotta and dark green with brass trim, and yellow and brown with brass trim.

The cattle car was painted in cream and maroon with nickel trim, terra-cotta and pea green with brass trim, terra-cotta and maroon with brass trim, and mojave and maroon with brass trim.

These reproduction cars differ from the originals in the following ways:

1. Under the paint is zinc plating which is a silver color.
2. The identification "MTH" is stamped in the floor.
3. "NYC" plates were mounted on the refrigerator instead of "Lionel Lines" and two of the number plates on the boxcar and cattle car.
4. The cars had no oil labels.

In February 1986, Mike's Train House came out with the 215 Tank Car, 216 Hopper, and 217 Caboose.

The tank car came in pea green with brass trim, ivory with brass trim, aluminum (silver) with nickel trim, aluminum (silver) with brass trim, and orange with brass trim.

The hopper was painted dark green with brass trim, dark green with nickel trim, red with brass trim, and red with nickel trim.

The caboose was painted orange with maroon roof and maroon trim, red with peacock roof and brass trim, pea green with red roof and brass trim, and red with red roof and nickel trim.

Mike's Train House has also reproduced the 211 Flatcar, 212 Gondola, 218 Dump Car (sells for $99), 219 Crane (sells for $150), and 220 Floodlight Cars in the original Lionel colors.

THE 500-SERIES FREIGHT CARS

In 1927, Lionel introduced a smaller version of the 200 Series to replace the equivalent 100 Series, which had a dated and drab look by this time. This group of freight cars, the 500 Series, complemented the larger, deluxe 200 Series and were painted in brighter and less realistic colors. Other features possessed by this and the 200 Series were brass or nickel plates and ornamentation, journal boxes on the trucks and latch couplers.

Initially, the 500 Series was composed of six cars: a gondola, a refrigerator car, an oil car, a lumber car, a cattle car, and a caboose. Lionel's initial 500-series line differed in several interesting ways from its initial 200-series line. In the 200 Series, the stock car and the boxcar were quite different in their side treatment (although the external dimensions are similar). The 213 Stock Car has stamped-out slats while the 214 Boxcar has moderately embossed large rectangular patterns. In the 500 Series, Lionel used modifications of the 513 die to produce the 514 Refrigerator. The 514 Refrigerator has the same slatted sides as the 513, but without the slats being punched out. Lionel did change the plate location for the 514 Refrigerator and added a long plate along the roof line.

The original 200 Series, while having both a boxcar and a cattle car, did not have a refrigerator car. But the 500-series line started with a stock and a refrigerator car in the line.

Lionel's initial line — as we indicated — included a 514 Refrigerator car. This car was offered for two years, 1927-1928, and then was replaced in 1929 by the 514R which is basically the same car but with an "R" added to the brass plate. Since the 514R Refrigerator was made two years later than the 514 Refrigerator, some design differences are evident. (We request our readers to compare the following details with their cars.) The 514 Refrigerator has the Type I latch couplers with the spring retaining brass insert, while the later 514R Refrigerator has the Type II latch couplers without the spring retaining brass insert. The 514 Refrigerators have truck king pins with holes for cotter pins, while the 514R Refrigerators have king pins with grooves for the offset washers. We would appreciate additional reader confirmations of these observations.

The observed samples of the 514 Refrigerator cars have large slots on its truck sides (Type I), while the 514R Refrigerator samples have the small holes on their truck sides (Type II). However, these comments are based on small numbers of observations. Hence reader reports are requested.

When Lionel changed the refrigerator car number to 514R in 1929, it created a new 514 Boxcar. This car again used the 513

Early 500-Series freight cars have brass plates and nickel journals. Later series cars retain the brass plates and have copper journals. Late series cars have nickel plates and nickel journals.

body without the slots punched out and retained the plate locations and door mechanisms of the original 513. With this change, the 500-series boxcar numbering exactly paralleled the 200-series numbering. In addition, the refrigerator cars of both series have had similiar numbering — 214R and 514R respectively.

In 1928 Lionel added the 516 Hopper to the 500-series line. (The 200-series line had featured a hopper since its 1926 inception.)

The last cars added to both the 200- and the 500-series lines were the floodlight cars — the 220 and the 520. Both cars shared the same superstructure and light unit. This superstructure was also used on the 820 O Gauge Floodlight Car. The 500-series cars also show other variations: oil labels, latch couplers, brakewheels, and plate lettering. These variations are discussed in some detail with the introduction to the 200-series cars.

There were three types of trucks used on the 500 Series. Type I, the early and less common type, has a large rectangular slot cut out of the side panel and nickel journals. Types II and III have a much smaller hole in the side frame with the ends of the bolster bar swaged through the hole. In these trucks, the journal boxes are copper or nickel. Type II trucks have eight horizontal springs, while Type III trucks have eight springs with a slight tilt. All of the 500-series cars are built on a deeply embossed frame, 11-1/2 inches long.

Even though the 500 Series could be called "Son of the 200 Series", it became half of an extremely attractive line of freight cars manufactured during the Classic Period. As in the deluxe series, Lionel paid attention to play value, although not with operating cars. Lionel supplied lumber loads, barrels, and fake coal piles for the hopper, and the doors on these cars opened. It was with rolling stock like this that Lionel consolidated its position as the preeminent manufacturer of toy trains in the United States.

Gd Exc Rst

511 FLATCAR: 1927-40, all have latch couplers and are rubber-stamped "LIONEL LINES" in either silver or gold on frame sides. The car came with a long wooden block scribed on its sides and top to resemble a lumber load. The original wooden load brings a $5.00 premium in the car's price.

(A) Dark green body, nickel journals, rubber-stamped gold lettering, brass stakes and Type II brakewheels on left side of car ends, number rubber-stamped in gold on car bottom, Type II couplers, Type II oil label. Koff, Graves, Hoffman, and Pauli Collections. **50 70 30**

(B) Same as (A), but nickel stakes and Type III oil label. C. Weber and R. Flanagan Collections. **50 70 30**

(C) Same as (A), except brakewheels on right side of car ends, copper journals and nickel stakes. Koff and Hoffman Collections. **35 50 20**

TOP SHELF: dark green 511 with copper journals, brass brakewheels, gold rubber-stamped lettering. Medium green 511 with nickel brakewheels, silver rubber-stamped lettering. CENTER SHELF: peacock 512 with brass brakewheels and barrels. Light green 512 with nickel plates and brakewheels and drums. BOTTOM SHELF: orange and green 513 with brass brakewheels and plates. Olive green and orange 513 with brass brakewheels and plates.

Gd Exc Rst

(D) Same as (C), but medium green body and nickel journals. Weaver Collection. **35 50 20**

(E) Same as (C), but brakewheels and stakes both nickel. Lotstein Collection. **35 50 20**

(F) Very dark green body (almost black), copper journals, rubber-stamped gold lettering, nickel stakes, brass Type II brakewheels on left of car sides, car number rubber-stamped in gold on car bottom, no oil label. Lotstein and Weaver Collections. **35 50 20**

(G) Dark green body, copper journals, rubber-stamped silver lettering, nickel stakes, brass Type II brakewheels. Sattler Collection. **35 50 20**

(H) Medium green body, nickel journals, rubber-stamped silver lettering, nickel stakes, Type IV brakewheels, Type II couplers, no oil label, trucks secured with horseshoe clip. **35 50 20**

(I) Same as (H), but gold rubber-stamped lettering. Lettering on (I) is .100" high while the lettering on (A) is .115" high. C. Weber and Graves Collections. **35 50 20**

512 GONDOLA: 1927-39, all had black frames and latch couplers, 11-1/2 inches long, came with a set of barrels ($3-5 premium in price of cars listed below) and / or toolbox with tools (see Accessory section for prices). Early and middle production cars had two supporting stanchions for each brakewheel. Later production cars eliminate the lower stanchion so that only one stanchion remains. Graves observation.

(A) Peacock body, brass plates, nickel journals, Type II oil label, brass Type II brakewheels, Type II couplers. Graves Collection. **40 55 25**

(B) Same as (A), except no oil label. Bergstrom Collection. **40 55 25**

(C Peacock body, brass plates, nickel journals, brass Type III brakewheels, no oil label, Type II couplers, trucks secured by horseshoe clip. Graves Collection. **40 55 25**

(D) Same as (B), but copper journals. Koff, Hoffman, and Weaver Collections. **40 55 25**

(E) Same as (C), but lighter peacock body. Pauli Collection. **60 80 35**

(F) Same as (C), but copper journals. C. Weber Collection. **40 55 25**

(G) 45N green body, nickel journals, nickel plates, brass brakewheels. Weaver Collection. **55 70 30**

(H) Same as (G), but nickel Type IV brakewheels, no oil label, Type II couplers and trucks secured by horseshoe clip. **55 70 30**

(I) Same as (G), but darker green body. Edmunds observation. **55 70 30**

513 CATTLE CAR: 1927-38, all have black frames and latch couplers, data lines on one plate read "CAPACITY 60000 WEIGHT 20000".

The other plate is lettered "LIONEL LINES", but the plates differ. On the orange-bodied cars, the black lettering of this plate is much heavier and more bold than the thin-lettered plate found on the olive green-bodied cars. We need to know whether these differences are in fact associated with the body colors and whether these thick- or thin-lettered plates also appear on other 500-series cars. Weaver photographs and observations.

(A) Olive green body, orange roof and door guides, nickel journals, brass plates and trim, brass Type II brakewheels, Type II couplers, Type II oil label. Pauli, Graves, and Weaver Collections. **75 125 35**

(B) Orange body, pea green roof and door guides, brass plates and trim, nickel journals, brass Type II brakewheels, Type II couplers, Type I oil label. Pauli and Hoffman Collections. **50 80 35**

(C) Same as (B), but Type II oil label. C. Weber Collection. **50 80 35**

(D) Same as (B), but Type III oil label. Graves Collection. **50 80 35**

(E) Same as (B), but plates have no borders. Edmunds observation. Further confirmation requested. **50 80 35**

(F) Same as (B), but copper journals and Type II oil label. Koff and Weaver Collections. **50 80 35**

(G) Cream body, maroon roof and door guides, nickel Type IV brakewheels, Type II couplers, nickel journals, nickel plates and nickel trim, no oil label. Rare. C. Weber Collection. **200 400 35**

514 REFRIGERATOR: 1927-28, black frame and latch couplers. Note: This car differs from the 514 Boxcar; it has a long, narrow plate along the top of the side which reads "LIONEL VENTILATED REFRIGERATOR". This car has "NO. 514" plates; it differs from the later 514R Refrigerator car, whose plates read "NO. 514R". Since its double doors open outward, it does not possess door guides as does the 514 Boxcar. All have Type II latch couplers and Type II brakewheels. Reader comments are requested concerning the relative scarcity of this car compared to the 514R version.

(A) White body, white doors, peacock roof, brass plates, nickel journals, brass Type II brakewheels and trim. Weaver Collection. **250 475 150**

(B) Same as (A), but cream body with cream doors. Sattler Collection. **225 300 125**

(C) Ivory (not white or cream) body, ivory doors, peacock roof, nickel journals, brass trim, brass plates, Type II brass brakewheels, Type II oil label, Type II couplers. Pauli, Koff, and Graves Collections. **300 700 150**

(D) Cream body, cream doors, flat dark Stephen Girard green roof, nickel journals, brass trim, brass borderless plates, Type II oil label. Pauli Collection. **275 600 150**

This car, more than any other example found in all the research done on the 500 Series, illustrates the exasperating dilemmas faced in collecting these cars. It was examined by three experienced collectors by placing it alongside an example with a peacock roof and comparing it with color charts. There is no way this car should have anything but a peacock roof. And yet, there it sits, defying analysis.

The car is obviously a factory error, but how could such a thing come to pass? One easy answer is to assume that the car was on display in a shop window, where sunlight faded the roof. One would also expect fading of other paint in that case, and no other colors show signs of deterioration. In addition, the bluish tinge to Lionel's peacock color is absent on this roof.

Another hypothesis has to do with production. We are not certain of the exact method, but Lionel used a spray-painting technique whereby the paint (pre-mixed) was put in metal sprayers. If the level of paint had been allowed to stand in the spray canister, pigment separation could have occurred to change the paint on a small number of cars until discovered. Another car we have found might bear out this hypothesis. See the entry for the 517(H) Caboose, where the main roof was a flat light red — including the cupola front and rear — but the cupola roof, which is a separate piece, is the normal red. (To further complicate the caboose, one of the cupola windows was not punched out — a possible double factory error!)

Gd Exc Rst

A third hypothesis is that Lionel tried a pre-production sample of a different shade of color for this car's roof, and that it somehow slipped out of the factory. If this car is, in fact, a pre-production sample, it must be extremely rare. Unfortunately, there is no way to prove this hypothesis after all these years.

Since we have uncovered two examples in the 500 Series where the roofs are a flatter gloss and a lighter color than the normal production run, we may have a chance to see if other examples exist. If they do, we have perhaps uncovered a major factory variation due to a painting quality control lapse. We hope this discussion will send collectors rummaging through their 500-series cabooses, box, cattle, and reefer cars — and their 200 Series as well — to report any further variations to us.

514 BOXCAR: 1929-40, black frame and latch coupler, one plate reads "CAPACITY 60000 WEIGHT 20000".

(A) Cream yellow body, orange roof and door guides, nickel journals, brass trim, brass Type II brakewheels, brass plates with borders, Type II couplers and oil labels. Koff and Pauli Collections. **75 100 40**

(B) Same as (A), but copper journals and no oil label. Graves Collection. **75 100 40**

(C) Yellow body, brown roof and door guides, nickel journals, nickel trim, nickel Type IV brakewheels, nickel plates, Type II couplers, no oil label, trucks mounted with horseshoe clip. Hoffman Collection. **100 175 40**

(D) Same as (C), but brass Type III brakewheels. Weaver Collection. **100 175 40**

(E) Same as (C), but "514" plate replaced by "LIONEL LINES" plate and "514" rubber-stamped on underside of frame. **125 200 50**

(F) Cream body, green roof and door guides, copper journals, brass trim, brakewheels, and plates. This car is pictured in the 1932 Lionel catalogue as part of set 361E on page 22. We would like to hear from a collector who possesses this car. Graves observation. **NRS**

514R REFRIGERATOR CAR: 1929-40, black frame and latch couplers, long narrow plate on top of side reads "LIONEL VENTILATED REFRIGERATOR", double doors open outward.

(A) Ivory body, peacock roof, nickel journals, brass trim, Type II brass brakewheels, brass borderless plates, Type II oil label, Type II couplers. Hoffman Collection. **120 150 70**

(B) Same as (A), but copper journals, Type III brakewheels, no oil label, trucks fastened with "horseshoe" retaining washer. C. Weber Collection. **120 150 70**

(C) Ivory body, light blue roof, nickel journals, nickel Type IV brakewheels, no oil label, Type II couplers, trucks mounted with horseshoe clip, nickel trim, nickel plates. Sattler Collection. **375 500 200**

(D) Same as (A), but cream body. Koff Collection. **135 175 70**

(E) Same as (A), but white body and copper journals. Weaver Collection. **120 150 70**

(F) White body, light blue roof, nickel journals, nickel trim, brass plates, Type IV brakewheels, Type II couplers, no oil label, trucks attached with horseshoe clip. C. Weber comment. **120 150 70**

(G) Same as (F), but nickel plates. C. Weber Collection. **120 150 70**

515 TANK CAR: 1927-40, black frame and latch couplers. See 215 entries for discussion of dome types.

NOTE: The 1983 edition listed two varieties as having burnt orange bodies. We have concluded that these are terra-cotta since burnt orange was first used on other items much later. Reader comments requested.

(A) Terra-cotta tank, nickel journals, brass trim, brass handrails, Type II couplers, Type III oil label. Pauli, Koff, Weaver, and Hoffman Collections. **90 125 60**

(B) Same as (A), but Type II oil label. Graves Collection. **90 125 60**

(C) Ivory tank, copper journals, brass trim, brass handrails, brass borderless plates, no oil label, Type II brakewheels. C. Weber, Pauli, and Hoffman Collections. **90 125 60**

(D) Same as (C), but "SUNOCO" decal added. Weaver Collection. **100 150 60**

(E) Light tan tank, copper journals, brass trim, brass handrails, Type III brakewheels, brass borderless plates, no oil label. Koff Collection. **120 150 70**

NOTE: In at least one report, the number plate on (E) has a more serif-style lettering like that on the nickel plates, as opposed to the more block style found on (C). C. Weber comment.

(F) Same as (C), but nickel journals. **120 150 70**

(G) Silver tank, "SUNOCO" decal, copper journals, brass trim, brass Type III handrails, brass plates, Type II couplers, no oil label. **100 150 60**

(H) Same as (G), but handrails are nickel. **100 150 60**

(I) Silver tank, "SUNOCO" decal, nickel journals, nickel trim, nickel Type IV handrails and nickel plates, Type II couplers, no oil label. Hoffman Collection. **100 150 60**

(J) Same as (I), but plates are brass. **100 150 60**

(K) Orange body, red "SHELL" decal, nickel journals, nickel trim, nickel handrails, Type IV brakewheels and nickel plates, trucks mounted with horseshoe clip, (very rare). **375 500 200**

516 HOPPER: 1928-40, red body, black frame and Type II latch couplers. The coal load brings a premium of $25.

(A) Nickel journals, stamped-steel coal load, brass ladders and trim, black-lettered brass-bordered plates, brass Type II brakewheels. Pauli Collection. **125 175 60**

(B) Same as (A), but copper journals. Koff Collection. **125 175 60**

(C) Same as (B), but no coal load. Weaver Collection. **100 150 50**

(D) Nickel journals, brass ladders and trim, brass plates, coal load, brass Type III brakewheels, rubber-stamped gold lettering with capacity data. This car was only available as part of a special coal train led by the black No. 318 engine. Koff, Graves, and Weaver Collections. **150 250 70**

(E) Same as (D), but Type II brakewheels. C. Weber Collection. **150 250 70**

NOTE: Variation (E) is reported with thinner lettering on the brass plates than on (B). Reader comments are requested to see if a pattern can be found as on the 513 Cattle Car.

(F) Same as (D), but no coal load. **125 225 60**

(G) Same as (D), but plates entirely absent from car, as are their mounting slots. Probable factory error, very rare. Pauli Collection. **500 750 NRS**

(H) Same as (A), but nickel journals, plates, and trim, Type IV nickel brakewheels. **150 225 60**

NOTE: We have had a report of a car in silver with nickel journals, either with or without capacity data stamping.

500-SERIES FREIGHTS

500-SERIES FREIGHT CARS

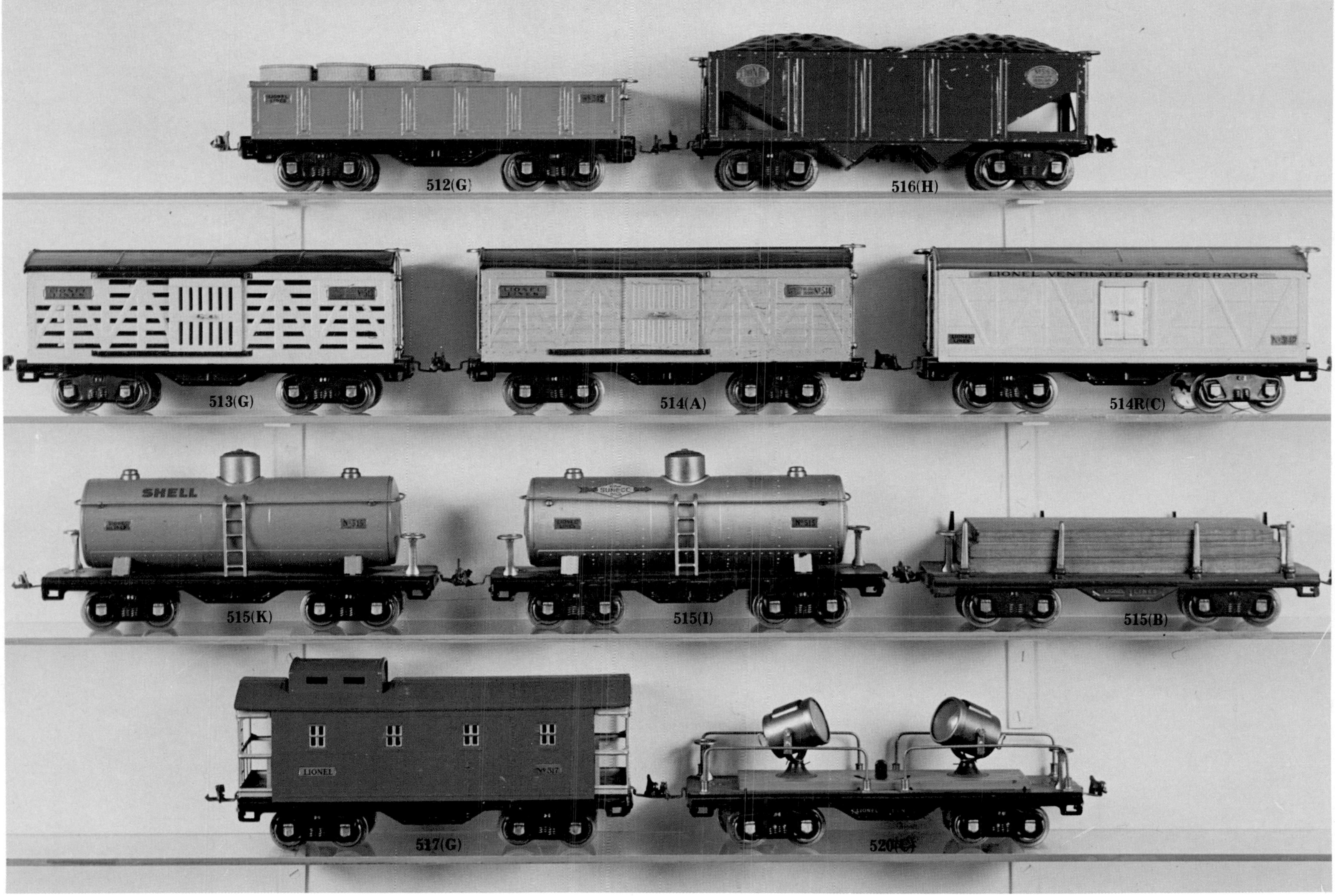

512(G) 516(H)

513(G) 514(A) 514R(C)

515(K) 515(I) 515(B)

517(G) 520

STANDARD FREIGHT SETS
400E
400T
212(D)
219(E)
220(C)
217(D)
220(A)
217(B)
212(B
219(B)
400E
217
218
219
212
390TX
517
390
516
516
516
390T
Coal Train 318E
390E
517
LIONEL LINES

Six different 515 Tank Cars. The cars are ordered by production from top to bottom. The earliest cars have brass trim and nickel journals, followed by cars with brass trim and copper journals. The last cars have nickel trim and nickel journals. TOP SHELF: terra-cotta tank with brass trim and nickel journals. Ivory tank with copper journals and brass trim. CENTER SHELF: silver tank with SUNOCO decal, brass trim, and copper journals. Silver tank with SUNOCO decal and nickel trim and journals. BOTTOM SHELF: orange tank, SHELL decal, and nickel trim and journals.

Gd Exc Rst

Further sightings are requested to determine whether this color is original.

517 CABOOSE: 1927-40, black frame and Type II latch couplers.

(A) Pea green body, red main roof, nickel journals, brass railings, brass borderless plates, orange windows, green cupola roof, red cupola ends, Type I oil label. Pauli and Hoffman Collections. **35 50 40**

(B) Same as (A), but Type II oil label. Graves Collection. **35 50 40**

(C) Same as (A), but brass window inserts. Koff and Weaver Collections. **35 50 40**

(D) Same as (A), but copper journals and brighter red roof and cupola ends. Koff Collection. **35 50 40**

(E) Same as (C), but copper journals and no oil label. D. Witman, R. Flanagan, and C. Weber Collections. **35 50 40**

NOTE: (E) is reported with plates with thick lettering while (B) has thin lettering. Reader comments are requested to see if there is a pattern as found on the 513 Cattle Car.

(F) Same as (A), but apple green body. Further confirmation requested. Bergstrom Collection. **75 100 —**

(G) Red body, red main roof, nickel journals, silver-painted railings and window inserts, borderless aluminum plates, red cupola, trucks mounted with horseshoe clip. Weaver Collection. **75 100 50**

(H) Same as (G), but brass plates. **75 100 50**

(I) Same as (G), but lighter flat red main roof, normal red cupola roof, one cupola hole not punched on car observed; probable factory error. This is an intriguing car because of its flat light red roof. For a discussion of how this car could have been produced this way, see the extended discussion about a similar car at entry 514(D). Lotstein Collection. **90 125 —**

(J) Same as (F), but "NO. 517" plate replaced by "LIONEL LINES" plate and number rubber-stamped on underside of frame. **90 125 —**

(K) Red body, black main roof, red cupola with black ends, orange windows, brass railings, brass plates, nickel journals. This was a special "coal train" caboose only available in a set with three special 516 Hopper cars and a 318 Locomotive. **250 400 —**

	Gd	Exc	Rst

520 FLOODLIGHT CAR: 1931-40, all have black frames and Type II latch couplers. Early versions had brakewheels on left side of car ends; later cars had them on right side. All have on-off light switch; same unit appeared on 820 O Gauge cars. All samples rubber-stamped "LIONEL LINES" in gold on side of frame.

(A) Terra-cotta base, brass Type III handrails, brass light casings, copper journals, rubber-stamped "520" on underside of frame. Weaver and Hoffman Collections. **75 125 40**

(B) Same as (A), but nickel journals. **75 125 40**

(C) Green base, nickel Type IV handrails, nickel light casings, nickel journals, rubber-stamped "520" on underside of frame. Graves, Hoffman, and Weaver Collections. **100 175 50**

Chapter III

Standard Gauge Passenger Cars

Features of an 18-series car from the mid-1920s. A late 10-series truck with electrical pickup and rectangular vertical bolster section that reaches the bottom edge of the side frame. P. Graves comments, R. Bartelt photograph.

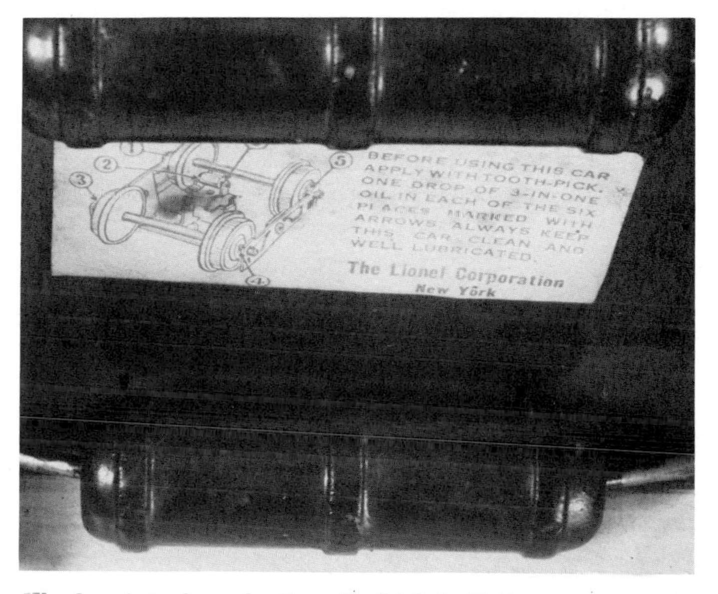

Wooden air tanks and a Type II oil label. P. Graves comments, R. Bartelt photograph.

Gd Exc Rst

NOTE: The 18 Pullman Series has been completely relettered to attempt to place the cars in proper chronological order.

18 PULLMAN: 1906-27, part of largest early series passenger cars. Came with matching 19 Combine and 190 Observation.

(A) 1906-10, dark olive green body and roof, solid clerestory, maroon doors and window sills, gold-painted window dividers, clear celluloid windows, red-speckled upper window celluloid, red-speckled celluloid lavatory windows, roof not removable, doors do not open, three high wooden knobs fastened to roof, open three-rivet trucks, short crinkle couplers, gold-painted pinhole steps, gold rubber-stamped on sides "18 PULLMAN 18" and "NEW YORK CENTRAL LINES", gold-painted door handle made from a nail end, not lighted, red primer on underside. D. Ely Collection. **700 1500 600**

(B) 1911-12, similar to (A), but low knobs, optional lighting kit available, serif letters but no scroll design. D. Ely Collection. **700 1500 600**

(C) 1914-17, dark olive green body and roof, maroon doors and window sills, gold-painted window dividers, clear celluloid windows, red-speckled celluloid in upper window section, removable roof, doors open, single-rivet trucks, regular hook couplers, gold rubber stamped "18 PULLMAN 18", black-painted wooden air tanks attached to floor underside, embossed "LIONEL MFG. CO." on floor, three-hole steps, pierced clerestory with tabs to hold celluloid, grooved diaphragms, matches 19 and 190. **150 200 70**

(D) 1916-17, yellow-orange body and roof, cream window sills and doors, gold-painted window dividers, clear celluloid lower windows, red-speckled upper windows, blue celluloid lavatory windows, stamped brass door handles, removable roof, doors open, single-rivet trucks, large crinkle hook couplers or hook couplers with ears, gold rubber-stamped "18 PULLMAN 18" and "NEW YORK CENTRAL LINES" on side, smooth diaphragms. Matches 19 and 190, sold with brass 7 or 54 as top-of-the-line set. D. Ely Collection. **275 600 175**

(E) Same as (D), but orange body and no embossing on floor. D. Ely comment. Confirmation requested. **NRS**

(F) Circa 1917, same as (E), but red-speckled celluloid in lavatory windows, blue-speckled celluloid in upper window and in clerestory, floor not embossed, no lettering on one end, "18" on right side of other end, "LIONEL / LINES / N.Y. / MADE IN U.S.A." on left. C. Weber Collection. **80 125 80**

(G) 1918-23, dark olive green body and roof, maroon doors and window sills, gold-painted window dividers, clear celluloid lower windows, blue-speckled celluloid in upper window, removable roof, doors open, single-rivet trucks, regular hook couplers, gold rubber-stamped "PARLOR CAR" with

LARGE EARLY PASSENGER CAR SETS

The top set on this page is composed of Lionel's earliest large cars with tall wooden roof knobs. Also note the railing on the observation with vertical rails. The second set also has knobs, but they are shorter and the observation car railing has an interlocking spoke design.

18, 19, 190 PASSENGER CARS

Lionel 190 Observation Cars came with several kinds of rear decks. The earliest cars had long decks with vertical slats, thin interlocking spoke railings, and finally fan blade designs. Then Lionel built the cars with a short deck and fan blade design as shown above.

Gd Exc Rst

scrollwork and "NEW YORK CENTRAL LINES" on sides, "18" on ends, wooden air tanks, floor not embossed, black or gold rubber-stamped "LIONEL CORPORATION" on floor underside or end, three-hole steps, pierced clerestory with tabs to hold celluloid, plain diaphragms. Matches 19 and 190. D. Ely Collection. **80 125 80**

(H) 1920-23, similar to 18(E), but dark orange sides and roof, gold window sills, maroon doors. Came with brass 7 or 54 as top-of-the-line set with matching 19 and 190. **275 600 100**

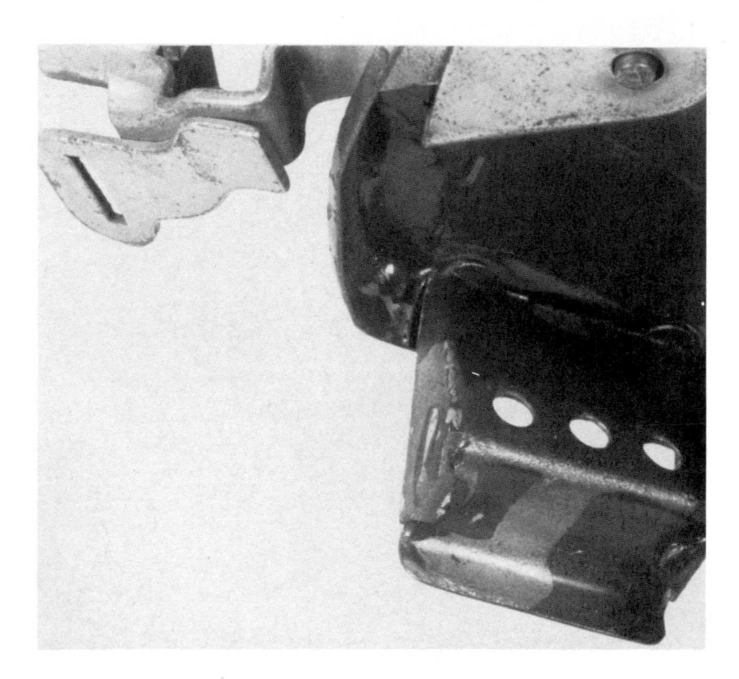

Construction of the steps can help date these cars. TOP PHOTO: an earlier No. 18 with three-hole soldered steps. Note the combination latch coupler with triangular body retainer. BOTTOM PHOTO: later construction with solid two-riser steps fastened to the body by tabs.

R. Bartelt photograph.

(I) 1923-27, dark olive green, similar to 18(E), but combination latch couplers or latch couplers, interior light bracket, roller pickup on one truck. **80 125 80**

(J) 1923-27, similar to 18(E), but mojave body and roof, combination latch couplers or latch couplers, with interior light bracket and roller pickup on one truck. Matches 19(I) and 190(I). **275 600 100**

(K) Same as (E), but no rubber-stamping on bottom, "PARLOR CAR" lettering below windows in gold on sides within scrollwork, rubber-stamped "18" in gold on right side of car ends and "LIONEL / LINES / N.Y. / Made in U.S.A." in four lines in gold on left side of car ends. Schuppner Collection. **NRS**

(L) Same as (I), except gold rubber-stamped "Made in U.S.A. / THE LIONEL CORPORATION / NEW YORK" on car bottom. J. Sattler Collection. **NRS**

(M) Same as (J), but light olive green. J. Sattler Collection. **NRS**

19 COMBINE:

(A) Matches 18(A) and 190(A). Gold rubber-stamped, in sans-serif lettering, "PULLMAN" and "NEW YORK CENTRAL LINES". Extremely rare. **900 1800 325**

(B) Matches 18(B) and 190(B). Extremely rare. **900 1800 325**

(C) Dark olive green, matches 18(C) and 190(C) or 190(D). **160 320 70**

TOP SHELF: an 18(J) Parlor Car. Note closely-spaced "NEW YORK CENTRAL LINES" lettering and chairs inside windows. BOTTOM SHELF: a 190 Observation with widely-spaced "NEW YORK CENTRAL LINES" lettering. Style of lettering differs at top, but not on bottom! P. Graves Collection.

R. Bartelt photograph.

Gd Exc Rst

(D) Yellow orange, matches 18(D) and 190(E). **225 375 100**
(F) Dark olive green, matches 18(G) and 190(F). **80 125 80**
(G) Dark olive green, matches 18(I) and 190(G). **80 125 80**
(H) Dark orange, matches 18(H) and 190(H). **275 600 100**
(I) Mojave, matches 18(J) and 190(I). **275 600 100**
(K) Matches 18(L). J. Sattler Collection. **NRS**
(L) Matches 18(M). J. Sattler Collection. **NRS**
(M) Matches 18(F), but embossed floor and all-red-speckled celluloid in windows. C. Weber Collection. **60 125 80**

190 OBSERVATION: 1914-18, 1923-27.
(A) Matches 18(A) and 19(A), vertical slat rail on long observation deck. **900 1800 350**
(B) Matches 18(B) and 19(B), vertical slat rail on long observation deck. **900 1800 350**
(C) Matches 18(C) and 19(C) (also see 190(D)). Interlocking spoke-wheel design rail with scalloped top edge on long observation deck. **150 200 55**
(D) 1914-18, matches 18(C) and 19(C). Fan-blade design rail with flat top railing on long observation deck. **150 200 80**
(E) Matches 18(D) and 19(D). Fan-blade rail with flat top railing, long observation. **275 600 100**
(F) Matches 18(G) and 19(F). **80 125 80**
(G) 1923-27, matches 18(I) and 19(G). Fan-blade design with flat top rail on short observation deck. **90 125 80**
(H) Dark orange sides and roof, matches 18(H) and 19(H). Fan-blade design rail with flat top railing, short observation deck. **275 600 100**
(I) Matches 18(J) and 19(I). Fan-blade design rail with flat railing top, short observation deck. **275 600 100**

29 DAY COACH: 1908-27.
(A) 1908, dark olive green body and roof, gold rubber-stamped "No. 29 N.Y.C. & H.R.R.R. No. 29" on sides. Nine windows, body with large clerestory openings, body same as No. 3 trolley, solid platform on lower panel-ends, three-rivet open trucks. **1000 2000 700**
(B) 1909, similar to 29(A), but platform on lower panel-ends open with twin railing, three-rivet open trucks. **1000 2000 700**
(C) Same as 29(B), but rubber-stamped "PENNSYLVANIA R.R." **1100 2100 750**
(D) 1910, maroon body and roof, gold rubber-stamped "No. 29 NYC & H.R.R.R. No. 29" on sides. Ten windows, platform ends open with twin railings, three-rivet open trucks, three high ventilators (knobs) on roof, nonremovable roof with no clerestory openings, short crinkle hook couplers, black-painted wooden air tank on each side, black steps pierced with many small holes. D. Ely Collection **1000 1500 750**
(E) Same as 29(D), but dark olive green body and roof. **800 1000 750**
(F) 1911, dark green body and roof, gold rubber-stamped "No. 29" twice on each side, "NEW YORK CENTRAL LINES" above windows, ten windows, platform ends open with twin railings, three-rivet open trucks, three low ventilators, nonremovable roof without clerestory openings, short crinkle hook couplers, black-painted wooden air tank on each side, black steps pierced with many small holes. Extremely rare. **2000 3000 —**
(G) 1912-14, dark olive green body and roof, maroon band through windows, gold rubber-stamped "29 NEW YORK CENTRAL LINES 29" on sides beneath windows, ten windows, platform ends open with twin gold-painted railings, single chain on each platform, single-rivet open trucks, removable roof with pierced clerestory, maroon interior, large crinkle hook couplers, black-painted wooden air tanks on each side, air tanks smaller than those on earlier 29s, three-hole gold-painted steps, "MFG." embossing on floor, 15-1/4". D. Ely Collection. **450 675 350**
(H) 1915-27, dark green body and roof, gold rubber-stamped "29 NEW YORK CENTRAL LINES 29" on sides beneath windows, ten windows, platform ends open with twin gold-painted railings, single chain on each platform, single-rivet open trucks, removable roof with pierced clerestory and tabs for holding celluloid strip, large crinkle hook couplers, black-painted wooden air tanks on each side, air tanks smaller than those on earlier 29s, three-hole gold-painted steps, 15-1/4". **375 600 275**
(I) Same as (H), but gold band beneath windows. D. Ely Collection. **NRS**
(J) Same as 29(G), but gold rubber-stamped "29 PENNSYLVANIA R.R. 29" on sides beneath window, 15-1/4". D. Ely Collection. **400 650 300**
(K) Same as (J), but rubber-stamping is "29 PENNSYLVANIA LINES 29". J. Sattler Collection. **NRS**

31 COMBINE:
(A) 1921-25, maroon body and roof, wood-grained baggage doors, gold rubber-stamped "PULLMAN" in elaborate scroll beneath windows, "NEW YORK CENTRAL LINES" above windows, black 100-series trucks, regular hook couplers, gold painted three-hole steps, clear celluloid lower windows, blue-speckled celluloid upper window, only baggage door opens, passenger doors at both ends, combination latch couplers, metal air tanks, 10-3/4". **60 85 40**
(B) Same as 31(A), but orange sides and roof, maroon baggage doors. **90 150 40**
(C) Same as 31(A), but dark olive green sides and roof, doors at one end only, steps at one end only, maroon window sills, gold window separator, wooden air tanks, "BAGGAGE" stamped under appropriate doors, number rubber-stamped on one end, Corporation rubber-stamping on the bottom, combination latch couplers. C. Weber Collection. **55 80 40**
(D) Same as 31(A), but brown sides and roof. **60 85 40**
(E) Orange sides and roof, wood-grained baggage doors, white window curtains, rubber-stamped "NEW YORK CENTRAL LINES" and "PULLMAN", maroon window sills, gold window separator, wooden air tanks, hook couplers with ears. C. Weber Collection. **90 150 40**

32 MAIL:
(A) Maroon sides and roof, matches 31(A). Four wood-grained baggage doors, no passenger doors. **60 85 40**
(B) Orange sides and roof, matches 31(B), four baggage doors and four passenger doors. **90 150 40**
(C) Dark olive green sides and roof, matches 31(C), four passenger doors, no steps, wooden air tanks, no "BAGGAGE" stamped on sides, combination latch couplers. C. Weber Collection. **55 80 40**
(D) Brown sides and roof, matches 31(D). **60 85 40**
(E) Matches 31(E). C. Weber Collection. **90 150 40**
(F) Same as (C), but regular hook couplers and large doorknobs. D. Ely Collection. **NRS**

There are three distinct series of 35 and 36 Passenger Cars, First (A)-(B), Second (E)-(K), and Third (N)-(T).

35 PULLMAN: First Series, 1912-13. Two embossed ribs under windows, gold rubber-stamped on sides between ribs

Small and Medium Size Early Passenger Cars

	Gd	Exc	Rst

"35 PULLMAN 35" and above windows "NEW YORK CENTRAL LINES", single-rivet, closed-side trucks, long crinkle hook couplers, gold-painted steps with three holes, red-speckled celluloid in upper windows, clear celluloid in lower windows, gold-painted window dividers, removable roofs, oval lavatory windows, embossed handrails.

(A) Dark blue (midnight blue), made as special for Montgomery Ward. Extremely rare. D. Ely Collection. **250 450 70**

(B) Dark olive green, maroon window sills. **80 100 70**

35 PULLMAN: Second Series, 1914-18. Smooth sides, gold rubber-stamped "PULLMAN" with elaborate scroll beneath windows, "NEW YORK CENTRAL LINES" above windows, "35" on ends, embossed "LIONEL MFG. CO." on floor, large crinkle hook couplers, gold-painted steps with three holes, blue-speckled celluloid in upper windows, clear celluloid in lower windows, gold-painted window dividers, removable roofs, square bottom lavatory windows with gold-painted outline.

(E) Dark olive green, rubber-stamped "35 PULLMAN 35", no scrollwork, no embossing or rubber-stamping on floor, 100-series flex trucks, long crinkle hook couplers, red celluloid window inserts. D. Ely Collection. **NRS**

(F) Dark olive green, maroon window sills. **30 50 30**

(G) Dark olive green, maroon window sills, gold rubber-stamped "CHESAPEAKE & OHIO R.R.", no number rubber-stamped anywhere, no floor embossing or rubber-stamping (no indication that Lionel produced it, no air tanks, no celluloid nor tabs to hold them, bench with no extension up for windows soldered to wall rather than stamping with tabs to hold celluloid. Probable department store special. C. Weber Collection. **NRS**

(H) Maroon, green window sills. **50 75 30**

(I) Orange, maroon window sills. **75 125 40**

(J) Same as (H), but standard latch couplers and solid brass steps. J. Sattler Collection. **NRS**

35 PULLMAN: Third Series, 1918-26. Smooth sides, gold rubber-stamped "PULLMAN" with elaborate scroll beneath windows, "NEW YORK CENTRAL LINES" above windows, "35" on one end, rubber-stamped "LIONEL CORPORATION" on ends or bottom, 100-series trucks, regular hook couplers, gold-painted steps with three holes, blue-speckled celluloid in upper windows, removable roofs, square bottom lavatory windows with gold-painted outlines. Gold rubber-stamped on bottom "Made in USA" and "The Lionel Corporation New York".

(N) Dark olive green, maroon window sills. **30 40 30**

(O) Maroon, green window sills. **25 35 20**

(P) Orange, maroon window sills. **90 150 30**

(Q) Brown, green window sills, white window shades. D. Ely Collection. **30 40 30**

(R) Orange, maroon window sills, white window shades. D. Ely Collection. **90 150 30**

(S) Same as (N), but combination latch couplers, wooden air tanks. C. Weber and D. Ely Collections. **30 40 30**

(T) Same as (O), but Type II oil sticker, early 500-series trucks, combination latch couplers, brass steps, metal air tanks with nickel ends. C. Weber Collection. **NRS**

36 OBSERVATION: First Series. 1912-13. Matches 35 Pullman, First Series. Gold rubber-stamped "36 Observation 36" between ribs, long observation deck.

(A) Matches 35(A). **200 450 40**

(B) Matches 35(B). **80 100 40**

36 OBSERVATION: Second Series. 1914-18. Matches 35 Pullman, Second Series. Gold rubber-stamped "OBSERVATION", with long deck.

(E) Matches 35(E). **NRS**

(F) Matches 35(F). **35 50 30**

(G) Matches 35(G). **NRS**

(H) Matches 35(H). **50 75 30**

(I) Matches 35(I). **75 125 40**

(J) Matches 35(J). J. Sattler Collection. **NRS**

36 OBSERVATION: Third Series. 1918-26. Matches 35 Pullman, Third Series. Gold rubber-stamped "OBSERVATION", short deck.

(N) Matches 35(N). **30 40 30**

(O) Matches 35(O). **30 40 30**

(P) Matches 35(P). **90 150 40**

(Q) Matches 35(Q). **30 40 30**

(R) Matches 35(R). **90 150 40**

(S) Matches 35(S). C. Weber Collection. **30 40 30**

(T) Matches 35(T), but latch couplers. C. Weber Collection. **NRS**

NOTE: There are three varieties of 180-series trucks. Type I is similar to a 100-series Type III, but the bolster is 1/16" higher. It has a solid side frame with embossed springs and rivets. The bolster is attached to the side frame with a large hollow rivet. Type II, used 1912-14, has an open side frame, embossed springs and rivets, and a large hole eyelet. Type III, used 1912-21, is the same as Type II, except it uses a hollow rivet.

180 PULLMAN: 1911-21.

NOTE: The 180 Series has been completely relettered to attempt to place the cars in proper chronological order.

One set of 180, 181, and 182 cars stamped "CANADIAN PACIFIC RAILWAYS" has been reported. These cars appear to have been factory decorated. K. Wills comments.

Gd Exc Rst

(A) 1911, maroon body and roof, gold rubber-stamped "180 PULLMAN 180" on sides beneath windows, "NEW YORK CENTRAL LINES" above windows. Dark olive green doors, red celluloid in upper part of windows, no openings in clerestory, black diaphragms, long straight hook couplers painted maroon and black, black-painted wooden air tanks, gold-painted steps pierced with many small holes, Type I 180-series trucks, red undercoat on underside of floor, floor embossed "LIONEL MFG. CO.", 12-1/2". D. Ely Collection. **100 150 90**

(B) 1911-13, maroon body and roof, gold rubber-stamped "180 PULLMAN 180" on sides beneath windows, "NEW YORK CENTRAL LINES" above windows. Dark olive green doors, no openings in clerestory, black diaphragms, long crinkle hook couplers, black-painted wooden air tanks, gold-painted steps pierced with many small holes, Type I 180-series truck, red undercoat on underside of floor, floor embossed "LIONEL MFG. CO.", 12-1/2". **100 150 90**

(C) 1914-17, maroon body and roof, gold rubber-stamped "PULLMAN" in elaborate scroll beneath windows, "180" on ends. Dark olive green doors, pierced clerestory with tabs to hold celluloid, black diaphragms, regular hook couplers, black-painted wooden air tanks, three-hole gold-painted steps, single-rivet 180-series trucks, underside painted maroon to match sides, floor embossed "LIONEL MFG. CO.", 12-1/2". **80 100 70**

(D) Same as (C), but rubber-stamped beneath windows "180 PULLMAN 180", pierced clerestory, but no tabs to hold celluloid, large crinkle hook couplers. Probable transition between (B) and (C). R. Kirchner Collection. **NRS**

(E) Same as (C), but gold rubber-stamped "PARLOR CAR" beneath windows, "NEW YORK CENTRAL LINES" above windows, pierced clerestory with red inserts, Type I 180-series trucks, regular hook couplers, floor embossed in two lines "LIONEL MFG. CO. / N.Y.", "No. 180" gold rubber-stamped on right side of one end, no other stamping on ends, four rows of seats. D. Dudley Collection. **NRS**

(F) Same as (C), but rubber-stamped "180 PULLMAN 180", blue celluloid throughout, large crinkle hook couplers, floor is not embossed or stamped, no stampings on ends, Type III 180-series truck. C. Weber Collection. **80 100 70**

(G) Same as (C), but gold rubber-stamped "CANADIAN PACIFIC RAILWAY" above windows, large crinkle hook couplers, stamped on one end "LIONEL / LINES / N.Y. / Made in U.S.A." to left of diaphragm and "NO. / 180" to the right. K. Wills observation. **NRS**

(H) Same as 180(C), but brown body and roof. **90 130 80**

(I) 1918-21, brown body and roof, similar to 180(C), but floor not embossed. Rubber-stamped "LIONEL CORPORATION" on ends or bottom. **90 130 80**

(J) 1918-21, maroon body and roof, similar to 180(C), but floor not embossed. Rubber-stamped "THE LIONEL CORPORATION" on ends or bottom. **80 90 70**

181 COMBINE: 1911-21.

(A) Maroon body and roof, matches 180(A). D. Ely comment. Confirmation requested. **100 140 90**

(B) Maroon body and roof, matches 180(B). **80 100 70**

(C) Maroon body and roof, matches 180(C). **90 125 80**

(D) Maroon body and roof, matches 180(D). R. Kirchner comment. Confirmation requested. **80 100 70**

(E) Matches 180(E), except floor is not embossed, and end is gold rubber-stamped "LIONEL / LINES / N.Y. / Made in U.S.A." on left and "No. 181" on the right. Gold rubber-stamped "PULLMAN" under the four windows and "BAGGAGE" under the oval windows, "NEW YORK CENTRAL LINES" above windows. D. Dudley Collection. **NRS**

(F) Matches 180(F), Type II 180-series trucks. C. Weber Collection. **80 100 70**

(G) Matches 180(G). K. Wills observation. **NRS**

(H) Brown body and roof, matches 180(H). **90 125 80**

(I) Brown body and roof, matches 180(I). **80 100 70**

(J) Maroon body and roof, matches 180(J). **80 100 70**

(K) Yellow orange body and roof, orange doors, gold rubber-stamped "PULLMAN" in elaborate scroll beneath windows, "NEW YORK CENTRAL LINES" above windows, black diaphragms, removable roof, pierced clerestory. **225 275 200**

NOTE: 181(K) and 182(K) properly belong in the 1914-17 period between variations (H) and (I). However, there are no reported examples of a matching 180 Pullman. Therefore it is reported last for convenience.

182 OBSERVATION: 1911-21.

NOTE: The earliest observations have a long platform with the support sloping downward to the outside. The next observations have long platforms with straight supports. The last observations have short platforms. The earliest platforms have vertical slat rails. The next platforms have an interlocking spoke-wheel design with scalloped top edge or fan-blade design with smooth top edge.

(A) 1911, maroon body and roof, matches 180(A) and 181(A). D. Ely comment. Confirmation requested. **NRS**

(B) 1911-13, maroon body and roof, matches 180(B) and 181(B). Observation rail with scalloped top edge, long deck. **100 140 90**

(C) Maroon body roof, matches 180(C) and 181(C). Observation rail with fan-blade design and smooth top edge, long deck. **80 100 70**

(D) Maroon body and roof, matches 180(D) and 181(D). R. Kirchner comment. Confirmation requested. **NRS**

(E) Matches 181(E). D. Dudley Collection. **NRS**

(F) Matches 180(F) and 181(F), Type II trucks. C. Weber Collection. **80 100 70**

(G) Matches 180(G) and 181(G). K. Wills observation. **NRS**

(H) 1914-17, brown body and roof, matches 180(H) and 181(H). Observation rail with fan-blade design and smooth top edge, long deck. **80 100 70**

(I) 1918-21, brown body roof, matches 180(I) and 181(I). Observation rail with fan-blade design and smooth top edge, short deck. **90 125 80**

(J) 1918-21, maroon body and roof, matches 180(J) and 181(J). Observation rail with fan-blade design and smooth top edge, short deck. **80 100 70**

(K) Yellow orange body and roof, orange doors, matches 181(K). Observation rail with fan-blade design and smooth top edge, long deck. (See note after 181(K).) **225 275 90**

190 OBSERVATION: See entry following 19 Combine.

309 PULLMAN: 1924-39, illuminated, 500-series trucks except some versions of (A), latch couplers (except (A), 13-1/4". Came with 310 Baggage and 312 Observation. Each car came with three plates below the windows. The left and right plates contain the car number. The middle plate contains the word "PULLMAN". Two different lettering styles can be found on these cars. One type features elaborate serif-style lettering within scrollwork. The other type features plainer serif-style lettering without scrollwork. J. Sattler observation. (See accompanying illustration.) The 309 and 312 came with two

Gd Exc Rst

different door styles. The early doors have large windows and the doors are supported by two crude hinges with a small coil spring to keep them closed. The small window doors are mounted by relatively long tabs which pass through the partition and are coiled within the body. Sets are found with all large doors, mixed doors, and small doors. Nevertheless, door types are useful when used with other characteristics in dating cars. A. G. Thomson observation.

TOP SHELF: "PULLMAN" lettering in larger serif letters within scrollwork. BOTTOM SHELF: Smaller serif letters, more widely spaced, without scrollwork.
R. Bartelt photograph.

(A) 1924, maroon body and roof, mojave window inserts, wood-grained door, large door windows, stamped "NEW YORK CENTRAL LINES" above windows, 100-, 200-, or 500-series trucks, combination latch couplers. **70 150 70**

(B) 1925-26, mojave body and roof, maroon window inserts, wood-grained door, nickel journals, large door windows, stamped "NYC LINES". **70 150 70**

(C) 1927-29, same as (A), but stamped "THE LIONEL LINES". **70 150 70**

(D) Same as (B), but stamped "THE LIONEL LINES". **70 150 70**

(E) 1927-30, pea green body and roof, orange window inserts and door, large or small door windows, nickel journals, stamped "THE LIONEL LINES". **70 150 70**

(F) 1930-33, light brown body, dark brown roof, cream window inserts and doors, large or small door windows, stamped "THE LIONEL LINES", nickel or copper journals. **85 175 80**

(G) 1931, maroon body, terra-cotta roof, cream window inserts and doors, large door window, stamped "NEW YORK CENTRAL LINES" above windows, nickel journals. Also reported by D. Ely with wood-grained doors. **90 175 70**

(H) 1934, medium blue body and door with small window, dark blue roof, cream window inserts, rubber-stamped "THE LIONEL LINES", copper journals. **120 250 80**

(I) 1934-35, apple green body, dark green roof, cream window inserts, apple green door with small window, rubber-stamped "THE LIONEL LINES", copper journals (rare). **120 250 90**

(J) 1935-39, pale blue body, silver roof, window insert and door, with small window, rubber-stamped "THE LIONEL LINES", nickel journals. **70 150 70**

(K) Light blue body and roof. Blue color identical to that found on 514R and late 814R Freight Car roofs. Gold rubber-stamped "THE LIONEL LINES" on insert below windows. Nickel journals, rubber-stamped Lionel identification on bottom. This car came as part of a set with an accompanying 390E "Blue Comet" Locomotive, a matching 310 Baggage, and a 312 Observation. This collector had color samples from the cars examined by a chemist using x-ray spectroscopy. Levels of barium, lead, and strontium in this car's paint were compared to paint samples from confirmed Lionel 514R and 814R Refrigerator Car roofs. The parallels in these levels of metallic pigments established beyond doubt that the paint on this car is genuine Lionel factory paint. This set is presently the only known example of this paint scheme, and it may in fact be one-of-a-kind. Editor's Note: The authentication process used is commendable. Adair Collection. **NRS**

310 BAGGAGE: 1924-39, illuminated, 500-series trucks, latch couplers, 13-1/4". Plates read "310", "BAGGAGE", "310". Came with 309 Pullman and 312 Observation.

(A) Matches 309(A), with dark green baggage door. **70 150 70**

(B) Matches 309(B), with dark green baggage door. **70 150 70**

(C) Matches 309(C), with dark green baggage door. **70 150 70**

(D) Matches 309(D), with dark green baggage door. **70 150 70**

(E) Matches 309(E), with orange baggage door (catalogued), dark green baggage door (uncatalogued). **70 150 70**

(F) Matches 309(F) with cream baggage door. **80 175 80**

(G) No baggage car made to match 309(G). **— — —**

(H) Matches 309(H), with light blue baggage door. **120 250 80**

(I) Matches 309(I), with apple green baggage door. **120 250 90**

(J) Matches 309(J), with silver baggage door. **70 150 70**

(K) Matches 309(K). Adair Collection. **NRS**

312 OBSERVATION: 1924-39, illuminated, 500-series trucks, latch couplers, 13-1/4". Plates read "312", "OBSERVATION", "312". Came with 309 Pullman and 310 Baggage.

(A) Matches 309(A). **70 150 70**

(B) Matches 309(B). **70 150 70**

(C) Matches 309(C). **70 150 70**

(D) Matches 309(D). **70 150 70**

(E) Matches 309(E). **70 150 70**

(F) Matches 309(F). **80 175 80**

(G) Matches 309(G). **90 175 70**

(H) Matches 309(H). **120 250 70**

(I) Matches 309(I). **120 250 90**

(J) Matches 309(J). **70 150 70**

(K) Matches 309(K). Adair Collection. **NRS**

CLASSIC ERA PASSENGER CARS
380
320
319
319
322
1835E
1835W
310(J)
309(J)
312
312(C)
309(C)
312(E)
310(C)
318
309(E)
310(E)
318E
312(G)
309(G)
LIONEL LINES
384T
384

LATE SMALL STANDARD PASSENGER SETS

Gd Exc Rst

319 PULLMAN: 1924-27, medium-sized passenger car of Classic Era, came in a variety of colors with different trucks. Rubber-stamped with different road names, mostly "LIONEL LINES" or "NEW YORK CENTRAL LINES". Combination latch, or later latch couplers, brass steps, 13-1/4". Maroon body and roof, wood-grained doors, mojave windows and number boards.
(A) 200-series trucks, rubber-stamped "LIONEL LINES". **70 100 70**
(B) Same as (A), but rubber-stamped "NEW YORK CENTRAL LINES". **70 100 70**
(C) Same as (A), but rubber-stamped "ILLINOIS CENTRAL". **100 145 90**
(D) Same as (A), but rubber-stamped "LIONEL ELECTRICAL RAILROAD". **100 145 90**
(E) 100-series Type V freight trucks, rubber-stamped "NEW YORK CENTRAL LINES". D. Witman Collection. **70 100 70**

320 BAGGAGE: 1925-27. (See 319 for background.) Part of series with 319 and 322. Maroon body and roof, wood-grained doors, mojave windows and number boards.
(A) 200-series trucks, rubber-stamped "LIONEL LINES". Matches 319(A). **70 100 70**
(B) Matches 319(B). R. Spong and A. Costa Collections. **130 250 90**
(C) Same as (A), but rubber-stamped "ILLINOIS CENTRAL". Matches 319 (C). **100 145 90**
(D) Same as (A), but rubber-stamped "LIONEL ELECTRICAL RAILROAD". Matches 319(D). **100 145 90**

322 OBSERVATION: 1924-27. (See 319 for background on series which includes 319 and 320.) Maroon sides and roof, wood-grained doors, mojave windows and number boards.
(A) 200-series trucks, rubber-stamped "LIONEL LINES". Matches 319(A). **70 100 70**
(B) Same as (A), but rubber-stamped "NEW YORK CENTRAL LINES". Matches 319(B). **70 100 70**
(C) Same as (A), but rubber-stamped "ILLINOIS CENTRAL". Matches 319(C). **100 145 90**
(D) Same as (A), but rubber-stamped "LIONEL ELECTRICAL RAILROAD". Matches 319(D). **100 145 90**
(E) Same as (B), but 100-series Type V freight trucks. Matches 319(E). D. Witman Collection. **70 100 70**

332 BAGGAGE: This car comes with two different small, late Standard Gauge passenger series. The first series consisted of the 332 Baggage plus 337 Pullman and 338 Observation. The 337 and 338 have single undivided windows. The second late, small series consisted of the 332 plus 339 Pullman and 341 Observation. The cars are 12 inches long and feature enameled inserts to create windows and number boards. All have 500-series trucks, latch couplers, nickel journals — without brass plates. They are rubber-stamped "RAILWAY MAIL" and "332" on each side and have black metal air tanks with nickel ends.
(A) Red body and roof, cream doors, windows, and number boards, rubber-stamped "THE LIONEL LINES". **45 75 45**
(B) Peacock body and roof, orange doors, windows, and number boards, rubber-stamped "THE LIONEL LINES". **45 75 45**
(C) Gray body and roof, maroon doors, windows, and number boards, rubber-stamped "THE LIONEL LINES". **45 75 45**
(D) Olive green body and roof, red doors, windows, and number boards. **50 90 45**
(E) State brown body, dark brown roof, cream doors, windows, and number boards, gold rubber-stamped "THE LIONEL LINES" and "RAILWAY MAIL". **100 250 45**
(F) Peacock body, dark green roof, orange doors, windows, and number boards. **60 100 45**
(G) Peacock body and roof, red doors, orange windows, and number boards, catalogued 1929 only. **75 125 45**
(H) Peacock body, dark green roof, orange windows, doors, and number boards, with "IVES LINES" decals over "THE LIONEL LINES" rubber-stamping. **90 140 60**
(I) Mojave body, maroon roof, maroon windows, doors, and number boards. C. Weber comment. **120 175 45**

337 PULLMAN: 1925-32. (See 332 for background.) Ten single undivided windows, rubber-stamped "NEW YORK CENTRAL LINES" or "THE LIONEL LINES" above windows, four brass steps, illuminated, 12".

NOTE: Letters assigned to variations of 337, 338, 339, and 341 are not in strict alphabetical order since they refer to related car variations.
(A) Red body and roof, cream doors, windows, and number boards, matches 332(A), rubber-stamped "THE LIONEL LINES". **45 75 45**
(B) Mojave body and roof, maroon windows, doors, and number boards, rubber-stamped "NEW YORK CENTRAL LINES", later 500-series trucks, Type II oil label. C. Weber Collection. **45 75 45**
(C) Same as (B), but lettered "THE LIONEL LINES", early 500-series trucks, Type II oil label. C. Weber Collection. **45 75 45**
(D) Olive green body and roof, red doors, windows and number boards, lettered "THE LIONEL LINES", Type II oil label, later 500-series trucks, brass air tank ends, matches 332(D). C. Weber Collection. **50 90 45**
(E) Olive green body and roof, maroon windows, doors, and number boards. **45 75 45**
(F) Pea green body and roof, cream windows, doors, and number boards. **100 200 45**
(G) - (I) intentionally not used.
(J) Olive green body and roof, maroon windows, doors, and number boards, rubber-stamped "ILLINOIS CENTRAL". Confirmation requested. **NRS**

338 OBSERVATION: (See 332 for background, matches 337 Pullman.) Ten single, undivided windows, brass observation railing, 12".
(A) Red, matches 337(A). **45 75 45**
(B) Mojave, matches 337(B). **45 75 45**
(C) Mojave, matches 337(C). C. Weber Collection. **45 75 45**
(D) Olive green and red trim, matches 337(D). **50 90 45**
(E) Olive green and maroon trim, matches 337(E). **45 75 45**
(F) Pea green, matches 337(F). **100 200 45**
(G)-(I) Intentionally not used.
(J) Olive green body and roof, maroon windows, doors, and number boards, rubber-stamped "ILLINOIS CENTRAL". Confirmation requested. **NRS**

339 PULLMAN: 1925-33. (See 332 for background on series.) Six windows divided horizontally and vertically, rubber-stamped "NEW YORK CENTRAL LINES" or "THE LIONEL LINES" above windows, four brass steps, illuminated, 12".
(B) Peacock body and roof, orange doors, windows, and number boards, matches 332(B), rubber-stamped "THE LIONEL LINES". **45 75 45**

THE STATE SETS

THE BLUE COMET AND STEPHEN GIRARD SETS
400E
400T
420
421
390E
390T
420
421
422
9E
424
425
425
424
Broadway Limited
392E
392TW
422
420
FAYE
WESTPHAL
STEPHEN GIRARD
CORAL ISLE
LIBERTY BELL
No 9E
LIONEL LINES
TEMPEL

431
419
408E
431
419
408
429
9
429
429
9E
380E

Gd Exc Rst

(C) Gray body and roof, maroon doors, windows, and number boards, matches 332(C). C. Weber Collection. **45 75 45**

(E) State brown body, dark brown roof, cream doors, gold-stamped windows and number boards, matches 332(E), rubber-stamped "THE LIONEL LINES". **100 250 45**

(F) Peacock body, dark green roof, orange doors, windows, and number boards. **60 100 45**

(H) Peacock body, dark green roof, orange windows, doors, and number boards, with "IVES LINES" decals over "THE LIONEL LINES" rubber-stamping. **90 140 60**

(I) Mojave body, maroon roof, windows, doors, and number boards. **120 175 45**

341 OBSERVATION: 1925-33. (See 332 and 339 for background on series.)

(B) Peacock body and roof, orange doors, windows, and number boards, matches 332(B), rubber-stamped "THE LIONEL LINES". **45 75 45**

(C) Gray body and roof, maroon doors, windows, and number boards, matches 332(C) and 339(C), rubber-stamped "NEW YORK CENTRAL LINES". See 339(C). C. Weber Collection and comment. **45 75 45**

(E) State brown body, dark brown roof, cream doors, windows, and number boards, matches 332(E), rubber-stamped. **100 250 45**

(F) Peacock body, dark green roof, orange doors, windows, and number boards, rubber-stamped. **60 100 45**

(H) Peacock body, dark green roof, orange windows, doors, and number boards, with "IVES LINES" decals over "THE LIONEL LINES" rubber-stamping. **90 140 60**

(I) Mojave body, maroon roof, windows, doors, and number boards. **120 175 45**

412 PULLMAN: 1929-35, brass plates with "CALIFORNIA" in black lettering with either serif or sans-serif letters, brass trim only on steps, handrails, nameplates. Part of "State Car" series: 412, 413, 414, 416; the largest Lionel passenger cars ever made (21-1/2"). Interior trim included two washrooms with sinks and toilets, interior doors, and individual passenger seats. Earlier cars have die-cast axle journals. They do decay and replacements are available. Later cars have stamped brass journals. Two body rivet designs are found. The later includes a new row of rivets outlining the car end section.

NOTE: Excellent reproductions of the State Car series have been made by Williams Reproductions. Reproductions have also been made from a lighter weight steel with plates lettered "LION LINES". The Williams cars are valued at $625 each in excellent condition. The "LION LINES" cars are valued at $470 each in excellent condition.

(A) Lighter green body, dark green roof, apple green window inserts, roof ventilators usually light green, a few are dark green. **850 1500 800**

(B) Same as (A), but yellow window inserts, usually came with 400E. **875 1600 825**

(C) Light brown body, dark brown roof, yellow window inserts, roof ventilators light or dark brown, some have yellow doors, came with 408E. **900 1800 850**

413 PULLMAN: 1929-35, "COLORADO", matches 412.

(A) Matches 412(A). **850 1500 800**

(B) Matches 412(B). **875 1600 825**

(C) Matches 412(C). **900 1800 850**

414 PULLMAN: 1929-35, "ILLINOIS", matches 412.

(A) Matches 412(A), 1929 only. **975 2100 900**

(B) Matches 412(B), reader verification requested. **NRS**

(C) Matches 412(C). **975 1800 950**

416 OBSERVATION: 1929-35, "NEW YORK", matches 412; celluloid insert on rear railing either "TRANSCONTINENTAL LIMITED" or "LIONEL LINES".

(A) Matches 412(A). **850 1500 800**

(B) Matches 412(B). **875 1600 825**

(C) Matches 412(C). **900 1800 850**

418 PULLMAN: 1923-32. This car with the matching 419 and 490 formed the first large passenger car series of the Classic Era. Introduced with the 402 as the top-of-the-line set in mojave, these cars later appeared in apple green. Gold rubber-stamped "PARLOR CAR" below windows and "NEW YORK CENTRAL LINES" above windows except (A) and (G), maroon window trim except (F) and (G), four brass step units, pierced roof clerestory, two knurled screws hold roof to body, light inside car, one pickup roller, gold rubber-stamped "418" on one end only, four black air tanks with nickeled ends. 1923 models were rubber-stamped "LIONEL CORP. U.S.A." on underside. Later models have oiling instruction labels. In 1927, a diner, 431 was added to the series. The cars have been expertly reproduced by Williams Reproductions.

(A) 1923-24, 10-series trucks, combination latch couplers, wood lithographed doors. **175 250 175**

(B) 1923, same as (A), but lettered "PULLMAN" below windows. P. Graves Collection. **175 250 175**

(C) 1923-24, same as (A), but maroon doors. **175 250 175**

(D) 1925, six-wheel trucks with nickel journals, latch couplers, and wood lithographed doors. **185 275 185**

(E) 1925, same as (D), but maroon doors. **185 275 185**

(F) Same as (D), except maroon doors and orange window trim. **185 300 185**

(G) Same as (D), except maroon doors, orange window trim, and "THE LIONEL LINES" above windows. **185 300 185**

(H) Same as (D), except maroon doors, red window trim, and apple green body and roof. **185 300 185**

NOTE: Williams Electric Trains has manufactured reproductions of the 418, 419, 490, 431, and 428, 429, and 430. "WRL" is embossed on major pieces of the body including the top ledge inside the car where the metal tabs hold the window material, inside of interior bulkheads and under vestibule ends. The cars are available in four colors: mojave, orange, dark green, and apple green. Window inserts are available in red, maroon, and orange. The cars are available with 200-series trucks or six-wheel, 418-style trucks. Decals with "NEW YORK CENTRAL LINES", and the numbers "418", "419", "490", "431", "428", and "429", and "430", are available. Hence it is expected that combinations of trucks, colors, window inserts, and numbers not originally created by Lionel will occasionally be offered for sale. The value of the cars in excellent condition, properly assembled, is about $150, except for the 431 Diner which brings $200.

419 COMBINATION: 1923-32, part of 418-, 419-, 490-series. (See 418 for background.) Combination cars, or "combines" for short, carry a mixed consist of passengers, baggage, and small freight items. They have three large passenger windows, a lavatory window, and two windows in baggage compartment on each side, two regular doors and one large baggage door on each side, gold rubber-stamped on lower side "BAGGAGE" and "PARLOR CAR", and "419" on end.

(A) Matches 418(A). **175 250 175**

(B) Matches 418(C). **175 250 175**

(C) Matches 418(D). **185 275 185**

(D) Matches 418(E). **185 275 185**

(E) Matches 418(F). **185 300 185**

	Gd	Exc	Rst
(F) Matches 418(G).	185	305	185
(G) Matches 418(H).	185	300	185

BLUE COMET CARS: 420, 421, and 422, specially painted locomotives. Catalogued initially with the 390E and later with the 400E Locomotive.

NOTE: In 1986 Mike's Train House of Columbia, Maryland reproduced the three Blue Comet cars in both brass and nickel trim. The three car sets were offered for $750. In addition, a fourth car marked "Halley" was offered for $250, in either nickel or brass trim. Note that 1985-86 marked the return of the Halley Comet to the vicinity of our planet after an absence of 76 years.

The reproduction cars differ from the originals as follows:

1. "MTH" is marked on the car roof, car floor, and the trucks.
2. Zinc chromate plating (gold color) under the paint.

420 PULLMAN: 1930-40, "FAYE", latch couplers, 18-3/4".

	Gd	Exc	Rst
(A) Medium blue with dark blue roof sections and vestibules, cream windows with brass trim, plates, and cast journals.	525	850	500
(B) Same as (A), but brass-stamped journals.	525	850	500
(C) Lighter blue with dark blue roof sections and vestibules, cream windows, mostly nickel trim, brass plates, nickel journals, frosted window glazing.	575	900	500
(D) Same as (C), but diaphragms painted lighter blue, all nickel trim.	700	1000	500

421 PULLMAN: 1930-40, "WESTPHAL", matches 420.

	Gd	Exc	Rst
(A) Matches 420(A).	525	850	500
(B) Matches 420(B).	525	850	500
(C) Matches 420(C).	575	900	500
(D) Matches 420(D).	700	1000	500

422 OBSERVATION: 1930-40, "TEMPEL", matches 420 and 421.

	Gd	Exc	Rst
(A) Matches 420(A).	525	850	500
(B) Matches 420(B).	525	850	500
(C) Matches 420(C).	575	900	500
(D) Matches 420(D).	700	1000	575

424 PULLMAN: 1931-40, brass plates "LIBERTY BELL", part of the Stephen Girard Series: 424, 425, and 426. These are late, medium-sized passenger cars, 16" long, found with Stephen Girard (light green) bodies and roofs, accented with dark green vestibules and roof areas. Six-wheel trucks, cream window inserts, operating doors, bench sides run longitudinally. All with brass plates and nickel or brass trim. Blue-speckled celluloid upper windows, clear celluloid lower windows, roof opens on hinges and latches; latch couplers. Reproductions have been made by Mike's Train House. The Stephen Girard Set which includes a set of three cars is currently $425. In addition an extra car lettered "Philadelphia" is also available. This Philadelphia car was never used by Lionel.

	Gd	Exc	Rst
(A) "LIBERTY BELL", brass trim.	325	500	325
(B) "LIBERTY BELL", nickel trim.	350	600	350
(C) Reproduction.	**	**	**

425 PULLMAN: 1931-40, brass plates "STEPHEN GIRARD" (See 424 for background.)

	Gd	Exc	Rst
(A) Brass trim.	325	500	325
(B) Nickel trim.	350	600	350
(C) Reproduction.	**	**	**

426 OBSERVATION: 1931-40, "CORAL ISLE" (See 424 for background.) Keystone on observation railing lettered "PENNSYLVANIA LIMITED".

	Gd	Exc	Rst
(A) Brass trim.	325	500	350
(B) Nickel trim.	350	600	375

427 DINER: Similar to 431, but was to have four-wheel, 200-series trucks, while 431 was catalogued with six-wheel trucks. 427 was catalogued in 1930 and to the best of our knowledge was not made. 431 Diners almost always have six-wheel trucks as catalogued. However, two examples of 431 Diners with factory affixed 200-series trucks have been discovered. It is argued that these are really 427 Diners misnumbered 431! We will leave this controversy to our readers... **Not Manufactured**

428 PULLMAN: 1926-30. Part of 428, 429, and 430 Series which featured 200-series trucks in contrast to the closely related 418, 419, and 490 Series with six-wheel trucks. Other than the trucks, colors and lettering appear identical. The cars have been expertly reproduced by Williams Electric Trains. (See note to 418 entry for more information.)

	Gd	Exc	Rst
(A) Dark green body and roof, maroon window inserts, wood lithographed doors, latch couplers, gold rubber-stamped "PARLOR CAR" on lower sides, "428" on one end, and "THE LIONEL LINES" above windows.	225	300	200
(B) Same as (A), but maroon doors.	225	300	200
(C) Same as (A), but orange window inserts and maroon doors.	225	300	200
(D) Orange body and roof, apple green window inserts and doors, gold rubber-stamped "PARLOR CAR" on lower sides, "428" on one end, "THE LIONEL LINES" above windows.	350	700	225

429 COMBINE: 1926-30. (See 428 for background on series.) Combination is part passenger, part baggage. It has three large passenger windows, a lavatory window, and two windows in the baggage compartment on each side, as well as two regular doors and one large baggage door on each side. Gold rubber-stamped on lower side "BAGGAGE" and "PARLOR CAR", "429" stamped on end. Reproductions available. See note following 418 entry.

	Gd	Exc	Rst
(A) Matches 428(A).	225	300	200
(B) Matches 428(B).	225	300	200
(C) Matches 428(C).	225	300	200
(D) Matches 428(D).	350	700	225

430 OBSERVATION: 1926-30. (See 428 for background on series.) The Observation has open rear deck with brass railings. Reproductions available. See note following 418 entry.

	Gd	Exc	Rst
(A) Matches 428(A).	225	300	200
(B) Matches 428(B).	225	300	200
(C) Matches 428(C).	225	300	200
(D) Matches 428(D).	350	700	225

431 DINER: 1927-32. Part of the 418, 419, and 490 Series and/or the 428, 429, and 430 Series. (See 418 and 428 for background on each series.) The Diner was generally not included in sets and is much scarcer than the other cars. It includes eight tables and 32 chairs in the dining room, and a small kitchen with stove and table. One light is provided for dining with one pickup roller attached to one truck providing the necessary current. The windows have blue-speckled celluloid in upper window section. The car comes with four brass steps and usually a roof attached with two knurled screws, although a few cars are known to have hinged roofs, probably for dealer display. The car usually has six-wheel 418-style trucks, although it is reported with 200-series trucks.

Two Lionel 385 Sets with 1767 Baggage, 1766 Pullman, and 1768 Observation (not shown). The upper set has the later nickel-trimmed locomotive with red cars with nickel trim. The lower set has the earlier brass and copper-trimmed locomotive with terra-cotta cars with brass trim.

Gd Exc Rst

Four black metal air tanks, latch couplers, and nickel journals adorn the car. Reproductions available. See note following 418.

(A) Mojave body, orange window inserts, maroon doors, six-wheel trucks, gold rubber-stamped "THE LIONEL LINES" above windows and "431" on one end only, knurled screws hold roof to body. **300 450 300**

(B) Same as (A), but hinged roof with several small hinges. **400 600 400**

(C) Same as (A), but maroon window inserts. **300 450 300**

(D) Dark green body, orange window inserts, 200-series trucks, gold rubber-stamped "THE LIONEL LINES" above windows, "431" gold stamped on one end only. **350 600 350**

(E) Orange body, apple green inserts, six-wheel trucks, gold rubber-stamped on one end only. **350 600 350**

(F) Apple green body, red window inserts, six-wheel trucks, gold rubber-stamped "THE LIONEL LINES" above windows, "431" on one end only. **350 600 350**

490 OBSERVATION: 1923-32. Part of 418, 419, 490 Series. (See 418 for background.) The Observation has an open rear deck with brass railing. Reproductions available, see 418 for details.

(A) Matches 418(A). **175 250 175**

(B) Matches 418(B). **175 250 175**

(C) Matches 418(C). **185 270 180**

(D) Matches 418(D). **185 270 180**

(E) Matches 418(E). **185 270 180**

(F) Matches 418(F). **185 300 185**

(G) Matches 418(G). **185 300 185**

1766 PULLMAN: 1934-40. These cars are Ives designs produced by Lionel under the Ives name in 1932. In 1934 they appeared with Lionel plates. There are two matching cars: 1767 Baggage and 1768 Observation. They have six-wheel trucks, latch couplers, lights, roof latch mechanisms. Earlier cars have terra-cotta sides, maroon roofs and fishbelly, cream windows and doors, and brass trim. Later cars have red sides, maroon roofs and fishbelly, aluminum windows and doors, and nickel trim. However, all catalogue illustrations show the earlier cars.

(A) Terra-cotta with brass trim. **300 600 300**

(B) Red with nickel trim. **300 500 300**

1767 BAGGAGE: 1934-40. (See 1766 for background.)

(A) Terra-cotta with brass trim. **300 600 300**

(B) Red with nickel trim. **300 500 300**

1768 OBSERVATION: 1934-40. (See 1766 for background.)

(A) Terra-cotta with brass trim. **300 600 300**

(B) Red with nickel trim. **300 500 300**

1910 PULLMAN: 1909-10, dark olive green body and roof, maroon doors and window sills, gold-painted window dividers, celluloid windows, roof not removable, doors do not open, three high wooden knobs fastened to roof, open, three-rivet trucks mounted close to car ends, short straight hook couplers, gold rubber-stamped on sides "1910 PULLMAN 1910" in letters without serifs. First Lionel closed vestibule passenger car. **800 1500 650**

Chapter IV
Standard Gauge Trucks

10 Series; three rivets; closed sides. These trucks are also called three rivet, flex trucks with closed sides. The earliest version has relatively narrow side frames as shown above. Later versions have wider side frames. The later version is illustrated on page 42 with the 12(A) Gondola.

10 Series; three rivets; open sides, embossed springs. Also called three rivet, open side flex trucks.

10 Series; earliest version of single-rivet truck, crimping at bolster bend, vertical sections of bolster match side frame. These are also called single-rivet flex trucks.

10 Series; later version of single-rivet truck, no crimping at bolster bend, vertical sections of bolster match side frame. Comes with two different rivet styles: the narrow flange type is shown above and the wide flange type is shown below. These are also called single-rivet, flex trucks.

10 Series; single-rivet; no crimping at bolster bend; vertical sections of bolster match side frame. Comes with two different rivet styles: the wide flange type is shown above and the narrow flange type is shown at the top of this column. These are also called single-rivet, flex trucks.

10 Series; latest version single-rivet truck, no crimping at bolster bend, vertical sections of bolster visible behind side frame. These are also called single-rivet, flex trucks.

Photograph not available

100 Series; Type I. Solid side frame, single-eyelet flex trucks with vertical sections of bolter with pointed ends. The eyelet is distinguished from the rivet of 100 Series, Type III by the absence of a wide outside flange on the eyelet. A Type I or Type II truck is illustrated on page 46 with the short 112(A) Gondola.

Photograph not available

100 Series; Type II. Solid side frame, single-eyelet flex trucks with vertical sections of bolster with rounded ends. The eyelet is distinguished from the rivet of the 100 Series, Type III by the absence of a wide outside flange on the eyelet. A 100 Series, Type I or II truck is illustrated on page 46 with the 112(A) short gondola.

Note rounded end of vertical section of bolster.

100 Series; Type III. Solid side frame, single-rivet, flex trucks with vertical sections of bolster with rounded ends. The rivet is distinguished from the eyelet found with Type I and II by its wide outside flange.

Photograph
not available

100 Series; Type IV; (same as Type V, but nickel).

100 Series; Type V; (same as Type IV, but black; used on 100-series Freights).

200 Series; embossed side frame, rectangular cutouts on each side, journal boxes. Came with and without roller pickup assemblies.

500 Series; early. Found in both freight and passenger cars. rectangular side slot, 1/8" high x 7/16" wide, no reinforcing bar. Came with and without roller pickup assembly.

500 Series; later. Found with freight and passenger cars. Two rectangular side slots which together are 1/8" high x 5/32" wide with reinforcing bar. Came with and without roller pickup assembly.

500 Series; latest. Found with freight and passenger cars. Two rectangular side slots which together are 1/8" high x 9/32" wide with reinforcing bar. Found with cars with brass trim and copper journals as well as cars with nickel trim and nickel journals. Came with and without roller pickup assembly.

Six-wheel Truck; used on 392 Tender

Chapter V
2-7/8 Inch Gauge

By James M. Sattler

Many interesting and significant new discoveries have been made about Lionel 2-7/8" Gauge cars and accessories since the last edition of this Chapter. These new discoveries add considerably to our present state of knowledge about these very rare items.

The number of original 2-7/8" Gauge items known to collectors is extremely limited. However, the recent assembly of a collection of 29 individual items of rolling stock and a number of original boxes and accessories has provided additional information and confirmation of previously-known information about Lionel's first production of train-related products.

Actual production of Lionel 2-7/8" Gauge cars and accessories was minute when compared to any later period of production, and it is doubtful that any person is still living who has first-hand knowledge of exactly what, when, how, and how many of each item was produced. While no production records have yet turned up to aid in the examination of the earliest period of Lionel production, a recent discovery of some of Lionel's earliest sales records provides new insight as to what was produced and sold. The only known Catalogues which show and describe 2-7/8" Gauge cars and accessories are the recently discovered 1902 and the more well-known 1903, 1904, and 1905 Lionel Catalogues. The 1906 Catalogue which introduced Standard Gauge does not mention or describe any 2-7/8" Gauge item, and therefore it can reasonably be assumed that actual production of 2-7/8" Gauge cars and accessories ceased sometime in 1905.

The 1902-1905 Lionel Catalogues, together with the less than fifty known surviving original specimens of the cars and accessories, and a very small number of original boxes, form the primary research materials relating to the commencement and subsequent developments of Lionel's earliest days of production, and they also afford some very interesting insights into Lionel's and America's turn-of-the-century history.

The 1902 Catalogue, for example, states:

"The goods described herein are offered for sale to the general public for the second year, although they have been in use for a long time by mechanical institutions for demonstrating purposes, as they give a thorough insight into the workings of the electric cars now so universally used. We received so many inquiries from the students and their friends for duplicate outfits that we decided to manufacture them in larger quantities, thereby reducing their cost and enabling us to offer them at a popular price."

Similarly, the 1903 and 1904 Catalogues state that the goods described "are offered for sale to the general public for the third year", and for the "fourth year", respectively, and the 1905 Catalogue states that Lionel had been constructing its goods "For the past five years." The recent discovery of a 1902 Catalogue shows that it follows similar patterns to those of its better-known 1903 versions.

Since no earlier Catalogues are known to exist, the commencement date of 2-7/8" Gauge production as 1901 must be deduced from the later Catalogue statements and other sources.

The generally-accepted view is that the production era of Lionel 2-7/8" Gauge "Electric Miniature Cars" was the five-year period from 1901 through 1905.

The first published work generally available to train collectors which mentions Lionel 2-7/8" Gauge trains is **Riding The Tinplate Rails** by Louis H. Hertz which was published in 1944 almost 40 years after production of these items ceased. Hertz states that "Actually, it was in 1901 that Joshua Lionel Cowen, then twenty-one years of age, who had already proved himself inventive in the electrical field, founded the original Lionel Mfg. Co. and made his first trains." Hertz also found that in 1937 when Lionel stock was placed on the open market, the company stated in a report filed with the Securities and Exchange Commission that the company had started business in 1901.

The conclusion that 1901 represents the commencement date of Lionel production is somewhat at variance with the 1902 Catalogue statement that although the goods were being offered for sale to the general public for the second year, "they have been in use for a long time . . . " For many later years the Lionel Catalogues used the advertising slogan "STANDARD OF THE WORLD" followed, for example, in the 1917 Catalogue by "FOR 17 YEARS" and in the 1920 Catalogue by "FOR TWENTY YEARS". If these numbers of years are counted backwards beginning with the year of the catalogue, the year of 1901 consistently results as the first year. However, in the 1923 and many later Catalogues, the advertising slogan was changed to "STANDARD OF THE WORLD SINCE 1900" and this slogan was also printed on the contemporaneous train set boxes. It might be said that the latter slogan is technically correct because if 1901 was the first year of production, then the goods had been made "since 1900". The actual commencement date of Lionel's 2-7/8" Gauge production may never be known for certain unless reliable documentation is found. The recently-discovered sales records only go back to about the middle of 1903, and therefore do not provide information about the actual commencement date of 2-7/8" Gauge production and sales.

As far as the Catalogues are concerned, it would be unwise in the extreme to blindly accept as true and accurate all of the statements found in Lionel Catalogues.

The Lionel 2-7/8" Gauge cars and equipment were amazingly advanced in view of subsequent developments in model railroading.

No. 100
Electric Locomotive

The Sattler Collection
ELECTRIC EXPRESS
No. 1
No. 2
No. 500(A)
B. & O.
No. 5.
METROPOLITAN.
EXPRESS
No. 100(A)
No. 5
No. 800
No. 1000(B)
No. 1000(A)
No. 300

Lionel began its train production with two-rail track and with one side of the wheels and axles insulated from the other. Although manually operated, all powered units had a reversing mechanism, the details of which varied over the years of production. All units, whether powered or trailers, had cast-iron frames and working coil springs.

The track was comprised of two strips of tin-plated steel inserted into slots or grooves cut in wooden ties. The track was supplied only in straight sections which had to be bent to form curves. The earliest track was composed of straight strips 1/16" thick and 3/8" wide, and of two different lengths of approximately 11" and 13" each. When the unequal lengths of rail were curved they would form a complete circle of eight sections having a diameter of approximately 34 inches.

The ties supplied with the earliest track were red-stained pieces of wood 4" wide, 1" thick, and 1/2" high with slots or grooves cut in one side 2-7/8" apart to admit the steel rails. Each section of the earliest track was supplied with five ties, two of which had plates of brass which fit into the slots or grooves and bent outward to lay flat against the top surface of the tie, and these brass plates were held in place by a single brass brad. The brass plates allowed the electrical contact to be made between the ends of the adjoining steel rails. The other three ties without the brass plates were to be spaced equally between the two end ties. The 1902 Catalogue suggested that: "A complete circle may also be formed, but it is not prudent to do so, as the continual friction on the wheels rounding the curve consumes a great deal more battery current than when car is run straight or slightly curved." This suggestion was eliminated in the later Catalogues.

The 1903 Catalogue indicated a change in the track and stated that the steel rails would be supplied with "offsets" which consisted of an L-shaped bend in one end of each rail and a hook-shaped bend in the other end. The sections of track, each one foot long, were joined by sliding the L-shaped end of one rail into the hook-shaped end of the adjoining rail. The ties supplied with the 1903 and later "offset" rails were reduced in size to 1/2" square and 4" long, and five ties were also supplied for each two-rail section of track. Interestingly, the 1905 Catalogue announced that the track was "Improved 1905"; however, the accompanying illustration is identical to that shown in the 1903 and 1904 Catalogues, and the description is identical to that in the 1904 Catalogue. The later and smaller ties were also stained red.

In addition to the track, Lionel offered a No. 320 "Switch and Signal", a No. 330 ninety-degree "Crossing", a No. 340 "Suspension Bridge" (the design of which changed in 1903), a No. 350 terminal track "Bumper" (the design of which changed between 1902 and 1904), and a No. 380 set of "Elevated Pillars". One of the interesting recently-discovered items is a No. 350 terminal track and "Bumper" in its original box. This particular example has a short section of track with ties which measure 4" wide, 1" thick, and 1/2" high and the "Improved" 1903-1905-type track to which the "Bumper" is attached. Power was supplied either by a set of dry cell batteries (Catalogue No. 301), or a "Plunge Battery" (Catalogue No. 302) consisting of four glass jars, each containing a carbon cylinder and pencil-shaped zinc, a 9" x 12" x 8" wooden box to keep the jars from touching, and a three-pound supply of electric sand to be added to three quarts of water to charge the four cells which were to be wired in series. An alternative power source utilized direct electric current through an outfit (Catalogue No. 370 in 1902 and 1903 only) of two glass jars, lead plates, a mixture of sulphuric acid and water, and a light bulb. Among the other recently-discovered accessory items are a No. 320 right-hand Switch and Signal, an early No. 340 "Suspension Bridge" with straight top members as illustrated in the 1902 catalogue, and two later No. 340 "Suspension Bridges" with arched top members as illustrated in the 1903, 1904, and 1905 Catalogues.

All powered units and all trailers had only four wheels. A realistic model, for the time, of link and pin-type couplers was used with link and metal pins which passed through holes in the coupler pockets and through corresponding holes in the links. Original links and pins are almost always missing when an occasional 2-7/8" Gauge item is found. 2-7/8" Gauge cars and accessories are definitely among the most difficult to acquire of all collectable train-related items.

As described in the accompanying list, there are at least twenty-six significantly different versions of 2-7/8" Gauge rolling stock. In addition, when minor variations are considered, such as types of wheels (either hollow brass or cast-iron), lettering variations (such as paint color differences or the presence or absence of design trim on the ends of destination boards of the 300 and 309 cars), the presence or absence of coupler pockets (on the wooden gondolas and the 300 and 309 cars), cast knobs or wire handles on the controllers, and the presence or absence of trolley poles (on the 300 and 1000 cars), there are well over thirty-two different collectable variations of rolling stock.

It should be understood, however, that some of the twenty-six significant versions described in the list may not have been made. To the author's knowledge, no examples of a 100 Electric Locomotive as a "trailer", or the 100 Electric Locomotive or the 400 Trailer in nickel, have survived, however, recently-discovered Lionel sales records indicate that some of these items were sold. Similarly, no example has yet surfaced of the motorized 500 Electric Derrick Car in light green. Original examples of all of the remaining items described in the list presently reside in collections.

WOODEN GONDOLAS

The generally accepted view is that the first item of 2-7/8" Gauge production was the uncatalogued motorized wooden gondola produced in 1901 or earlier. Two distinct variations of the motorized wooden gondola have been found. The first, which is sometimes referred to as the "Type I", has a red-stained finish and mortised and tenoned corners, and lacks any steps, handrails, or coupler pockets. Because of the rather primitive construction features of this version, it is believed to be the earliest 2-7/8" Gauge item ever produced, and the generally accepted production date is 1901 or possibly earlier.

The second variation, often referred to as the "Type II", is similar; however, it has a natural brown-stained finish and brass corner braces. It also appears with steps, handrails, and a coupler pocket. This variation is described exactly in the recently discovered 1902 Catalogue, although the cut illustrating this item incorrectly shows the words "Electric Express" in a darkened circle. All original examples found to date of both versions of the wooden gondola bear the words "Electric Express" in a straight gold line 5-1/2" long on each side. One of the interesting recent discoveries is a pair of Type II wooden gondolas, reportedly from the old Lionel showroom, one motorized and the other a non-motorized "TRAIL CAR". As prophetically stated on page 6 of the 1902 Lionel Catalogue:

"These cars coupled together make a very interesting and entertaining outfit."

Another recent discovery is an original wooden double box for a pair of wooden gondolas (not verified, however, as the original wooden box for the pair of wooden gondolas reportedly from the old Lionel showroom) and a second original wooden box for a single wooden gondola. The construction of these wooden boxes bears a striking resemblance to the construction of the wooden gondolas themselves.

One of the most overworked, and in many cases misused, words commonly heard in train collecting is "rare". As applied to the wooden gondola, however, there is hardly another adjective that fairly or more accurately can be used. All versions of the Lionel wooden gondola are among the rarest items confronted in train collecting. At this writing, the number of surviving examples of the Type II wooden gondolas outnumber the number of the Type I wooden gondolas by eight to one.

No. 100 Electric Locomotives

The first model of a locomotive ever made by Lionel was the No. 100 Electric Locomotive. The No. 100, which always bore the designation "No. 5" on its sides and ends, was modeled after the 1,800-horsepower electric locomotives which hauled trains through the Camden-Waverly tunnel section under the City of Baltimore, as a part of the Baltimore and Ohio Railroad. The prototype had four articulated sets of wheels, which Lionel reduced to two. The Lionel model, like all powered 2 7/8" Gauge items, had an electric motor which was entirely below floor level.

Although the Catalogues all state that the "Actual size" of the No. 100 is "12 inches long", in fact the overall length of the No. 100 is 10-1/2". A longer measurement could only be derived by also including the two fully-extended link couplers.

The No. 100 is only rarely found with a light green body and roof and a black frame. The 1903 Catalogue states that "All parts are japanned and lettered in harmonious colors." The term "japanned" means to give a coat of "japan" which in turn refers to a type of varnish or lacquer having a hard, brilliant finish, and it most commonly refers to a black coating used on metal and fixed by heating. The light green finish on the early locomotives is definitely and distinctly of a different type of finish than that which appears on maroon and black examples. The light green finish chips easily, and when the finish chips or flakes off the shiny, tinned metal underneath is readily visible.

The 1904 and 1905 Catalogues changed the word "japanned" to "enameled", and consequently it is reasonable to assume that the light green models were of 1903 or possibly earlier production, while the maroon and black versions followed the Catalogue language change. Therefore, the maroon and black versions can be fairly dated as 1904 or later production. At least one No. 100 has been found with gold-colored paper stickers on both sides stamped "C & St. L" on the left sides of the center door and "No. 5" on the right sides.

There is a significant difference in the manner by which the bodies are held to the frames in the light green and the maroon and black versions. The light green locomotives have two 1/2" holes in the bottom of the floor through which portions of the cast-iron frame pass to hold the body to the frame. In the maroon and black versions these holes are not present and the body is fastened to the cast-iron frame by means of two screws with square nuts on the inside of the body. The reversing switches are also very different, and in this regard there is a curiosity which arises out of the Catalogue illustrations. The 1904 and 1905 Catalogues both contain an illustration of the underside of a car which "represents the mechanism contained in all our motor cars". The 1903 Catalogues do not contain such an illustration. The reversing switch shown in the 1904 and 1905 illustrations is identical to that found on the light green locomotives; however, the maroon and black locomotives have a reversing switch which is circular and concentric. As is the case in the prewar and postwar eras, the Catalogues cannot be taken as accurate in all instances, and in this particular case it may well be that the 1904 and 1905 Catalogues used an illustration of a 1903 or earlier mechanism.

The 1904 and 1905 Catalogues also describe a "Special Show Window Display" outfit with a nickel-plated No. 100 Electric Locomotive with all working parts constructed of phosphor-bronze. No example of a nickel-plated No. 100 is known to exist, but recently-discovered Lionel sales records indicate that some sales of the outfits catalogued as No. 700, "SPECIAL SHOW WINDOW DISPLAY", were sold. As the catalogues are concerned, it was only the No. 700 outfits which contained the nickel-plated No. 100. It is anticipated that one of the No. 700 outfits will eventually be found.

The light green electric locomotives are in the same category, as far as scarcity is concerned, as the wooden gondolas. If a nickel-plated No. 100 should turn up, it would be more rare than the light green version. Relatively speaking, the maroon and black versions are "common". The Catalogues do not show, and no one has yet found, a No. 100 Locomotive in a non-motorized version.

No. 200 and No. 400 Steel Gondolas

In 1903 Lionel replaced the wooden gondola with a steel version. The earliest steel gondolas had two ribs on each side and were "japanned" in light green to match the light green No. 100. These gondolas were also lettered "B. & O." and it appears that the same stamp was used both on the No. 100 Locomotives and the No. 200 Gondolas.

Beginning with the 1904 Catalogue, the steel gondola was shown with "Lake Shore" lettering. One of the most interesting recent discoveries were a pair of light green "LAKE SHORE" steel gondolas, one motorized and the other a "TRAIL CAR". Neither of these cars have the ribs on the sides that characterize the known examples of the light green "B & O" steel gondolas. All other examples with "LAKE SHORE" lettering found to date have been enameled in maroon with gold trim and lettering. The 1904 and 1905 Catalogues also list a deluxe nickel-plated steel gondola as a non-motorized "Trailer" with the "Special Show Window Display" outfit. No examples of the nickeled versions have been found to date, but as with the nickel-plated No. 100, it is anticipated that one of the nickel-plated steel gondolas will eventually turn up.

Examples of light green steel gondolas have been found both motorized and non-motorized and with both "B & O" and "LAKE SHORE" markings. As in the case of the No. 100 Locomotives, the maroon and black versions of the No. 200 and No. 400 steel Gondolas are seen much more often than their light green counterparts.

No. 300 and No. 309 Open Trolleys

Another early production item, possibly contemporaneous with the wooden gondolas, is the No. 300 Electric Trolley Car. This item, catalogued in 1902, 1903, 1904, and 1905, used a body supplied by Morton E. Converse & Company to which was

No. 300
2-7/8" Gauge Trolley with Converse body

LEFT: 100(B) Electric Locomotive. The pin in the right coupler is not original. RIGHT: 300 Electric Trolley with "CITY HALL PARK" destination board visible on roof. R. Sullens Collection.

added a wooden subfloor and a Lionel cast frame, motor, and controller. (These trolleys have an aluminum stamped Lionel emblem tacked to the underside of the wood floor.) The bodies were also used and sold by the Converse company in a trackless pull toy version, but when found their painting and lettering is usually much different than the Lionel versions, although the author has examined one original Converse trolley painted in the same colors and configured as the Lionel versions.

All examples of the No. 300 found to date have been generally similar in maroon, pea green, and cream paint colors, lettering, and trim; however, variations are found in the color of the lettering on the destination boards and in the presence or absence of design trim on the ends of the destination boards. The lettering on the destination boards appears either in red or in black on white reversible boards. The black lettering versions also have a design on both sides of the lettering. Some examples have been found with a stamped-steel reversible trolley pole, but most do not have the pole.

Beginning in 1904 and continuing in 1905, a No. 309 Electric Trolley Trailer was illustrated and described in the Catalogues which was the same as the No. 300, but without a motor. It appears that coupler pockets were added to the post-1904 versions.

Both the No. 300 and the No. 309 are relatively easy to find, with the No. 309 being the much more difficult of the two.

No. 500 and No. 600 Derrick Cars

One of the most intriguing cars, and certainly the piece with the greatest "play value", is the derrick car.

The No. 500 is a motorized version which has a manually-operated drum to which is attached a metal chain and a cast-iron hook. The cast-iron hook is almost always missing when a derrick is found. To the author's knowledge, the only known original cast-iron hook is the one on his light green derrick "TRAIL CAR". That hook is painted bright red. The No. 600 was identical except for the absence of the motor and the controller.

The derrick cars were only catalogued in 1903 and 1904, and are among the most difficult to find of all the 2-7/8" Gauge pieces. Due to the height of the derrick car boom, it appears that its introduction in 1903 was responsible for a change in design of the No. 340 Suspension Bridge from a clearance height of about 10", as shown in the 1902 Catalogue, to about 14", as shown in the 1903 to 1905 Catalogues. The design change was to eliminate the two upper straight horizontal members at both top ends of the bridge and to substitute two arched members, which would allow for more than sufficient clearance for the derrick car boom which rose a total of 11" above the height of the track. Interestingly, the No. 300 Electric Trolley Cars which have been found with trolley poles, also rise exactly 11" above the height of the track, and it is possible that such cars with poles may represent only 1903 and later production, because only the 1903 and later Suspension Bridges would allow the trolley poles to pass under the top members of the bridges. The catalogues are of no assistance to such a determination, because none of the catalogue illustrations shows a No. 300 Electric Trolley Car with a trolley pole. Although the No. 600 Derrick Trailer is known to exist in both light green and maroon and black versions, the motorized No. 500 Electric Derrick is only known to exist in maroon and black.

No. 800 and No. 900 Boxcars

This car is sometimes called the "Jail Car" because of the bars in the windows. It is the only 2-7/8" Gauge item with opening doors. All known examples are maroon and black with "Metropolitan Express" in gold on both sides.

Both the No. 800 and No. 900 are among the more commonly seen 2-7/8" Gauge items, with the No. 900 being the scarcer of the two.

No. 1000 and No. 1050 Passenger Cars

The No. 1000 and No. 1050 Passenger Cars are only shown in the 1905 Catalogue. These "late production" items are found most often with either "Metropolitan St. R. R. Co." or "Maryland St. Ry. Co." lettering, although at least one example with "Philadelphia R. T. Co." lettering is known.

The colors are the familiar maroon and black, with variations of the maroon running almost to red.

At least one example has been found with a 6-1/2" brass trolley pole painted black which is mounted on a swiveling and sprung base. No Lionel identification appears anywhere on these cars.

Conclusion

Because of their extreme scarcity, 2-7/8" Gauge pieces are seldom seen even by seasoned train collectors. No known collection has more than nine different original pieces. Many long-time train collectors who have been knowledgeable about Lionel train production for more than thirty years have never had the opportunity to acquire a single piece. Moreover, the vast majority of Lionel train collectors have never even seen an original piece of 2-7/8" Gauge other than in photographs; and interestingly, most collectors display little or no interest in 2-7/8" Gauge.

In car collecting, the same is true of the Duesenberg. The lack of interest in the Lionel 2-7/8" Gauge may well stem from the fact that during their lifetime most train collectors will never have the chance to acquire an original 2-7/8" Gauge item. But, like the Duesenberg, the inability to own one has not had a dampening effect upon the prices at which these items infrequently change hands. The fact of the matter is, however, that it is usually only the most experienced collectors who are interested in and who are willing to make the financial commitment required to acquire specimens of the earliest, and certainly the most unique, of all Lionel trains.

Because of the great scarcity of 2-7/8" trains and the small number of active collectors who often communicate one with the other, sales of 2-7/8" Gauge items usually are conducted privately and are only rarely offered for public sale.

Reproductions of some of the 2-7/8" cars were made from 1957 to 1961 by McCoy Manufacturing Company of Kent, Washington. None of the McCoy reproductions were made with motors, and none of them were embossed in the floor bottoms with the name "Lionel Mfg. Co." All of the McCoy reproductions were rubber-stamped in gold on the underside with either "REPRODUCTION BY McCOY" or "McCOY'S OF KENT". This rubber-stamping can easily be removed.

The cast portions of the McCoy reproductions were made using original Lionel 2-7/8" Gauge parts as patterns and they were die-cast in "white metal" (sometimes called "zamac") and are subject to deterioration and crumbling. The McCoy reproductions are very faithful to their Lionel counterparts in most respects; however, the dimensions of the cast portions are slightly smaller than Lionel originals due to a shrinkage factor in the die-castings. The paint colors and the size, style, and color of the lettering and numbering of the McCoy reproductions differ considerably from the Lionel originals.

McCoy made approximately 100 sets of 2-7/8" Gauge cars and each set consisted of one each of: a B & O No. 5 Locomotive, a steel "Lake Shore" gondola, a derrick car, a "Metropolitan Street" boxcar or "jail" car, and a passenger trailer car (sometimes referred to as a 2-7/8" Gauge "closed end trolley"). Each set sold for $300.00 and, when available, individual cars were sold for $60.00 each.

In addition to the cars in the sets, McCoy also made wooden bottoms, side frames, wheels, and axles which were installed on about 20 to 25 original Converse pull toy bodies to simulate the Lionel No. 309 non-motorized "Electric Trolley Trailer". It is not known whether these items were marked as reproductions. McCoy also made one "Metropolitan Street" boxcar or "jail" car body entirely of copper and brass which was installed on the standard frame and given by McCoy to veteran train collector Russ Hafdahl for his birthday in 1961. This particular item is now in the author's collection.

Due to their age and relatively early appearance in train collecting, the McCoy 2-7/8" Gauge reproductions are highly prized and command significant prices today.

James Cohen of Trumbull, Connecticut has made approximately 200 2-7/8" Gauge car reproductions and plans to make more. To date he has reproduced the No. 400 steel Gondolas in both the green "B & O" and the maroon and black "Lake Shore" versions, the maroon and black No. 900 Boxcar or "Jail" Car, the No. 600 Derrick Cars in both the green and the maroon and black versions, and the No. 1050 Passenger Car trailers in all three of the known Lionel lettering variations. Cohen made a prototype No. 100 "B. & O." Locomotive in 1977, and plans to make more copies. He has also made the No. 400 steel Gondola in nickel-plated brass and the No. 600 Derrick Cars with nickel-plated brass bottoms with black-painted booms.

All of Cohen's original tooling for the 2-7/8" Gauge cars came from McCoy, but due to difficulties with the shrinkage factor in the "white metal" die-castings, Cohen had new patterns made to have the cast portions made of cast-iron. Therefore, except for some very early examples, most of the Cohen reproductions differ from the McCoy reproductions in that the cast portions are made of cast-iron rather than die-cast "white metal", and the dimensions of the cast portions of Cohen's more recent reproductions are more accurate to the Lionel originals than the McCoy reproductions. The paint colors and lettering of the Cohen reproductions also differ slightly from the Lionel originals. Most of the Cohen reproductions bear a gold rubber-stamping on the underside which reads:

REPRODUCTION BY
JAMES COHEN
69 STEMWAY ROAD
TRUMBULL, CONN. 06611

and none have been embossed by Cohen with "Lionel Mfg. Co." in the floors.

The Cohen reproductions are also faithful reproductions in most respects to the original Lionel cars, but having been made in recent years they usually appear to be much shinier and cleaner than either the now over twenty-five-year-old McCoy reproductions or the Lionel originals, although the author has seen examples of the Cohen reproductions which have been "weathered" to create an appearance very similar to original Lionel specimens.

Great care should be exercised to avoid paying the price of a Lionel original for an unmarked (and / or fraudulently embossed) McCoy or Cohen reproduction. The absence of a motor and the absence of the embossing of "Lionel Mfg. Co." in the floors are the two easiest, although not always reliable, ways to tell an original from a reproduction. Cohen is in the process of making reproduction motors for 2-7/8" Gauge cars. Depending upon the accuracy of such motors, either a McCoy or Cohen reproduction could be motorized to appear like a Lionel original. Cohen also plans to reproduce the following 2-7/8" Gauge track and accessories: Sectional Track, Switch and Signal, Crossing, Suspension Bridge, Track Bumper, and Elevated Pillars.

Gd VG Exc

100 WOODEN GONDOLA: Not catalogued, believed to be manufactured in 1901, wooden gondola, 14-1/2" long, 4-1/2" wide, and 4-1/8" high, red-stained finish, mortised and tenoned corners, metal tag attached to underside with two brads which reads: "MFG. BY LIONEL MFG. CO. NEW YORK", motorized, cast-iron frame 11-5/8" long and 1-7/8" high, wheels 2" in diameter, round journals, cast knob on controller, no steps, no coupler pocket. Reportedly, the earliest

Gd VG Exc

examples of these cars are initialed by Joshua Lionel Cowen himself. "Electric Express" in gold 5-1/4" long on both sides. This version is referred to as the "Type I" wooden gondola. Only one example is known to exist. **NRS**

NOTE: In the 1902 Catalogue the first item shown and described is the No. 300 "ELECTRIC TROLLEY CAR" and the second item is the No. 200 hardwood "ELECTRIC EXPRESS". The No. 100 does not appear in the 1902 Catalogue. However, since there are two distinct variations of the hardwood gondola, the first being "uncatalogued" (so long as a 1901 or earlier Catalogue does not appear), and being finished in red with mortised and tenoned corners, and the second variation being the now "catalogued" version (i.e., in the recently-discovered 1902 Catalogue) which is finished in brown with brass corner plates, handrails, and steps as described on page 5 of the 1902 Catalogue, I submit that documentation will eventually surface which will indicate that (1) the first 2-7/8" Gauge car manufactured by Lionel was the first variation of the hardwood gondola and (2) the first variation of the hardwood gondola was assigned the number "100". I also submit that, with the changes in the color and construction of the hardwood gondola as described in the 1902 Catalogue, the subsequent number "200" was logically assigned to that second variation. I further submit that due to the discontinuance of the hardwood gondola in 1903 in favor of the steel gondola, the then-unused catalogue number "100" was re-assigned to the then-new B & O No. 5 "ELECTRIC LOCOMOTIVE".

200 WOODEN GONDOLA: Catalogued 1902 only, 14-1/2" long, 4-1/2" wide, and 4-1/8" high, natural brown-stained finish, brass corner braces and brass handrails and steps, metal tag attached to underside with two brads which reads: "MFG. BY LIONEL MFG. CO. NEW YORK", motorized, cast-iron frame 11-5/8" long and 1-7/8" high, cast-iron wheels 2" in diameter, round journals, cast knob on controller, coupler pocket on controller, "Electric Express" in gold 5-1/4" long on both sides. This version is referred to as the "Type II" wooden gondola. Eight examples are known to exist. **NRS**

100(A) ELECTRIC LOCOMOTIVE: Catalogued 1903, 1904, and 1905. Catalogues do not show or describe colors and so the light green version cannot be conclusively dated, but the light green versions are believed to be the earliest. $6.00 in some 1903 Catalogues, $7.00 in all others, steel reproduction of 1,800-horsepower electric locomotives used by the B & O R R for hauling trains through the tunnels of Baltimore, 10-1/2" long, 4-1/4" wide, and 6-5/8" high, light green body and roof with black-painted cast-iron frame and gold-painted trim on controller, motorized, hollow brass wheels 2" in diameter, rectangular journals, wire handle on controller, coupler pockets on both ends, "LIONEL MFG. CO. N.Y." stamped in floor bottom readable from underside, two portions of cast-iron frame pass through two 1/2" diameter holes in floor bottom and attaches to floor bottom without screws, reversing switch has tabs, "B. & O." in gold 2" long on left of both sides, "No. 5" in gold 1-3/8" long on right of both sides and on both ends. Less than five examples known to exist. **NRS**

100(B) ELECTRIC LOCOMOTIVE: See 100(A) for Catalogue and Catalogue price information. Description same as 100(A), but with cast-iron wheels 2" in diameter and with maroon body and black roof and frame, cast-iron frame attaches to floor bottom by means of two screws with nuts on inside on floor bottom, no 1/2" holes in floor bottom, reversing switch is circular without tabs, many differences in motor and in the manner in which wires connect from motor to reversing switch, lettering same as 100(A). One of the most common 2-7/8" Gauge items available. **3000 4000 6000**

100(C) ELECTRIC LOCOMOTIVE: Uncatalogued. Description same as 100(A), except that gold paper stickers appear on both sides with "C & St. L" to left of center door and "No. 5" to right of center door. **NRS**

100(D) ELECTRIC LOCOMOTIVE: Catalogued 1904-05. $25.00 for set, not catalogued individually. Description same as 100(A), but all parts are nickeled and polished, motor mechanism is constructed throughout of phosphor-bronze, catalogued only as a component of "Special Show Window Display", lettering unknown. No known examples, but Lionel sales records indicate that some were sold. **NRS**

200(A) ELECTRIC EXPRESS: Catalogued 1903 for $6.00, steel gondola, 12-1/4" long, 4-1/2" wide, and 4-1/8" high, both light green and dark green examples have survived with black-painted cast-iron frame 11" long and 1-7/8" high, two ribs on each side, one-piece gold-painted handrails and steps at each corner, motorized, stamped brass wheels 2" in diameter, rectangular journals, cast knob handle on controller, coupler pockets on both ends, "B. & O." in gold on both sides (Note: 1903 Catalogue shows other lettering on sides of car with "CAPACITY 80,000" on left side and "WEIGHT 35,000" on right side, but as found no such lettering is present.) **4000 5000 7000**

200(B) ELECTRIC EXPRESS: Catalogued 1904-05 for $6.00, steel gondola, 12-1/4" long, 4-1/2" wide, and 4-1/8" high, light green, black-painted cast-iron frame 11" long and 1-7/8" high, no ribs on sides, one-piece handrails and steps at each corner, motorized, stamped brass wheels 2" in diameter, rectangular journals, wire handle on controller, coupler pockets on both ends, "LIONEL MFG. CO. N.Y." stamped in floor bottom readable from underside, "Lake Shore" in gold 3-1/4" long on both sides, "CAPACITY 80,000 LBS." in gold on left lower corners on both sides, "WEIGHT 35000 LBS." in gold on lower right corners on both sides. (Note: no comma appears in "35000", but a comma does appear in "80,000".) **4000 5000 6000**

200(C) ELECTRIC EXPRESS: Catalogued 1904-05 for $6. Description same as 200(B), but painted maroon with gold-edge trim, inner portions of gondola body and underside are painted a flat reddish-brown that is not as glossy or as maroon as the exterior portions of gondola body (the same flat paint also appears as an undercoat on the exterior portions of the gondola body), cast-iron wheels 2" in diameter, lettering same as 200(B) **NRS**

300 ELECTRIC TROLLEY CAR: Catalogued 1903-05. $7.00 in 1903-04, $8.00 in 1903 other Catalogue and in 1905, Steel Open Trolley Car, 16-1/2" long, 5" wide, and 8-1/8" high, maroon, pea green, and cream with yellow design trim, 4-1/2" long destination boards on top of each side which are reversible, six cream seats with red back design trim which are reversible, wood subframe 15" long and 3-3/4" wide, black-painted cast-iron frame 11" long and 1-7/8" high, no steps or handrails, motorized, either hollow brass or cast-iron wheels 2" in diameter, rectangular journals, wire handle on controller, no coupler pockets, found with or without 6" stamped-steel trolley pole which is attached to a wire which protrudes through roof and subroof and into metal frame (but not through wooden subframe). No Lionel identification appears anywhere, "CITY HALL PARK" and "175" in yellow on both ends 3-1/2" long, "UNION DEPOT" and "CITY HALL PARK" in red or white

Gd VG Exc

reversible destination boards with no designs on either side. (Note: some examples have same lettering in black on white reversible destination boards with a design on both sides.) One of the most common 2-7/8" Gauge items to turn up. **2000 3000 4000**

309 ELECTRIC TROLLEY TRAILER: 1904-05, $3.25 in 1904, $3.75 in 1905 Catalogue. Description same as 300, but without motor and known to exist only with cast-iron wheels 2" in diameter, lettering same as 300. **2000 3000 4000**

400(A) EXPRESS TRAILER CAR: 1903, $2.25 and $2.50 in distributor Catalogue. Description same as 200(A) and 200(B) Electric Express, but without motor, lettering same as 200(A) and 200(B). **NRS**

400(B) EXPRESS TRAIL CAR: 1903, $2.25 and $2.50 in distributor Catalogue. Description same as 200(C), but without motor, lettering same as 200(B). **2000 3000 4000**

400(C) TRAILER: 1904-05, sold only as set for $25. Description same as 200(B), but all parts are nickeled and polished, motor mechanism is constructed throughout of phosphor-bronze, catalogued only as a component of "Special Show Window Display", lettering unknown. No known examples, but Lionel sales records indicate that some were sold. **NRS**

This "iron hand swinging crane" swung over a siding and muscled machinery and other freight items weighing up to ten tons on and off flatcars and boxcars at the Reading Company's Hamburg, Pennsylvania station. The block and tackle was raised and lowered by a small handle near the base of the boom on the shielded side. The lever visible on the open (geared) side operates a friction brake. Cranes like this were common, and they probably inspired Lionel's 500 and 600 four-wheel 2-7/8" Derricks. Photograph and comment by Rev. Philip Smith.

500(A) ELECTRIC DERRICK CAR: 1903-04, $7.00 in 1903-04, $8.00 in distributor 1903 Catalogue, Steel Derrick Car, 14-1/2" long, 4-1/2" wide, and 10-7/8" high, cast-iron derrick 8-1/2" high, light green with gold trim and black-painted cast-iron frame 11" long and 1-7/8" high, no handrails or steps, motorized, cast-iron wheels 2" in diameter, rectangular journals, wire handle on controller, coupler pockets on both ends, no lettering. No known examples. **NRS**

500(B) ELECTRIC DERRICK CAR: 1903-04, $7.00 in 1903-04, $8.00 in other 1903 Catalogue. Description same as 500(A), but painted maroon with gold trim, no lettering. **3000 4000 5500**

600(A) DERRICK TRAILER: $3.25 in 1903-04, $4.00 in distributor 1903 Catalogue. Description same as 500(A), but without motor and with "LIONEL MFG. CO." stamped in bottom of car body readable from top, no lettering. One of the rarest 2-7/8" Gauge items. **3500 5000 7500**

600(B) DERRICK: Catalogue dates and prices same as 600(A). Description same as 500(B), but without motor, no lettering. **3500 5000 7500**

800 BOXCAR: Catalogued 1904 and 1905. Catalogue price $7, steel boxcar (sometimes called the "Jail Car" because of the bars on the windows), 14-1/2" long, 4" wide, 7-1/8" high, maroon with black roof and black-painted cast-iron frame 11" long and 1-7/8" high, gold-painted bars in windows, opening doors with gold-painted door knobs, one-piece gold-painted handrails and steps, motorized, cast-iron wheels 2" in diameter, rectangular journals, wire handle on controller, coupler pockets on both ends of car, no Lionel identification on car, inner portions of car body are painted a flat reddish-brown that is not as glossy or as maroon as exterior portions of car body (the same flat paint also appears as an undercoat on the exterior portions of car body), "METROPOLITAN" in gold 2-3/8" long on left side of door on both sides of car, "EXPRESS" in gold 1-3/4" long on right side of door on both sides of car. One of the most common 2-7/8" Gauge items to be found. **2000 3000 4000**

900 BOX TRAILER CAR: Catalogued 1904-05, sold for $3.25. Description same as 800, but without motor, lettering same as 800. **2000 3000 4000**

1000(A) PASSENGER CAR: Catalogued 1905 at $7.00, steel closed-sided passenger cars, 14-3/4" long, 4-1/2" wide, and 7-1/4" high (excluding trolley pole), maroon with black roof and black-painted cast-iron frame 11" long, motorized, cast-iron wheels 2" in diameter, rectangular journals, wire handle on controller, coupler pockets on both ends, found with or without 6-1/2" sprung trolley pole made of brass and painted black, no Lionel identification appears anywhere, "METROPOLITAN St. R.R. Co." in gold 7-3/4" long on both sides and "416" in gold 3/4" long on both ends. One of the rarest 2-7/8" Gauge items to turn up. **3500 5000 7500**

1000(B) PASSENGER CAR: Years and price not catalogued. Description same as 1000(A), "MARYLAND ST. RY. Co." in gold 7" long on both sides and "BROADWAY" in gold 2-3/4" long on both ends. One of the rarest 2-7/8" Gauge items to be found. **3500 5000 7500**

1050(A) PASSENGER CAR TRAILER: 1905 catalogued, sold for $3.25. Description same as 1000(A), but without motor, lettering same as 1000(A). Very rare. **3500 5000 7500**

1050(B) PASSENGER CAR TRAILER: Years and prices not catalogued. Description same as 1000(B), but without motor, lettering same as 1000(B). Very rare. **3500 5000 7500**

1050(C) PASSENGER CAR TRAILER: Years and prices not catalogued. Description same as 1050(A), but in brighter red with black roof and black-painted frame, "PHILADELPHIA R.T. CO." in gold on both sides. Very rare. **3500 5000 7500**

BATTERIES, TRACK, AND ACCESSORIES

Gd VG Exc

301 BATTERIES: 1903-05, set of four for $1.20, dry cell battery with wire and directions for connecting (early 1903 Catalogue shows "Everbest Dry Cell" batteries, early 1904 Catalogue states that "Eastern dry cell No. 3" would be supplied, early 1905 Catalogue states that "Climax Dry Cell" would be supplied). No surviving examples known. **NRS**

302 PLUNGE BATTERY: Catalogued in 1902 only. Price of complete battery, with full charge, $2.50, consisting of four glass jars, each containing a carbon cylinder and pencil-shaped zinc, and a wooden box measuring 9" x 12" x 8". The jars were charged with three pounds of "electric sand" which was added to three quarts of water to make a full charge for the four cells. The cells were connected in series - that is, the carbon of one to the zinc of the other. The jars had to be kept apart, and the wooden box was supplied to hold the four jars apart so they would not touch. No surviving examples known. **NRS**

303 CARBON CYLINDERS: Catalogued in 1902 only. Price per cylinder $.25. No surviving examples known. **NRS**

304 COMPOSITE ZINCS: Catalogued in 1902 only. Price each $.07. No surviving examples known. **NRS**

306 GLASS JARS: Catalogued in 1902 only. Price per jar $.125. No surviving examples known. **NRS**

310 THE TRACK: 1902 and earlier, steel tin-plated rails and wooden ties, rails are straight strips of tin-plated steel 3/8" high, 1/16" thick, and about 13-3/8" long; ties are red stained pieces of wood 4" wide, 1" thick and 1/2" high and grooved to admit the insertion of the rails, the grooves are 2-7/8" apart. Some ties have plates of brass which fit into the grooves and are bent outward to cover the outside portions of the ties and are held in place by a single brass brad. These brass plates allow the electrical contact to be made by the ends of the adjoining rails. Rails were only supplied in equal length straight sections and had to be bent (with the inside rails cut shorter) to make curved sections. Two rails and five ties comprised one complete section of track. Two of the five ties have brass plates. **NRS**

310 THE TRACK: 1903-05, 24 rails and 60 ties for $1.50, steel tin-plated rails and wooden ties, rails are straight strips of tin-plated steel 3/8" high, 1/16" thick, and about 12" long with one end bent into an L-shaped offset and the other end bent into a hook or a hoop shape to accept insertion of the L-shaped end of an adjoining section; ties are unstained and unpainted pieces of wood 4" wide, 1/2" thick, and 1/2" high, and grooved to admit the insertion of the rails. The grooves are 2-7/8" apart. The offsets on the ends of the rails had to be turned outward and the five ties per two sections of rails were used, the sections were joined by sliding the L-shaped end of one into the hook-shaped end of the other, rails were supplied in two different lengths with the shorter length used on the inside of a curve, and a complete circle was formed by using eight sections of track. The 1905 Catalogue states that "The Track" was "Improved 1905", however, the track illustrated and described in the 1905 Catalogue is identical to that illustrated and described in the 1903 and 1904 Catalogues. Two rails and five ties comprised one complete section of track. **NRS**

320 SWITCH AND SIGNAL: 1902-05, $1.50, turnout 17-1/2" long, 8" high, and 4-1/2" wide, lever which shifts the track changes the signal at the same time, signal discs are red and white, signal is cast-iron. **NRS**

330 CROSSING: 1902-05, $.50, 90 degree crossover, cross-rails mounted on a base 6" square. **NRS**

340 SUSPENSION BRIDGE: 1902, $1.50, suspension-type bridge, 24" long, 10" high, 6" wide, braces are cast-iron with wooden end and center ties, the end top members are straight and allow clearance of only cars under 10" in overall height. Very rare. **NRS**

340 SUSPENSION BRIDGE: 1903-05, $1.50, suspension-type bridge, 24" long, 14" high, 6" wide, braces are cast-iron with wooden end and center ties, the end top members are arched to allow high clearance for cars to pass through bridge. The arched members have the words "REDUCED SPEED" cast on one side. **NRS**

350 BUMPER: 1902, only $.50, terminal track bumper (without spring), 4" long, 4" high, and 3" wide, supplied with one tie to be inserted between the joints of the last two sections of the track instead of a tie with a brass plate to cut off the current before the car strikes the bumper to lessen the impact. **NRS**

350 BUMPER: 1903-05, $.50, terminal track bumper, spring-loaded, 4" long, 4" high, and 3" wide, supplied with one short section of track. **NRS**

370 JARS AND PLATES: 1902-03, $.50 in 1920, $.60 in 1903, outfit consisting of two glass jars 2" by 1-1/4" by 3-1/2" and lead plates 1" wide and 1/16" thick supplied for the purpose of utilizing direct electric current to operate powered items, jars were to be filled with water and sulfuric acid and connected in series to a 110-volt current and a 32 candle-power lamp bulb. No surviving examples known. **NRS**

380 ELEVATED PILLARS: 1904-05, 12 pillars for $2.00, cast-iron posts 8-1/2" high with 6" wide bases supplied with screws and washers for attaching wooden ties to posts for elevation of trackwork, including switches, bridges, crossings, and bumpers. Price per pillar. **30 50 75**

700 SPECIAL SHOW WINDOW DISPLAY: 1903-05, $25.00, outfit consisting of No. 100 Electric Locomotive and No. 400 Trailer, both items nickeled and polished, mechanism is constructed of phosphor-bronze, supplied with No. 340 Suspension Bridge and 24 feet of track. No known examples, but Lionel sales records indicate that some outfits were sold. **NRS**

912
911
913
912
0077
0075
0074
004TW
0047
0046
0045
004E
0044
0027
0025
003T
003E
0024
0017
0016
002TW
0015
002E
0014
001TW
0014
LIONEL LINES
SHELL
NEW YORK CENTRAL
N.Y.C.
SUNX 258P
0015
0017
001E
092 Tower
00 Gauge

Chapter VI
OO Gauge

By Robert S. Friedman, D.D.S.

The year was 1938, and Lionel needed a new steam locomotive to match the success of the O Gauge 700E Scale Hudson it had brought out the previous year. The new engine was to be yet another Hudson, but a smaller size duplicate of the 700E Scale Hudson. The OO Hudson was built to a scale of 5/32nds to the foot as opposed to the 8/32nds of the O Gauge Hudson.

To quote the 1938 Lionel catalogue. "Visualize the great O Gauge scale model Lionel Hudson reduced to 5/8ths its size and you will have the new Lionel OO Gauge locomotive for the OO model has been made from exactly the same blueprints, reduced to scale 15-1/4" in length . . . . Nothing has been overlooked - nothing left undone!"

The engine and tender, which were manufactured from 1938 to 1942, were produced in four different versions. There were two super detailed versions, one for three-rail track and one for two-rail track, as well as a less detailed or modified version of each. The two-rail versions were designed to run on Lionel's solid T-rail two-rail track, which had a 48" diameter curve. This track looked far more realistic than the tubular three-rail track with its 27" inch diameter curve.

The four cars that accompanied the new OO Hudson were all die-cast metal. They were a boxcar, a hopper, a tank car, and a caboose. The OO Hudson was a Lionel original, but the cars unfortunately were not. The four Lionel cars were copies of the same cars made by the Scalecraft Company of Chicago. Lionel had copied the Scalecraft cars which came as kits and had slightly changed the ladders and trucks and made small modifications to the castings. Scalecraft had a patent on the truck suspension; consequently, Lionel had to pay Scalecraft a royalty because of this. When the Lionel and Scalecraft cars are placed next to one another, it is difficult to see the differences. The accompanying photographs will illustrate the difficulties.

Other companies offered OO equipment at the time, but none had as direct a relationship with Lionel as did Scalecraft. Some of these other companies were Nason, Famoco, Star Lines, Amity, Kemtron, and many more.

My knowledge of Lionel OO has come from searching out the various publications which have run articles about Lionel OO, questioning people at train meets and stores who had information about OO, and by carefully examining my own collection over and over again. The information presented by me in this chapter is as accurate and documented as I could make it. Surely some one of you reading this chapter will have some new or different information than that which you see here. Please be kind enough to send it along so that we may all share it in future editions.

Knowingly or unknowingly, many fine people have greatly contributed to my knowledge of OO. To name a few, if I may: William J. Krone and George J. Adamson for their fine articles in the TCA Quarterlies; Don Shaw of "The Train Station"; Tom McComas and James Tuohy for the OO Chapter in Vol. III of their series; Carl Shaw of Madison Hardware; and two fine collectors and runners of OO, Tony Cavanna and George E. Jones. To Bruce Greenberg, a special thanks for allowing me the pleasure of updating this chapter for his book.

Presentation Set

Gd Exc Rst

001 PRESENTATION SET: 1938, consists of locomotive numbered 5342 (we are not certain as to which one), 0014 yellow Lionel Lines Boxcar, 0015 silver Sunoco Tank Car, 0016 gray Southern Pacific Hopper, and 0017 Pennsylvania Caboose. This set was contained within a dark brown leather-covered wooden case 20-1/2" long, 15-1/4" wide, and 2" thick. The case lid is hinged to the bottom of the case at rear. Inside the case are die-cut hard cardboard dividers 1/4" thick, suspended at points to allow rolling stock to be held in place. The lid and sides have compartments to hold track— six straight on each side and twelve curved across lid. The case interior is lined with red velvet material; there is gold lettering inside the lid. The case also has a leather carrying handle. A matching transformer case with a leather carrying strap, 3-3/4" wide, 4-3/4" deep, and 5-1/2" high, holds a 1040 Transformer. This set was probably made by Lionel for special presentations and awards ceremonies as a public relations device. As such, there are probably very few sets of this nature still intact today. Exter Collection. This set was based on the simpler salesman set which came in a plain wooden box. **NRS**

Engines and Tenders

OO Engines and tenders came in both super detailed and modified versions. The super detailed locomotive has boiler turret caps, booster steam pipes, a feedwater pump, flag stanchions on the pilot, a front coupler, full valve gear, headlight number boards, complete piping, a power reverse

Gd Exc Rst

cylinder, and a turbo generator. The modified locomotive has none of the above.

The super detailed coal tender has four corner rails, one handrail, four stanchions, and an air brake cylinder. The modified coal tender has none of the above.

001 STEAM LOCOMOTIVE: 1938-42, 4-6-4, Hudson prototype, black boiler and frame, 9" long, rubber-stamped "5342" in silver below cab window. Came with 12-wheel New York Central tender, 6-1/2" long. Locomotive and tender are super detailed, for use on three-rail track, catalogued as 001.

(A) 1938 only, locomotive with miniature drawbar pin and chain. Came with 001W Whistle Tender. Neither locomotive nor tender are stamped "001". **120 225 110**

(B) 1938 only, same as (A), but with 001T Tender without whistle. **120 225 110**

(C) 1939-42, miniature drawbar pin and chain replaced by spring-loaded pin without chain, "001" stamped on inside of cab roof as well as "001W" stamped on bottom of tender with whistle. **120 225 110**

(D) 1939-42, same as (C), but with "OO1T" stamped on bottom of tender without whistle. **120 225 110**

002 STEAM LOCOMOTIVE: 1939-42, 4-6-4, Hudson prototype, black boiler and frame, 9" long, rubber-stamped "5342" in silver below cab window and "002" on inside of cab roof. Came with 12-wheel New York Central tender stamped "002W" or "002T" on bottom, 6-1/2" long. Locomotive and tender are modified, for use on three-rail track.

(A) Locomotive with 002W Tender with whistle. **100 200 95**

(B) Locomotive with 002T Tender without whistle. **100 200 95**

Two-Rail Engines and Tenders

Lionel "OO" engines of the 001 and 002 Series were designed to run on conventional tubular three-rail track, while the 003 and 004 Locomotives were designed to run on T-rail two-rail track. In order for this to be accomplished, the following changes in design of the running gear had to be made: the locomotive center double pickup was removed; the trucks were insulated, and the left side drivers were made of Bakelite with metal rims. The tender single center pickup was removed, the right side wheels of the tender trucks were insulated, and the trucks themselves were insulated from the tender body. The electrical connections between the locomotive and the tender were accomplished by a plug from the tender to a jack on the brushplate and then to the E-unit. The other connection was by way of the tender drawbar and the spring-loaded pin of the locomotive. The two-rail cars, as well as the kit cars, came with all the wheels insulated and could be run on either two or three-rail track.

003 STEAM LOCOMOTIVE: 1939-42, 4-6-4, Hudson prototype, black boiler and frame, 9" long, rubber-stamped "5342" in silver below cab window and "003" on inside of cab roof. Came with 12-wheel New York Central tender stamped "003W" or "003T" on bottom, 6-1/2" long. Locomotive and tender are super detailed, for use on two-rail track.

(A) Locomotive with 003W Tender with whistle. **130 275 100**

(B) Locomotive with 003T Tender without whistle. **120 250 95**

004 STEAM LOCOMOTIVE: 1939-42, 4-6-4, Hudson prototype, black boiler and frame, 9" long, rubber-stamped "5342" in silver below cab window and "004" on inside of cab roof. Came with 12-wheel New York Central tender stamped "004W" or "004T" on bottom, 6-1/2" long. Locomotive and tender are modified, for use on two-rail track.

(A) Locomotive with 004W Tender with whistle. **120 245 110**

(B) Locomotive with 004T Tender without whistle. **110 225 100**

0081K LOCOMOTIVE AND TENDER KITS: Catalogued 1938. Existence not verified. **NRS**

0081KW LOCOMOTIVE AND WHISTLE TENDER KITS: Catalogued 1938. Existence not verified. **NRS**

NOTE: The OO tenders had one other feature of interest, which was that the tone chamber was an integral part of the body casting and could not be replaced separately. If the field or casting were defective, the entire tender had to be returned for repair.

OO BOXCARS

Super detailed boxcars have an air brake cylinder under the frame. Modified boxcars do not have the air brake cylinder.

0014 BOXCAR: 1938-42, 6-7/8", super detailed, three-rail.

(A) 1938 only, yellow body, maroon catwalk and door guides, black ladders, black decal lettering "LIONEL LINES 0014", and a red and blue Lionel "L" emblem. **40 80 20**

(B) 1939-42, tuscan body and catwalk, may have black ladders, white decal lettering "PENNSYLVANIA 0014". **25 50 20**

0024 BOXCAR: 1939-42, 6-7/8", tuscan body and catwalk, may have black ladders, white decal lettering "PENNSYLVANIA 0024", modified, three-rail. **25 50 20**

0044 BOXCAR: 1939-42, 6-7/8", tuscan body and catwalk, may have black ladders, white decal lettering "PENNSYLVANIA 0044", super detailed, insulated wheels for two-rail operation. **25 50 20**

TOP: Scalecraft's B & LE Boxcar. BOTTOM: Lionel's 0014(B) Pennsylvania Boxcar. Lionel's steps at the corners are slightly smaller than Scalecraft's. Lionel's wheels are larger. Note that the Lionel catwalk protrudes slightly beyond the roof, while the Scalecraft's catwalk ends are flush with the car ends.

Gd Exc Rst

0044K BOXCAR: 1939-42, 6-7/8", same as 0044, but in unpainted kit, may have been factory painted with gray primer. **50 100 40**

0074 BOXCAR: 1939-42, 6-7/8", tuscan body and catwalk, may have black ladders, white decal lettering "PENNSYLVANIA 0074", modified, insulated wheels for two-rail operation. **25 50 20**

OO HOPPER CARS

Super detailed hopper cars have an air brake cylinder on top of the frame. Modified hopper cars were not manufactured.

0016 HOPPER CAR: 1938-42, 5-1/2", super detailed, three-rail.

(A) 1938 only, uncatalogued, gray hopper, black decal lettering "SP 0016" and a round "SOUTHERN PACIFIC LINES" emblem. **35 75 20**

(B) Catalogued 1938, gray hopper, black decal lettering, "LIONEL LINES 124947", and a red and blue Lionel "L" emblem. **Not Manufactured**

(C) 1939-42, black hopper, white decal lettering "SP 0016" and a round "SOUTHERN PACIFIC LINES" emblem. **35 65 30**

(D) Catalogued 1941, but existence not verified, black hopper, white decal lettering, "READING" plus six digits. **NRS**

0046 HOPPER CAR: 1939-42, 5-1/2", super detailed, insulated wheels for two-rail operation.

(A) Black hopper, white decal lettering, "SP 0046" and a round "SOUTHERN PACIFIC LINES" emblem. **25 50 20**

(B) Same as 0016(D), but for two-rail operation. **25 50 20**

0046K HOPPER CAR: 1939-42, 5-1/2".

(A) Same as 0046(A), but in unpainted kit, may have been factory painted with gray primer. **40 75 35**

(B) Same as 0046(B), but in unpainted kit, may have been factory painted with gray primer. **NRS**

Lionel's 0046(A) car (bottom) shows several differences from its Scalecraft counterpart (top). Note the air brake cylinder at left on frame. Lionel's bay doors are much closer to the car center. Also note the double row of rivet patterns on the Lionel car.

OO TANK CARS

Super detailed tank cars have an air brake cylinder under the frame. Modified tank cars do not have the air brake cylinder.

0015 TANK CAR: 1938-42, 5-3/4", super detailed, three-rail operation.

(A) 1938 only, uncatalogued, silver tank, black frame with no number stamp on bottom, black decal lettering "THE SUN OIL CO.", "S.O.C.X. 0015", plus a small Sunoco herald at the opposite end. **25 50 20**

(B) catalogued 1938, silver tank, black frame, black decal lettering "LIONEL LINES 601614" and Sunoco-style herald, **Not Manufactured**

(C) 1939-40, black tank, black frame with "0015" silver-stamped on bottom, white decal lettering "SHELL", "S.E.P.X. 8126". **25 50 20**

(D) 1941-42, silver tank, black frame with "G 0015" silver-stamped on bottom, black decal lettering "S.U.N.X. 2599", and large Sunoco herald. **25 50 20**

(E) Same as (D), but with "0015" stamped on bottom. C. Weber Collection. **50 20 20**

(F) catalogued 1941, but existence not verified, black tank, black frame, white decal lettering "S.U.N.X. 0015", and Sunoco herald. **NRS**

0025 TANK CAR: 1939-42, 5-3/4", modified, three-rail operation.

(A) 1939-40, 1942, black tank, black frame, silver-stamped "0025" on bottom, white decal lettering "SHELL, S.E.P.X. 8126", three-rail. **25 50 20**

(B) 1941-42, silver tank, black frame with "0025" silver-stamped on bottom, black decal lettering "S.U.N.X. 2599", and large Sunoco herald. **25 50 20**

0045 TANK CAR: 1939-42, 5-3/4", super detailed, insulated wheels for two-rail operation.

(A) 1939-40, 1942, black tank, black frame with "0045" silver-stamped on bottom, white decal lettering "SHELL, S.E.P.X. 8126". **25 50 20**

(B) 1941-42, silver tank, black frame with "0045" silver-stamped on bottom, black decal lettering "S.U.N.X. 2599", and large Sunoco herald. **25 50 20**

(C) Same as 0015(E), but for two-rail operation. **25 50 20**

The Lionel 0015(C) Tank Car differs significantly from its Scalecraft equivalent (top). Note differences in brakewheel design and placement, inclusion of corner steps, and design of air brake cylinder. In addition, the Lionel dome is taller and narrower than that on the Scalecraft car.

Gd Exc Rst

0045K TANK CAR: 1939-42, 5-3/4".

(A) Same as 0045(A), but in unpainted kit, may have been factory painted with gray primer, no number on frame. 50 100 40

(B) Catalogued 1941, but existence not verified, same as 0045(C), but in unpainted kit, may have been factory painted with gray primer, no number on frame. **NRS**

0075 TANK CAR: 1939-42, 5-3/4", modified, insulated wheels for two-rail operation.

(A) 1939-40, 1942, black tank, black frame with "0075" silver-stamped on bottom, white decal lettering "SHELL, S.E.P.X. 8126". 25 50 20

(B) 1941-42, silver tank, black frame with "0075" silver-stamped on bottom, black decal lettering "S.U.N.X. 2599", and large Sunoco herald. 25 50 20

(C) 1942 only, uncatalogued, gray tank, color may have been primer of kit cars, black frame with "0075" silver-stamped on bottom, white decal lettering "SHELL S.E.P.X. 8126". 25 50 20

OO CABOOSES

The super detailed caboose has a stove pipe with hood on the roof and a drain pipe under the frame. The modified caboose has none of these details.

0017 CABOOSE: 1938-42, 4-5/8", super detailed, three-rail operation.

(A) Manufactured 1938 only, but catalogued as 0047 in 1940, red body, maroon catwalk, white decal lettering "PENNSYLVANIA 0017". The red color of the 1938 caboose is lighter than that of all the following years. 25 50 20

(B) 1939-42, red body and catwalk, white decal lettering "N.Y.C. 0017". 25 50 20

(C) Catalogued 1938, red body and catwalk, black decal lettering "LIONEL LINES 477626". **Not Manufactured**

Lionel's 0017(A) Caboose differs in many respects from its Scalecraft counterpart (top). The brakewheels differ in design and placement. Lionel's version has a battery box as well as a drain pipe. The rivet detail on the sides did not help Lionel's lettering!

0027 CABOOSE: 1939-42, 4-5/8", modified, three-rail operation, red body and catwalk, white decal lettering "N.Y.C. 0027". 25 50 20

0047 CABOOSE: 1939-42, 4-5/8", super detailed, insulated wheels for two-rail operation.

(A) Catalogued 1940, but existence not verified, red body, maroon catwalk, white decal lettering "PENNSYLVANIA 0047". **NRS**

(B) Red body and catwalk, white decal lettering "N.Y.C. 0047". 25 50 20

0047K CABOOSE: 1939-42, 4-5/8".

(A) catalogued 1940, but existence not verified, same as 0047(A), but in unpainted kit, may have been factory painted with gray primer. **NRS**

(B) Same as 0047(B), but in unpainted kit, may have been factory painted with gray primer. 50 100 40

0077 CABOOSE: 1939-42, 4-5/8", modified, insulated wheels for two-rail operation, red body and catwalk, white decal lettering "N.Y.C. 0074". 25 50 20

What OO Gauge might have become: Had Lionel continued its development of OO Gauge after World War II, we might have seen cars like the Rock Island Caboose (top), or the Scalecraft open vestibule Passenger Coach (center), or the Texas & Pacific Stock Car (bottom).

OO TRACK, SWITCHES, AND CROSSOVER

		Gd	Exc
	Two-Rail Track: 48" circle		
0031:	Curved Track, 1939-42.	10	12
0032:	Straight Track, 1939-42.	15	18
0034:	Connection Curved Track, 1939-42.	15	18
	Three-Rail Track: 27" circle		
0051:	Curved Track, 1939-42.	5	8
0053:	Straight Track, 1939-42.	5	8
0054:	Connection Curved Track, 1939-42	10	12
0061:	Curved Track, 1938.	5	8
0062:	Straight Track, 1938.	5	8
0063:	1/2 Curved Track, 1939-42.	10	12
0064:	Connection Curved Track, 1938.	10	12
0065:	1/2 Straight Track, 1939-42.	10	12
0066:	5/6 Straight Track, 1939-42.	10	12
0070:	90 degree Crossover, 1939-42.	18	25
0072:	Remote Control Switches, 1939-42.	120	175

Chapter VII

Crossovers, Switches, Uncoupling Units, Power Supplies, Motors, and Track

Note: For OO Gauge equipment, see Chapter VI.

Switch controller. Roger Bartelt photograph.

	Gd	Exc	Rst

011 DISTANT CONTROL: 1933-37, non-derailing switches, with 222 Controller, pair, O Gauge.

(A) 1933, green base.	20	40	20
(B) 1934-37, black base.	20	40	20

012 REMOTE CONTROL SWITCHES: 1927-33, pair, O Gauge.

(A) 1927-31, unpainted base. L. Bohn comment.	12	30	10
(B) 1932-33, green base. L. Bohn comment.	12	30	10

013 O GAUGE DISTANT CONTROL SWITCH AND PANEL BOARD SET: one pair 012 Switches, one 439 Illuminated Panel Board. 55 125 50

20 90 DEGREE CROSSOVER: 1909-32, Standard Gauge.

(A) 1909-13, open-base version with small center square without enameled center. 2 5 3

(B) 1914-26, open-base version with small center square with enameled center. 2 5 3

(C) 1927-32, closed-base version with green enamel. 2 5 3

(D) 1927-32, closed-base version with black enamel. 2 5 3

20X 45 DEGREE CROSSOVER: 1928-32, Standard Gauge, 16-1/2" x 9", green base. 3 7 2

020 90 DEGREE CROSSOVER: 1915-42, O Gauge.

(A) 1915-16, tin base.	2	5	—
(B) 1927-33, green enamel base.	2	5	—
(C) 1934-42, black enamel base.	2	5	—

020X 45 DEGREE CROSSOVER: 1917-42, O Gauge, 11-1/2" x 6".

(A) 1917-26, tin base.	3	7	—
(B) 1927-33, green base.	3	7	—
(C) 1934-42, black base.	3	7	—

21 90 DEGREE THREE-RAIL CROSSOVER: 1906, Standard Gauge, 8". 7 15 —

21 LIGHTED LANTERN SWITCHES: 1915-25, Standard Gauge, right-hand and left-hand. 10 20 10

021 LIGHTED LANTERN SWITCHES: 1915-37, O Gauge.

(A) 1915-22, right-hand and left-hand, green base. 8 20 8

(B) Same style as (A), but unpainted. L. Bohn comment. 8 20 8

(C) 1923-33, improved with fiber strip at cross points, dark olive base, nickel plates. C. Rohlfing Collection. 8 20 8

(D) 1934-37, black base, nickel plates. C. Rohlfing Collection. 8 20 8

22 MANUAL THREE-RAIL SWITCH AND SIGNAL: 1906-25, right-hand and left-hand, Standard Gauge, with signal discs, unpainted tinplate base. Switches are illuminated by lamp socket which has a wire running to a solder point on the center rail. Came in plain cardstock box with "No. 22" rubber-stamped in large black serif lettering on one end. D. Ely and M. Miles Collections. 10 25 15

022 MANUAL SWITCHES: 1915-37.

(A) 1915-22, O Gauge right-hand and left-hand. 15 30 15

(B) 1923-37, improved with fiber strip at cross points. 15 30 15

022 REMOTE SWITCHES: 1938-42, with controllers and plugs. Die-cast control cover and controller, continued into postwar, but with Bakelite control cover and controller. Legend on identification plate differs from postwar models. 25 50 20

042 MANUAL SWITCHES: 1938-42, pair, O Gauge, continued into postwar. 15 30 15

210 ILLUMINATED LANTERN SWITCH: 1926, 1934-42, Standard Gauge, manual switches.

(A) 1926, green base (pair).	10	25	12
(B) 1934-42, black base (pair).	10	25	12

220 LANTERN SWITCH: 1926, same as 210, but not lighted, for Standard Gauge (pair). 10 25 12

222 ELECTRIC DISTANT CONTROL ILLUMINATED SWITCHES: 1926-32, Standard Gauge remote switches (pair).

(A) Green base, flat Bakelite control lever. G. Koff Collection. 20 40 20

(B) 1931 only, non-derailment feature. 20 40 20

223 DISTANT CONTROL SWITCH: 1932-42, same as 222, but with non-derailing feature, pair.

(A) 1932-33, green base with fiber insert.	30	75	30
(B) 1934-42, black base (pair).	30	75	30

225 DISTANT CONTROL SWITCH AND PANEL BOARD SET: 1929-32, includes one pair 222 Distant Control Switches (right and left) and one 439 Illuminated Panel Board, Standard Gauge. 75 150 60

711 O72 SWITCHES: 1935-42, remote control with two die-cast controllers for tubular track with a diameter of 72", non-derailing feature. Note that replacement switch lanterns are available (price quoted includes switch lanterns and controllers). There are two major versions of O72 switches. One used a small frog and rail while the other used the large

Gd Exc Rst

frog. The late version works better. Reissued by Lionel, Inc. in 1987. R. Bartelt, R. LaVoie, and A. G. Thomson comments. **75 150 75**

720 O72 CROSSING: 1935-42, 90 degree with black base for tubular track, 14-1/2" wide. **7 15 7**

721 O72 SWITCHES: 1935-42, manual for tubular, 72" diameter track. **45 100 45**

730 O72 CROSSING: 1935-42, 90 degree with black base for solid T-rail track. **20 35 10**

731 O72 SWITCHES: 1935-42, remote control for solid T-rail, 72" diameter track. **85 175 75**

1021 O27 CROSSOVER: 1934-42, Winner, 90 degree, O27. **1 2 1**

1024 O27 MANUAL SWITCHES: 1937-42, hand-operated switches, 9-1/8" long x 5-1/8" wide, not illuminated, pair. **2 5 4**

1121 O27 REMOTE CONTROL SWITCHES: 1937-42, remote control for O27 track, with illuminated controller, switches (pair). Prewar control boxes were metal and had integral red-painted levers. Postwar boxes were Bakelite and the levers were attached to the base instead of the box cover. The prewar mechanism box on the switches was square metal with celluloid light indicator inserts. Its postwar equivalent had a rounded plastic box with plastic light indicator inserts, although early postwar switches also have die-cast mechanism box. Original Lionel box brings $5 premium. R. LaVoie and C. Rohlfing comments. **15 25 15**

1550 O27 WINDUP SWITCH: 1933-37, pair of manually-operated switches; two rails spaced the same as outside rails of O27 track, pair. **2 5 4**

1555 O27 WINDUP CROSSOVER: 1933-37, 90 degree, for two-rail windup track, two rails spaced the same as outside rails of O27 track. **1 2 1**

MOTORS, TRANSFORMERS, AND RHEOSTATS.

Motors

Gd Exc Rst

A: 1904, Lionel Miniature Motor, 2-7/8" x 2-7/8" x 2-1/4". **50 100 50**

B: 1906-16, New Departure Motor, 3-1/4" x 3" x 2". **50 100 50**

C: 1906-16, New Departure Motor, wound to run on single or double cell. **50 100 50**

D: 1906-14, New Departure Motor, reversing device, cutoff switch, 3-5/16" tall, eyelet on top, maroon base and winding housing, chrome ends, decal says "NEW DEPARTURE / TYPE D". D. Ely Collection. **50 100 50**

E: 1906-14, New Departure Motor, two-speeds. **50 100 50**

F: 1906-14, New Departure Motor, two-speeds, reversible. **50 100 50**

G: 1909-14, Battery Fan Motor. **50 100 —**

K: 1904-06, Power Motor for sewing machines. **50 100 —**

L: 1905, Power Motor for sewing machines. **50 100 —**

M: 1915-20, Battery Motor Peerless, one-speed, one direction. **30 75 —**

R: 1915-20, Battery Motor Peerless, operates backward and forward. Black base 4-5/8" x 2-5/16", red fiberboard forward / reverse switch, motor is similar to that found in U-frame four-wheel Standard Gauge No. 33 Locomotive, drives a 2" brass gear with a wide belt drive spool on the other end of the brass gear axle. In addition, a 7/16" slotted drive wheel is affixed on the same end of the armature shaft. This second drive permits two-speed operation. A brass plate, 3/8" by 1-3/8" reads in sans-serif lettering "PEERLESS BATTERY MOTOR / TYPE "R" / THE LIONEL MANUFACTURING COMPANY / NEW YORK". Came in a dark gray box with silver rubber-stamped lettering on one end: "PEERLESS / BATTERY MOTOR / TYPE R / MADE BY / THE LIONEL MANUFACTURING CO. / NEW YORK". Has sales slip from the "Central Electric & Lock Co. / 13 N. Thirteenth St. / Philadelphia, PA" which is dated "1/22/1916". From this we can assume that this model was manufactured in 1915. D. Ely Collection. **30 75 30**

Y: 1915-20, Battery Motor Peerless, three speeds, operates backward and forward. **40 80 40**

1 BILD-A-MOTOR: 1928-31, three-speed reversible motor, 5-1/2" x 3" x 3", red or black base and trim on main pulley wheel, nickel-plated motor sides, converts to O motor. One observed sample came in a two-piece box consisting of a base with sides and lid with sides that covered the base. At one end of the box lid is a white label 2-1/4" wide by 3" high that reads: "No. 1 / "BILD-A-MOTOR" / TRADE-MARK PATENTS PENDING" with an illustration of the motor followed by some additional description. On the lid top is black rubber-stamped "11-83T". D. Ely comment. Weaver Collection. **60 125 50**

2 BILD-A-MOTOR: 1928-31, three-speed reversible motor, 7" x 3-5/8" x 4", converts to Standard motor, red or black base. D. Ely comment. **60 125 50**

043 BILD-A-MOTOR GEAR SET: Converts O Gauge No. 1 Motor to No. 2 "Bild-A-Motor" for Standard Gauge. Box has label pasted on ends; box originally meant for No. 58 Lamp Post. D. Ely Collection. **NRS**

Transformers

Transformers are usually bought to operate trains and related items. Hence, if a transformer is not operating it has little if any value. (If a transformer is repairable, after it is repaired it will yield the values indicated.) Several of the larger models, V and Z, have some minimal value (even if completely burned out) for knobs and nuts. In the listing that follows, we report only Good and Excellent conditions and require that the transformer be in operating condition to yield the price indicated. We have only listed transformers for 110-120 volts, 50-60 cycle current, since the others have little if any practical use.

Earlier transformers have brass plates mounted on the side, later at the top. The later varieties have nickel plates mounted on top. L. Bohn comments.

A: 1921-37, click-type Rheostat

(A) 1921-31, early, 40 watts. **1 2 —**

(B) 1931-37, late, 60 watts. **1 3 —**

B: 1916-38, click-type Rheostat

(A) 1916-17, first, 50 watts. **1 2 —**

(B) 1917-21, early, 75 watts. **1 3 —**

(C) 1921-31, late, 50 watts. **1 2 —**

(D) 1931-38, latest, 75 watts. **1 3 —**

K: 1913-38, click-type Rheostat

(A) 1913-17, early, 150 watts. **2 5 —**

(B) 1917-21, middle, 200 watts. **4 8 —**

	Gd	Exc	Rst

(C) 1921-38, late, 150 watts, 3-1/4" x 1-3/4" brass plate with black background and embossed brass lettering on the side. C. Rohlfing Collection. **2 5 –**

(D) Same as (C), but same size nickel plate with black lettering on the side. C. Rohlfing Collection. **2 5 –**

L: 1913-38, click-type Rheostat

(A) 1913-16, early, no Rheostat, 75 watts. **1 2 –**

(B) 1933-38, late, click-type Rheostat, 50 watts. **1 2 –**

N: 1941-42, click-type Rheostat, 50 watts. **1 2 –**

Q: 1914-15, 1938-42, click-type Rheostat

(A) 1914-15, early, no rheostat, 50 watts. **1 2 –**

(B) 1938-42, late, dial-type rheostat, 75 watts. **7 12 –**

R: 1938-42, dial-type Rheostat, 100 watts. **10 20 –**

Lionel S-Type transformer version (A). R. Bartelt photograph.

S: 1914-17, 1938-42, click-type Rheostat

(A) 1914-17, 50 watts. **1 2 –**

(B) 1938-42, later production, dial-type rheostat, 80 watts, whistle and reversing controls, also made postwar. Diamond Collection. **7 12 –**

T: 1919-28, click-type Rheostat

(A) 1914-17, early, 75 watts. **1 3 –**

(B) 1917-21, middle, 150 watts. **2 5 –**

(C) 1921-22, late, 110 watts. **2 4 –**

(D) 1922-28, latest, 100 watts. Brass plate 3-1/4" x 1-3/4" with blackened background and embossed brass lettering on side, brass control arm, brass binding posts and nuts, cloth-covered cord. C. Rohlfing Collection. **2 5 –**

(E) 1922-28, latest, 100 watts. Brass plate 2-1/2" x 7/8" with blackened background and embossed brass lettering on top of transformer, nickel control arm, binding posts and nuts, rubber cord. C. Rohlfing Collection. **2 5 –**

(F) 1922-28, latest, 100 watts. Nickel plate 3-1/4" x 1-3/4" with black lettering on side, nickel control arm, binding posts and nuts, rubber cord. C. Rohlfing Collection. **2 5 –**

U: 1932-33, click-type Rheostat "ALADDIN", 50 watts. **1 2 –**

V: 1938-42, dial-type Rheostat, 150 watts. Continued into postwar production. **25 45 –**

W: 1932-33, click-type Rheostat.

(A) 1932-33, early, "ALADDIN", 75 watts. Label says "WINNER TOYS, INC., NEW YORK". D. Ely Collection. **1 3 –**

(B) 1938-42, late, click-type Rheostat, 75 watts. **1 3 –**

Z: 1938-42, dial-type Rheostat, 250 watts. Continued into postwar production. **35 60 –**

106: 1911-14, click-type Rheostat. **3 9 –**

1017: 1932-33, transformer in lithographed tin station. **15 40 –**

1027: 1933-34, transformer in lithographed tin station. **15 40 –**

1029: 1935-39, lever-type Rheostat, 25 watts. **1 2 –**

1030: 1935-38, lever-type Rheostat, built-in whistle control, 40 watts. **2 3 –**

1031: Uncatalogued, circa 1938, lever-type Rheostat, 40 watts. C. Rohlfing Collection. **2 3 –**

1036: Uncatalogued, circa sometime between 1941 and 1948, lever-type Rheostat, 40 watts. C. Rohlfing Collection. **2 3 –**

1037: 1940-42, lever-type Rheostat, 40 watts. **1 2 –**

1038: Uncatalogued, circa 1940, lever-type Rheostat, 30 watts. Dated by date code on original box. R. LaVoie and C. Rohlfing Collections. **2 3 –**

1039: 1937-40, lever-type Rheostat, 35 watts. **1 2 –**

1040: 1937-39, lever-type Rheostat, built-in whistle control, 60 watts. **5 10 –**

1041: 1939-42, lever-type Rheostat, built-in whistle control, 60 watts. Continued into postwar production. **5 10 –**

Rheostats

81: 1927-33, Controlling Rheostat.

Lionel's "Multi-Volt transformers" did not produce a continuous variable voltage output. Rather, when the voltage was increased (or decreased), a momentary current interruption occurred. This was not a problem until 1926, since Lionel's locomotives rolled freely and a short current interruption was barely noticeable if the engine was highballing (as was usually the case). However, in 1926 Lionel introduced the pendulum reverse unit to compete with Ives' automatic reversing unit. The Lionel design was such that a momentary interruption caused the locomotive to abruptly change direction with humorous or disastrous consequences. Consequently, Lionel needed a device to vary the transformer voltage without interrupting the current flow.

Lionel already had a potential candidate for the job, the No. 88 Battery Rheostat. With some structural changes and some change in the wire resistance, Lionel created a continuous variable voltage output by linking the rebuilt 88 (now an 81) with its transformers. Wire resistance changed when the 88 was redesigned into the 81. Standard Gauge was originally designed for a maximum of 12 volts from batteries. From the time of O Gauge, the design was for 18 volts maximum from AC. The wire resistance had to be different because much more heat was generated with AC. In addition, the locomotive, car, and accessory bulbs had to be changed from 12 to 18 volts. The 81 consists of resistance wire wound around a ceramic core. One end of the resistance wire is connected to the unit frame. (This arrangement has implications for current draw and current waste. Transformer output was dissipated in heat!) The balance of the circuit was completed through a spring steel slide which ran along the top side of the coil. The spring steel slide is connected by an on / off switch to two bars which ground into the frame. The unit has a black stamped-steel frame with two terminal posts. A green-painted stamped-steel cover is tabbed and screwed to the black steel frame. An embossed brass plate is affixed to the top of the green steel cover. L. Bohn comment. Weisblum Collection. **1 3 5**

Gd Exc Rst

88: 1915-27, Battery Rheostat. 1 3 —

95: 1934-42, Controlling Rheostat, this unit is the same as the 81 Controlling Rheostat above, but it substitutes a red push button for the fiber on / off toggle of the 81. This change probably relates to the introduction of the modern three-position E-units in Lionel trains about this time (1933). A momentary current interruption would be very useful for sequencing the reversing unit.
(A) Black frame, dark green cover, brass plate. D. Ely and C. Rohlfing Collections. 1 3 5
(B) Same as (A), but nickel plate. D. Ely Collection. 1 3 5

107 DIRECT CURRENT REDUCER: 1911, four porcelain tubes mounted on a steel base 8" x 10" and 3/4" thick. The tubes were protected and ventilated by a perforated, asbestos-lined steel cover. A sliding lever regulates the voltage. Four porcelain supports with screws were supplied so that the reducer could be fastened to a wall or table.
(A) For 110 volts. Weisblum Collection. NRS
(B) For 220 volts. NRS

108: 1912 only, Battery Rheostat. NRS

170 DIRECT CURRENT REDUCER: 1914, for 220 volts DC. This device came from a practical need. Since Lionel had to contend with AC in some cities, battery-powered DC in some areas, and line voltage DC in some Eastern cities, the motors were wound "universal" to work with both currents. With line voltage DC, transformers were impossible, since DC cannot be transformed. Therefore, the direct current reducer had to be used. It was merely a 110 volt resistance coil with taps. Since only about 10 volts were needed for the train, the other 100 volts were dissipated through considerable heat. When 110 volt AC became available, practical transformers were made which did not have to dissipate such terrific amounts of heat. L. Bohn comment. NRS

TRACK, TRACK BEDS, LOCKONS, CONTACTORS, AND TRIPS

Straight Standard track comes in three types: Type 1—three narrow width ties, about 1906-20; Type 2–three wide ties, about 1920-30; and Type 3—four black ties, 1930-40.

Curved track comes in three types: Type 1 — four narrow ties, 1906-24; Type 2 — four narrow ties with wire connections, 1925-30; and Type 3 — five black ties, 1930-42. ("Leading 0s" are shown but not used in indexing.)

NOTE: For OO Gauge track sections, see Chapter VI.

Gd Exc Rst

C: 1906-42, three-rail, curved track, Standard. .50 1 —

1/2 C: 1906-42, three-rail, curved track, half-section Standard Gauge. .50 1 —

CC: 1915-22, curved with battery connections, Standard Gauge. .75 1.50 —

MS: 1933-38, mechanical straight track, 9" long. .30 .50 —

MWC: 1933-38, mechanical curved track, 27" diameter. .30 .50 —

OC: 1915-42, O Gauge curved. .25 .50 —

1/2 OC: 1934-42, O Gauge half-section, curved. .25 .50 —

OCC: 1915-22, curved track with battery connection, O Gauge. .25 .50 —

OCS: 1934-42, insulated curved track, O Gauge, 10" long. .25 .50 —

OSS: 1934-42, insulated straight track, O Gauge. .25 .50 —

OTC: 1923-36, lockon, O Gauge. .25 .50 —

RCS: 1938-42, remote-control track set, O Gauge. 1.50 3 —

S: 1906-42, three-rail, straight, Standard Gauge. .50 1 —

1/2 S: 1906-42, three-rail, straight half-piece, Standard Gauge. .50 1 —

SC: 1915-22, straight with battery connections, Standard Gauge. .50 1 —

SCS: 1934-42, insulated curved, Standard Gauge. .50 1 —

SS: 1923-42, special track for train-operated accessories. .50 1 —

STC: 1923-36, lockon, Standard Gauge. .25 .50 —

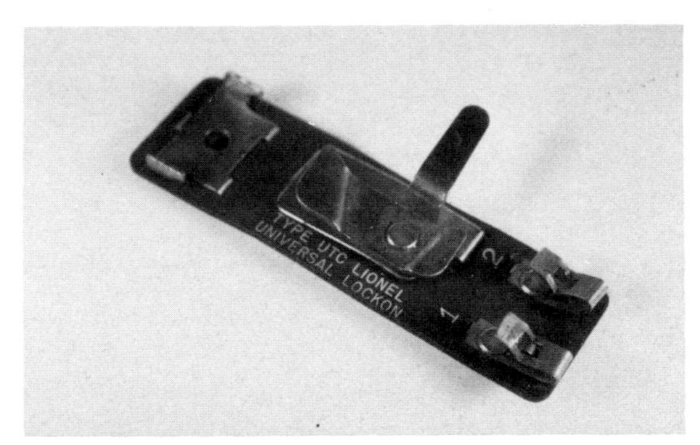

The UTC Lockon works with O, 027, and Standard Gauge track. R. Bartelt photograph.

UTC: 1937-42, lockon, for use with O or Standard Gauge. .25 .50 —

30: 1931-37, silent track bed (curved), Standard Gauge. 2 5 —

030: 1931-39, silent track bed (curved), O Gauge. 2 5 —

31: 1931-37, silent track bed (straight), Standard Gauge. 2 5 —

32: 1931-37, silent track bed for 90 degree crossing. 2 5 —

33: 1931-37, silent track bed for 45 degree crossing, Standard Gauge. 2 5 —

033: 1931-39, silent track bed for 45 degree crossing, O Gauge. 2 5 —

34: 1931-37, silent track for switches, Standard Gauge. 2 5 —

034: 1931-39, silent track bed for switches, O Gauge. 2 5 —

41: 1936-42, accessory contactor. 1 2 —

60: 1906-12, automatic trip fits on side of track to reverse trains. Standard Gauge track trip made from a 2-7/8" rail bent around and attached to two green ties. Came in a box marked "LIONEL MFG. CO., 381 BROADWAY, N.Y.". D. Ely Collection. 2 5 —

62: 1914, automatic reversing trip. 2 5 —

	Gd	Exc	Rst

760: Tubular curved track. Sixteen sections of O72" in diameter, (price for set of 16 sections). Also produced in postwar period and by Fundimensions. Note that a completely compatible version of this track is being made and sold by A. Kriswalus of Endicott, New York (and others). Kriswalus' track has a slightly different tie and is currently priced at about $35 for sixteen pieces. **25 35 25**

761: 1934-42, O72 curved, one piece of O72 tubular curved track. **1 2 1**

762: 1934-42, O72 straight, one piece of 14-3/8" O72 tubular straight track. **1 2 1**

762: 1934-42, O72 insulated straight, same as 762, but with one insulated outside rail to operate various accessories as the train passes over it. Came with lockon. **2 3 2**

771: 1935-42, O72 curved, one section of O72 solid T-rail curved track with screws, wrench, nuts, and fishplates for assembly; 16 sections form a circle 72" in diameter. **3 6 2**

772: 1935-42, O72 straight, one section of O72 solid T-rail straight with screws, wrench, nuts, and fishplates for assembly; matches 771. **4 10 4**

773: 1936-42, O72 T-rail, Fishplate Outfit, 100 screws, 100 nuts, 50 fishplates, and wrench. **25 30 —**

1013: 1932-42, O27 curved track, one section of O27 tubular track, forms circle with diameter of approximately 27". First called "Winner", then "Lionel-Ives" and "Lionel, Jr.", and finally O27. **.10 .25 —**

1018: 1932-42, O27 straight track, 9" long, one section of O27 tubular straight track, mates with 1013 (see 1013 for background). **.10 .25 —**

1019: 1938-42, remote-control track, mates with O27 track, five-rail straight section for uncoupling and unloading rolling stock, with two-button controller. (Note that insulation from the four-conductor wire is often badly decayed. Replacement four-conductor wire is available.) **1 2 1**

Chapter VIII
Catalogued Sets

By Roger Bartelt and Marsha A. Davis

We have organized the set data in this chapter initially by catalogue years since this is the most important feature. We then list the Gauge type - smallest Gauge first, largest Gauge last since this helps a person more easily locate the set. And finally, we list the set numerically under each Gauge heading.

We have omitted track, lockons, track uncouplers, rheostats, and light bulbs from these listings. These items are easily acquired and have limited value. However, if the set included switches or special accessories we include these in the listings. In the special cases of the Magic Electrol or Teledyne equipped sets, we have listed the appropriate controllers because they are an integral part of the set. Also, the name after the set number will be omitted. The name of the set in parenthesis is a collectors reference.

1915

O Gauge

70: 700 Locomotive, two 600s.
71: 701 Locomotive, two 601s.
72: 701 Locomotive, 602, two 601s.
73: 702 Locomotive, 602, two 601s.
74: 704 Locomotive, 610, 611, 612.
75: 703 Locomotive, 610, 611, 612.
76: Same as 71, but with reversing locomotive.
77: Same as 72, but with reversing locomotive.
90: 700 Locomotive, 800, 801.
91: 701 Locomotive, 820, 822.
92: 701 Locomotive, 820, 821, 822.
93: 702 Locomotive, 820, 821, 822.
300: 710 Locomotive and Tender, two 601s, (catalogued, but not made).
301: 710 Locomotive and Tender, 602, two 601s, (catalogued, but not made).
400: 710 Locomotive and Tender, 820, 822, (catalogued, but not made).
401: 710 Locomotive and Tender, 820, 521, 822, (catalogued, but not made).

Standard Gauge

34: 33 Locomotive, 35, 36.
37: 33 Locomotive, two 112s.
39: 38 Locomotive, two 116s.
40: 38 Locomotive, two 35s, 36.
41: 38 Locomotive, 112, 113, 114, 116, 117.
43: 51 Locomotive and Tender, two 29s.
44: 42 Locomotive, two 29s.
50: 51 Locomotive and Tender, 180, 181, 182.
52: 53 Locomotive, 180, 181, 182.
420: 42 Locomotive, 19, 18, 190.
421: 54 Locomotive, 19, 18, 190.
620: 6 Locomotive and Tender, 18, 19, 190.

1916

1916 Sets are the same as 1915 with the following exceptions:

O Gauge

78: 701 Locomotive, 602, two 601s
94: 706 Locomotive, 820, 822.

Standard Gauge

37: 33 Locomotive, 112, 117.
39: 38 Locomotive, 116, 117.

1917

O Gauge

160: 150 Locomotive, two 600s.
161: 150 Locomotive, 800, 801.
162: 152 Locomotive, 601, 602.
163: 152 Locomotive, 820, 822.
164: 154 Locomotive, 602, two 601s.
165: 154 Locomotive, two 820s, 822.
166: 156 Locomotive, two 610s, 612.
167: 154 Locomotive, two 820s, 822, 020X Crossing.
168: 154 Locomotive, 602, two 601s, 020X Crossing.
214: 203 Motor Car, two 900s.
215: 203 Motor Car, two 702s.

Standard Gauge

34: 33 Locomotive, 35, 36.
37: 33 Locomotive, 112, 117.
38: 38 Locomotive, 35, 36, 112, 113, 114, 116, and 117 Freights.
39: 38 Locomotive, 116, 117.
40: 38 Locomotive, two 35s, 36.
41: 38 Locomotive, 112, 113, 114, 116, 117.
43: 51 Locomotive and Tender, two 29s.
44: 42 Locomotive, two 29s.
50: 51 Locomotive and Tender, 180, 181, 182.
52: 53 Locomotive, 180, 181, 182.
420: 42 Locomotive, 19, 190, 18.
421: Same as Set 420, but 54 Locomotive.
422: 42 Locomotive, 11, 12, 13, 14, 15, 16, 17.
423: Same as Set 422, but 54 Locomotive.
620: 6 Locomotive and Tender, 18, 19, 190.
621: Same as Set 620, but 7 Locomotive.
622: 6 Locomotive and Tender, 11, 12, 13, 14, 15, 16, 17.
623: Same as Set 622, but 7 Locomotive.

1918

O Gauge

160: 150 Locomotive, two 600s.
161: 150 Locomotive, 800, 801.
162: 152 Locomotive, 602, 601.
163: 152 Locomotive, 820, 822.
164: 154 Locomotive, two 601s, 602.
165: 154 Locomotive, two 820s, 822.
166: 156 Locomotive, two 210s, 612.
214: 203 Motor Car, two 900s.
215: 203 Motor Car, two 702s.

Standard Gauge

34: 33 Locomotive, 35, 36.
37: 33 Locomotive, 112, 117.
39: 38 Locomotive, 116, 117.
40: 38 Locomotive, two 35s, 36.
41: 38 Locomotive, 112, 113, 114, 116, 117.
43: 51 Locomotive and Tender, two 29s.
44: 42 Locomotive, two 29s.
50: 51 Locomotive and Tender, 180, 181, 182.

52: 53 Locomotive, 180, 181, 182.
420: 42 Locomotive, 18, 19, 190.
421: Same as Set 420, but 54 Locomotive.
422: 42 Locomotive, 11, 12, 13, 14, 15, 16, 17.
423: Same as Set 422, but 54 Locomotive.
620: Same as Set 420, but 6 Locomotive.
621: Same as Set 620, but 7 Locomotive.
622: Same as Set 422, but 6 Locomotive and Tender.
623: Same as Set 422, but 7 Locomotive and Tender.

1919

O Gauge

159: 158 Locomotive, two 901s.
160: 150 Locomotive, two 600s.
161: 150 Locomotive, 800, 801.
162: 152 Locomotive, 602, 601.
163: 152 Locomotive, 820, 822.
164: 154 Locomotive, two 601s, 602.
165: 154 Locomotive, two 820s, 822.
166: 156 Locomotive, two 610s, 612.
214: 203, two 900s.
215: 203, two 702s.

Standard Gauge

34: 33 Locomotive, 35, 36.
37: 33 Locomotive, 112, 117.
39: 38 Locomotive, 116, 117.
40: 38 Locomotive, two 35s, 36.
41: 38 Locomotive, 112, 113, 114, 116, 117.
43: 51 Locomotive and Tender, two 29s.
44: 42 Locomotive, two 29s.
50: 51 Locomotive and Tender, 180, 181, 182.
52: 53 Locomotive, 180, 181, 182.
420: 42 Locomotive, 18, 19, 190.
421: Same as Set 420, but 54 Locomotive.
422: 42 Locomotive, 11, 12, 13, 14, 15, 16, 17.
423: Same as Set 422, but 54 Locomotive.
620: Same as Set 420, but 6 Locomotive.
621: Same as Set 620, but 7 Locomotive.
622: Same as Set 422, but 6 Locomotive and Tender.
623: Same as Set 422, but 7 Locomotive and Tender.

1920

O Gauge

155 150 Locomotive, 603, 604.
157 158 Locomotive, two 600s.
159 158 Locomotive, two 901s.
160: 150 Locomotive, two 600s.
161: 150 Locomotive, 800, 801.
162: 152 Locomotive, 602, 601.
163: 152 Locomotive, 820, 822.
164: 154 Locomotive, two 601s, 602.
165: 154 Locomotive, two 820s, 822.
166: 156 Locomotive, two 610s, 612.
167: 154 Locomotive, two 820s, 822, 020X.
168: 154 Locomotive, 602, two 601s, 020X.
214: 203, two 900s.
215: 203, two 702s.

Standard Gauge

34: 33 Locomotive, 35, 36.
37: 33 Locomotive, 112, 117.
39: 38 Locomotive, 116, 117.
40: 38 Locomotive, two 35s, 36.
41: 38 Locomotive, 112, 113, 114, 116, 117.
43: 51 Locomotive and Tender, two 29s.
44: 42 Locomotive, two 29s.
50: 51 Locomotive and Tender, 180, 181, 182.
52: 53 Locomotive, 180, 181, 182.
420: 42 Locomotive, 18, 19, 190.
421: Same as Set 420, but 54 Locomotive.
422: 42 Locomotive, 11, 12, 13, 14, 15, 16, 17.
423: Same as Set 422, but 54 Locomotive.
424: 42 Locomotive, 190, 18, 12, 13, 121, 19, 14, 15, 16, 17, 120, two 67s, two 65s, 66, two 21s, 217, K Transformer.
620: Same as Set 420, but 6 Locomotive.
621: Same as Set 420, but 7 Locomotive.
622: Same as Set 422, but 6 Locomotive and Tender.
623: Same as Set 422, but 7 Locomotive and Tender.

1921

O Gauge

155 150 Locomotive, 603, 604.
157 158 Locomotive, two 600s.
159 158 Locomotive, two 901s.
160: 150 Locomotive, two 600s.
161: 150 Locomotive, 800, 801.
162: 152 Locomotive, 601, 602.
163: 152 Locomotive, 820, 822.
164: 154 Locomotive, two 601s, 602.
165: 154 Locomotive, two 820s, 822.
166: 156 Locomotive, two 610s, 612.

Standard Gauge

34: 33 Locomotive, 35, 36.
37: 33 Locomotive, 112, 117.
39: 38 Locomotive, 116, 117.
40: 38 Locomotive, two 35s, 36.
41: 38 Locomotive, 112, 113, 114, 116, 117.
43: 51 Locomotive and Tender, two 29s.
44: 42 Locomotive, two 29s.
45: 38 Locomotive, 31, 32, 35, 36.
50: 51 Locomotive and Tender, 180, 181, 182.
420: 42 Locomotive, 18, 19, 190.
421: Same as Set 420, but 54 Locomotive.
422: 42 Locomotive, 11, 12, 13, 14, 15, 16, 17.
423: Same as Set 422, but 54 Locomotive.
424: 42 Locomotive, 190, 18, 12, 13, 121, 19, 14, 15, 16, 17, 120, two 67s, two 65s, 66, two 21s, 217, K Transformer.
620: Same as Set 420, but 6 Locomotive.
621: Same as Set 420, but 7 Locomotive.
622: Same as Set 422, but 6 Locomotive and Tender.
623: Same as Set 422, but 7 Locomotive and Tender.

1922

O Gauge

155: 150 Locomotive, 603, 604.
157: 158 Locomotive, two 600s.
159: 158 Locomotive, two 901s.
160: 150 Locomotive, two 600s.
161: 150 Locomotive, 800, 801.
162: 152 Locomotive, 601, 602.
163: 152 Locomotive, 820, 822.
164: 154 Locomotive, two 601s, 602.
165: 154 Locomotive, two 820s, 822.
166: 156 Locomotive, two 610s, 612.
169: 156 Locomotive, 610, 612.
172: 150 Locomotive, three 600s, 68, 62, 118.
173: 150 Locomotive, two 603s, 604, 118, six 60s, 106.
174: 154 Locomotive, 602, two 601s, two 022s, 106, 121, six 60s, two 62s, 68, 119.
176: 156 Locomotive, two 610s, 612, 109, eight 60s, 62, 121, 119, two 022s.

177: Scenic Railway, 150 Locomotive, two 603s, 604, 069, 62, 119, pair 022s, five 60s, 124, six houses, bridge.

178: Scenic Railway, 150 Locomotive, two 603s, 604, 124, 62, 069, five 60s, four houses, bridge, 118.

NOTE: Scenic Railway Train Sets include pre-wired and finished train board or table with legs.

Standard Gauge

34: 33 Locomotive, 35, 36.

37: 33 Locomotive, 112, 117.

39: 38 Locomotive, 116, 117.

40: 38 Locomotive, two 35s, 36.

41: 38 Locomotive, 112, 113, 114, 116, 117.

43: 51 Locomotive and Tender, two 29s.

44: 42 Locomotive, two 29s.

45: 38 Locomotive, 31, 32, 35, 36, two 22s.

183: Scenic Railway, 38 Locomotive, two 35s, 36, 124, 120, 69, 62, two 67s, eleven 60s, bridge, foot bridge, nine metal houses.

420: 42 Locomotive, 18, 19, 190.

421: Same as Set 420, but 54 Locomotive.

422: 42 Locomotive, 11, 12, 13, 14, 15, 16, 17.

423: Same as Set 422, but 54 Locomotive.

424: 42 Locomotive, 18, 19, 190, 12, 13, 14, 15, 16, 17, two 67s, two 65s, 66, two 21s, 217, 121, 120, K Transformer.

620: 6 Locomotive and Tender, 18, 19, 190.

621: Same as Set 620, but 7 Locomotive.

622: 6 Locomotive and Tender, 11, 12, 13, 14, 15, 16, 17.

623: Same as Set 622, but 7 Locomotive.

1923

O Gauge and 072 Gauge

177: Scenic Railway, 34 Train Set, 155 Train Set, 191, 189, five 184s, two 104s, 110, 124, two 59s, five 58s, 57, 62, 69, 89, three 60s.

178: Scenic Railway, 155 Train Set, 57, 62, 118, four 58s, two 110s, 124, five 184s, 89, 069, five 60s.

NOTE: Scenic Railway Train Sets include pre-wired and finished train board or table with legs.

Standard Gauge

The "Classic Era" begins with the 380 and the 402 Locomotive.

34: 33 Locomotive, 35, 36.

37: 33 Locomotive, 112, 117.

39: 38 Locomotive, 116, 117.

40: 38 Locomotive, two 35s, 36.

41: 38 Locomotive, 112, 113, 114, 116, 117.

43: 51 Locomotive and Tender, two 18s.

44: 42 Locomotive, two 18s.

45: 38 Locomotive, 31, 32, 35, 36.

Standard Gauge

155: 150 Locomotive, 603, 604.

157: 158 Locomotive, two 600s.

159: 158 Locomotive, two 901s.

160: 150 Locomotive, two 600s.

161: 150 Locomotive, 800, 801.

162: 152 Locomotive, 601, 602.

163: 152 Locomotive, 820, 822.

164: 154 Locomotive, two 601s, 602.

165: 154 Locomotive, two 820s, 822.

166: 156 Locomotive, two 610s, 612.

169: 156X Locomotive, 610, 612.

172: 150 Locomotive, three 600, 68, 62, 118.

173: 150 Locomotive, two 603s, 604, 118, six 60s, 106.

174: 154 Locomotive, 602, two 601s, two 022s, 106, 121, six 60s, two 62s, 68, 119.

176: 156 Locomotive, two 610s, 612, 109, eight 60s, 62, 121, 119, two 022s.

180: Scenic Railway, 160 Train Set, 127, two 58s, three 184s, two 60s, 62, 89.

308: 380 Locomotive, 18, 19, 190.

390: 380 Locomotive, 12, 15, 14, 17.

403: 402 Locomotive, 418, 419, 490.

420: 42 Locomotive, 18, 19, 190.

421: Same as Set 420, but 54 Locomotive.

422: 42 Locomotive, 11, 12, 13, 14, 15, 16, 17.

423: Same as Set 422, but 54 Locomotive.

424: 42 Locomotive, 18, 19, 190, 12, 13, 14, 15, 16, 17, two 67s, two 65s, 66, two 21s, 217, 121, 120, K Transformer.

440: 380 Locomotive, two 18s.

620: 6 Locomotive and Tender, 18, 19, 190.

621: Same as Set 620, but 7 Locomotive.

622: Same as Set 422, but 6 Locomotive and Tender.

623: Same as Set 422, but 7 Locomotive and Tender.

1924

O Gauge

169: 156X Locomotive, 610, 612.

174: 264 Locomotive, two 603s, 604, two 022s, 106, 121, six 60s, two 62s, 68, 119.

176: 254 Locomotive, two 610s, 612, one pair 022s, 109, 121, eight 60s, 62, 68, 199.

255: 153 Locomotive, 603, 604.

257: 150 Locomotive, two 600s, OTC, eight OC Track.

259: 150 Locomotive, 901, 801, OTC, eight OC Track.

260: 152 Locomotive, 629, 630.

261: 152 Locomotive, 800, 801.

264: 253 Locomotive, two 603s, 604.

265: 253 Locomotive, two 820s, 822.

266: 254 Locomotive, two 610s, 612.

268: 256 Locomotive, two 710s, 712.

Standard Gauge

34: 33 Locomotive, 35, 36.

41: 38 Locomotive, 112, 113, 114, 116, 117.

340: 50 Locomotive, 31, 35, 36.

342: 318 Locomotive, two 319s, 322.

344: 380 Locomotive, 18, 190.

345: 380 Locomotive, 12, 14,15, 17.

346: 380 Locomotive, 18, 19, 190.

370: 33 Locomotive, 112, 114, 117.

403: 402 Locomotive, 418, 419, 490.

404: 402 Locomotive, 11, 12, 13, 14, 15, 16, 17.

405: 402 and 5 Locomotives, 418, 419, 490, 11, 12, 13, 14, 15, 16, 17, three pairs 22s, two 23s, 121, 191, 180, four 184s, K Transformer, 69, two 77s, eight 60s, 89, 65, 66, 120, 101, two 59s, four 57s.

1925

O Gauge

91: 153 Locomotive, 800, 804, 801.

92: 152 Locomotive, 629, 630.

94: 153 Locomotive, two 629s, 630.

95: 253 Locomotive, two 820s, 821, 822.

96: 153 Locomotive, two 603s, 604.

97: 251 Locomotive, two 605s, 606.

98: 253 Locomotive, two 610s, 612.

174: Same as Set 96, but with one pair 022s, 106, 121, six 60s, two 62s, 119.

176: Same as Set 98, but with one pair 022s, 109, 121, eight 60s, 62, 68, 119.

257: 150 Locomotive, two 600s.

266: 254 Locomotive, two 610s, 612.

268: 256 Locomotive, two 710s, 712.

Standard Gauge

41: 318 Locomotive, 112, 113, 114, 116, 117.

342: 318 Locomotive, two 339s, 341

343: 380 Locomotive, two 319s, 320, 322.

344: 380 Locomotive, 18, 190.

345: 380 Locomotive, 12, 14, 15, 17.

350: 8 Locomotive, 35, 36.

351: 8 Locomotive, 112, 114, 117.

352: 10 Locomotive, two 337s, 338.

403: 402 Locomotive, 418, 419, 490.

404: 402 Locomotive, 11, 12, 13, 14, 15, 16, 17.

405: 402 and 5 Locomotives, 418, 419, 490, 11, 12, 13, 14, 15, 16, 17, three pairs 22s, two 23s, 121, 191, 180, four 184s, K Transformer, 69, two 77s, eight 60s, 89, 65, 66, 120, 101, two 59s, four 57s.

1926

O Gauge

NOTE: All 1926 O Gauge sets include an 068 Crossing Sign.

41E: Same as Set 41, but 318E Locomotive.

92: 152 Locomotive, 629, 630.

93: 250 Locomotive, 629, 630.

95: 253 Locomotive, two 820s, 821, 822.

97: 251 Locomotive, two 605s, 606.

98: 253 Locomotive, two 610s, 612.

174: Same as Set 296, but with one pair 022, 106, 121, six 60s, two 62s, 119.

266: 254 Locomotive, two 610s, 612.

268: 256 Locomotive, two 710s, 712.

290: 152 Locomotive, 901, 801.

291: 252 Locomotive, 800, 801, 803, 804.

294: 252 Locomotive, two 529s, 530.

296: 252 Locomotive, two 607s, 608.

299: 254 Locomotive, 813, 814, 817.

Standard Gauge

41: 318 Locomotive, 112, 113, 114, 116, 117.

342: 318 Locomotive, 310, 309, 312.

342E: Same as Set 342, but 318E Locomotive.

343: 380 Locomotive, two 319s, 320, 322.

343E: Same as Set 343, but 380E Locomotive.

344: 380 Locomotive, 18, 190.

344E: Same as Set 344, but 380E Locomotive.

345: 380 Locomotive, 12, 14, 15, 17.

345E: Same as Set 345, but 380E Locomotive.

347: 8 Locomotive, 337, 338.

347E: Same as Set 347, but 8E Locomotive.

348: 380 Locomotive, 428, 429, 430.

348E: Same as Set 348, but 380E Locomotive.

350: 8 Locomotive, 35, 36.

351: 8 Locomotive, 112, 114, 117.

351E: Same as Set 351, but 8E Locomotive.

352: 10 Locomotive, 332, 339, 341.

352E: Same as Set 352, but 10E Locomotive.

403: 402 Locomotive, 418, 419, 490.

403E: Same as Set 403, but 402E Locomotive.

405: 402 and 5 Locomotives, 418, 419, 490, 11, 12, 13, 14, 15, 16, 17, three pairs 22s, two 23s, 121, 191, 180, four 184s, K Transformer, 69, two 77s, eight 60s, 89, 65, 66, 120, 101, two 59s, four 57s.

405E: Same as Set 405, but 402E Locomotive.

406: 402 Locomotive, 211, 212, 213, 214, 215, 216, 217.

406E: Same as Set 406, but 402E Locomotive.

1927

O Gauge

NOTE: All 1927 O Gauge Sets include an 068 Crossing Sign.

97: 251 Locomotive, two 605s, 606.

97E: Same as Set 97, but 251E Locomotive.

98: 253 Locomotive, two 610s, 612.

174: 252 Locomotive, two 607s, 608, one pair 021s, 106, 122, six 60s, two 62s, 119.

249: 248 Locomotive, 831, 807.

266: 254 Locomotive, two 610s, 612.

266E: Same as Set 266, but 254E Locomotive.

268: 256 Locomotive, two 710s, 712.

269: 251 Locomotive, 812, 813, 814, 815, 817.

269E: Same as Set 269, but 251E Locomotive.

290: 152 Locomotive, 901, 801.

292: 248 Locomotive, 629, 630.

293: 252 Locomotive, 803, 804, 805, 807.

294: 252 Locomotive, two 529s, 530.

296: 252 Locomotive, two 607s, 608.

299: 254 Locomotive, 813, 814, 817.

299E: Same as Set 299, but 254E Locomotive.

Standard Gauge

342: 318 Locomotive, 310, 309, 312.

342E: Same as Set 342, but 318E Locomotive.

343: 380 Locomotive, two 319s, 320, 322.

343E: Same as Set 343, but 380E Locomotive.

344: 380 Locomotive, 18, 190.

344E: Same as Set 344, but 380E Locomotive.

347: 8 Locomotive, 337, 338.

347E: Same as Set 347, but 8E Locomotive.

348: 380 Locomotive, 428, 429, 430.

348E: Same as Set 348, but 380E Locomotive.

352: 10 Locomotive, 332, 339, 341.

352E: Same as Set 352, but 10E Locomotive.

353: 8 Locomotive, 511, 512, 517.

353E: Same as Set 353, but 8E Locomotive.

354: 10 Locomotive, 511, 512, 513, 514, 517.

354E: Same as Set 354, but 10E Locomotive.

355: 318 Locomotive, 511, 512, 513, 514, 515, 517.

355E: Same as Set 355, but 318E Locomotive.

356: 380 Locomotive, 211, 213, 215, 217.

356E: Same as Set 356, but 380E Locomotive.

403: 402 Locomotive, 418, 419, 490.

403E: Same as Set 403, but 402E Locomotive.

406: 402 Locomotive, 211, 212, 213, 214, 215, 216, 217.

406E: Same as Set 406, but 402E Locomotive.

407E: 408E and 380E Locomotives, 418, 419, 490, 431, 211, 212, 213, 214, 215, 216, 217, 218, 219, 81, 84, K Transformer, three pair 222s, two 23s, 124, 189, 191, three 184s, 438, 101, 140L, twelve 60s, 78, 80, two 77s, 89, two 76s, 69, 436, 437, two 67s, four 56s, two 57s, two 59s.

409E: 408E Locomotive, 418, 419, 490, 431.

410E: Same as Set 406, but 408E Locomotive.

1928

O Gauge

NOTE: All 1928 O Gauge Sets include an 068 Crossing Sign.

97: 251 Locomotive, two 605s, 606.

97E: Same as Set 97, but 251E Locomotive.

174: 252 Locomotive, two 607s, 608, one pair 021s, 106, 122, six 60s, two 62s, 119.

175E: 254E Locomotive, two 610s, 612, 080, 069, 90, 106, one pair 021s, 437, 119L, two 56s, eight 60s.

249: 248 Locomotive, 831, 807.

268: 256 Locomotive, two 710s, 712.

269: 251 Locomotive, 812, 813, 814, 815, 817.

269E: Same as Set 269, but 251E Locomotive.

292: 248 Locomotive, 629, 630.

293: 252 Locomotive, 803, 804, 805, 807.

294: 252 Locomotive, two 529s, 530.

266: 254 Locomotive, two 610s, 612.

266E: Same as Set 266, but 254E Locomotive.

296: 253 Locomotive, two 607s, 608.

299: 254 Locomotive, 813, 814, 817.

299E: Same as Set 299, but 254E Locomotive.

Standard Gauge

342: 318 Locomotive, 310, 309, 312.

342E: Same as Set 342, but 318E Locomotive.

347: 8 Locomotive, 337, 338.

347E: Same as Set 347, but 8E Locomotive.

348E: 380E Locomotive, 428, 429, 430.

352: 10 Locomotive, 332, 339, 341.

352E: Same as Set 352, but 10E Locomotive.

353: 8 Locomotive, 511, 512, 517.

353E: Same as Set 353, but 8E Locomotive.

354: 10 Locomotive, 511, 512, 513, 514, 517.

354E: Same as Set 354, but 10E Locomotive.

355E: 318E Locomotive, 511, 512, 513, 514, 515, 517.

357E: 380E Locomotive, 212 with tool set, 218, 219, 217.

403E: 402E Locomotive, 418, 419, 490.

407E: 408E and 380E Locomotives, 418, 419, 490, 431, 211, 212, 213, 214, 215, 216, 217, 218, 219, two 81s, 84, K Transformer, three pair 222s, two 23s, 124, 189, 191, three 184s, 438, 101, 140L, twelve 60s, 78, 80, two 77s, 89, two 76s, 69, 436, 437, two 67s, four 56s, two 57s, two 59s.

409E: 408E Locomotive, 418, 419, 490, 431.

410E: 408E Locomotive, 211, 212, 213, 214, 215, 216, 217.

1929

O Gauge

NOTE: All 1929 O Gauge Sets include an 068 crossing sign.

Steam returns to Standard Gauge.

97: 251 Locomotive, two 605s, 606.

97E: Same as Set 97, but 251E Locomotive.

174: 253 Locomotive, two 607s, 608, one pair 021s, 106, 122, six 60s, two 62s, 119.

175E: 254E Locomotive, two 610s, 612, 080, 069, 90, 106, one pair 012s, 437, 119L, two 56s, eight 60s.

249: 248 Locomotive, 831, 807.

266: 254 Locomotive, two 610s, 612.

266E: Same as Set 266, but 254E Locomotive.

267: 4 Bild-a-Loco Locomotive, two 605s, 606,.

268: 256 Locomotive, two 710s, 712.

269: 251 Locomotive, 812, 813, 814, 815, 817.

269E: Same as Set 269, but 251E Locomotive.

292: 248 Locomotive, 629, 630.

293: 252 Locomotive, 803, 804, 805, 807.

294: 252 Locomotive, two 529s, 530.

295: 253 Locomotive, 811, 812, 817.

296: 253 Locomotive, two 607s, 608.

299: 254 Locomotive, 812, 813, 814, 817.

299E: Same as Set 299, but 254E Locomotive.

Standard Gauge

340E: 318E Locomotive, three 516s, 517, Coal Train.

342: 318 Locomotive, 310, 309, 312.

342E: Same as Set 342, but 318E Locomotive.

347: 8 Locomotive, 337, 338.

347E: Same as Set 347, but 8E Locomotive.

349: 9 Bild-a-Loco Locomotive, 428, 429, 430.

349E: Same as Set 349, but with "Distant Control" unit.

352: 10 Locomotive, 332, 339, 341.

352E: Same as Set 352, but 10E Locomotive.

353: 8 Locomotive, 511, 512, 517.

353E: Same as Set 353, but 8E Locomotive.

354: 10 Locomotive, 511, 512, 513, 514, 517.

354E: Same as Set 354, but 10E Locomotive.

355E: 318E Locomotive, 511, 512, 513, 514, 515, 517.

357E: 380E Locomotive, 212 with tool set, 218, 219, 217.

391: 390 Locomotive and Tender, 511, 512, 517.

391E: Same as Set 391, but with "Distant Control" unit.

392: 390 Locomotive and Tender, 332, 339, 341.

392E: Same as Set 392, but with "Distant Control" unit.

393: 390 Locomotive and Tender, three 516s, 517.

393: Same as Set 393, but with "Distant Control" unit.

394E: 390E Locomotive and Tender, 310, two 309s, 312.

395: 390 Locomotive and Tender, 511, 512, 513, 514, 515, 517.

395E: Same as Set 390, but with "Distant Control" unit.

403E: 402E Locomotive, 418, 419, 490.

407E: 408E and 380E Locomotives, 418, 419, 490, 431, 211, 212, 213, 214, 215, 216, 217, 218, 219, 84, K Transformer, three pair 222s, two 23s, 124, 189, 191, three 184s, 438, 101, 140L, twelve 60s, 78, 80, two 77s, 89, two 76s, 69, 436, 437, two 67s, four 56s, two 57s, two 59s.

409E: 408E Locomotive, 418, 419, 490, 431.

410E: 408E Locomotive, 211, 212, 213, 214, 215, 216, 217.

411E: 381E Locomotive, 412, 413, 414, 416, Transcontinental Limited (State Set).

1930

Lionels first O Gauge Steam Type Engines.

O Gauge

NOTE: All 1930 O Gauge Sets include 068 Crossing Sign.

97: 251 Locomotive, two 605s, 606.

97E: Same as Set 97, but 251E Locomotive.

174: 253 Locomotive, two 607s, 608, one pair 021s, 106, 122, six 060s, 62, 89, 119.

176E: 260E Locomotive, two 710s, 712, 080, 069, 90, 106, one pair 021s, 437, 119L, two 56s, eight 060s.

229: 257 Locomotive and Tender, 831, 807.

232: 257 Locomotive and Tender, 629, 630.

233: 258 Locomotive and Tender, 902, 803, 804, 806, 807.

234: 258 Locomotive and Tender, two 529s, 530.

236: 258 Locomotive and Tender, two 607s, 608.

239E: 260E Locomotive and Tender, 812, 813, 814, 815, 817.

240E: 260E Locomotive and Tender, 811, 810, 812 with tools, 817.

241E: 260E Locomotive and Tender, two 710s, 712.

249: 248 Locomotive, 831, 807.

266: 254 Locomotive, two 610s, 612.

266E: Same as Set 266, but 254E Locomotive.

267: 4 Bild-a-Loco Locomotive, 043 Gear Set, two 605s, 606.

292: 248 Locomotive, 629, 630.

293: 252 Locomotive, 803, 804, 805, 807.

294: 252 Locomotive, two 529s, 530.

295: 254 Locomotive, 811, 812, 817.

295E: Same as Set 295, but 254E Locomotive.

296: 253 Locomotive, two 607s, 608.

299: 251 Locomotive, 812, 813, 814, 817.

299E: Same as Set 299, but 251E Locomotive.

Standard Gauge

342E: 318E Locomotive, 310, 309, 312, Baby State Set.

347: 8 Locomotive, 337, 338.

347E: Same as Set 347, but 8E Locomotive.

349E: 9E Bild-a-Loco Locomotive, 428, 429, 430.

352E: 10E Locomotive, 332, 339, 341.

353: 8 Locomotive, 511, 512, 517.

353E: Same as Set 353, but 8E Locomotive.

354E: 10E Locomotive, 511, 512, 513, 514, 517.

358E: 390E Locomotive and Tender, 212 with tool set, 218, 219, 217.

385: 384 Locomotive and Tender, 337, 338.

385E: Same as Set 385, but 384E Locomotive.

386: 384 Locomotive and Tender, 512, 513, 517.

386E: Same as Set 386, but 384E Locomotive.

387: 384 Locomotive and Tender, 332, 339, 341.

387E: Same as Set 387, but 384E Locomotive.

393E: 390E Locomotive and Tender, three 516s, 517.

394E: 390E Locomotive and Tender, 310, 309, 312.

395E: 390E Locomotive and Tender, 511, 512, 513, 514, 515, 517.

396E: 390E Locomotive and Tender, 420, 421, 422, The Blue Comet (one year only with 390).

407E: 408E and 390E Locomotives, 412, 413, 414, 416, 212, 217, 218, 219, K Transformer, four pair 222s, two 23s, 208, 209, 124, 189, 191, three 184s, 438, 101, 140L, twelve 60s, 78, 80, two 77s, 89, two 128s, 300, 140L, twelve 85s, 78, 80, two 77s, 69, 840, two 67s, two 56s, 87, 79, 195.

409E: 381E Bild-a-Loco, 412, 413, 416, (State Set).

410E: 408E Locomotive, 211, 212, 213, 214, 215, 216, 217.

411E: 408E Locomotive, 412, 413, 414, 416, Transcontinental Limited (State Set).

423E: 390E Locomotive and Tender, 212, 213, 214, 215, 216, 217.

1931

O Gauge

NOTE: All 1931 O Gauge Sets except those with 260E Locomotives include an 068 Crossing Sign.

131: 248 Locomotive, 831, 804, 807.

132: 248 Locomotive, 603, 604.

133: 262 Locomotive, 262T, 902, 804, 807.

134: 252 Locomotive, two 603s, 604.

135: 262 Locomotive, 262T, 812, 810, 817.

136: 262 Locomotive, 262T, 603, 604.

138: 253 Locomotive, two 613s, 614.

139: 261 Locomotive and Tender, 831, 807.

142: 4 Bild-a-Loco, two 605s, 606.

142E: Same as Set 142, but 254E Locomotive.

144: 262 Locomotive, 262T, two 613s, 614.

148: 261 Locomotive, 529, 530.

174: 253 Locomotive, two 607s, 608.

176: 260E Locomotive, two 710s, 712, 069.

233: 262 Locomotive, 262T, 902, 806, 803, 804, 807.

236: 262 Locomotive, 262T, two 607s, 608.

239E: 260E Locomotive, 260T, 812, 814, 815, 813, 817.

240E: 260E Locomotive, 260T, 812 with tools, 810, 811, 817.

241E: 260E Locomotive, 260T, two 710s, 712.

292: 248 Locomotive, 629, 630.

293: 252 Locomotive, 804, 805, 803, 807.

296: 253 Locomotive, two 607s, 608.

296E: Same as Set 293, but 253E Locomotive.

299: 251 Locomotive, 812, 813, 814, 817.

299E: Same as Set 299, but 251E Locomotive.

Standard Gauge

342E: 318E Locomotive, 310, 309, 312, Baby State Set.

347: 8 Locomotive, 337, 338.

358E: 400E Locomotive, 400T, 212 with tools, 219, 220, 217.

360: 8 Locomotive, 332, 337, 338.

360E: Same as Set 360, but 8E Locomotive.

361: 318 Locomotive, 511, 512, 514, 517.

361E: Same as Set 361, but 318E Locomotive.

362: 384 Locomotive, 384T, 309, 312.

362E: Same as Set 362, but 384E Locomotive.

364E: 9E Locomotive, two 424s, 426, (Steven Girard Set).

363E: 390E Locomotive, 390T, 511, 514R, 515, 516, 517.

368E: 390E Locomotive, 390T, two 424s, 426, Pennsylvania Limited (Stephen Girard Set).

386: 384 Locomotive, 384T, 512, 513, 517.

386E: Same as Set 386, but 384E Locomotive.

394E: 390E Locomotive, 390T, 309, 310, 312.

396E: 390E Locomotive, 400T, 420, 421, 422, The Blue Comet.

407E: 400E Locomotive, 408E, two 81s, 412, 413, 414, 416, 212, 217, 220, 219, K Transformer, four pair 222s, two 23s, 208, 209, forty-seven S Tracks, twenty C Tracks, two 1/2S Tracks, 128, 300, 140L, twelve 85s, 78, 80, two 77s, 69, 840, two 67s, four 56s, 87, 79, 195, sixteen STC Lockon Connections.

409E: 381E Locomotive, 412, 413, 416, The Olympian (State Set).

411E: 408E Locomotive, 412, 413, 414, 416, (State Set).

423E: 400E Locomotive, 400T, 211, 212, 213, 214, 215, 216, 217.

432E: 400E Locomotive, 400T, 419, 418, 490.

433E: 400E Locomotive, 400T, 412, 413, 416, 20th Century Limited (State Set).

1932

O Gauge

133: 262 Locomotive, 262T, 902, 804, 807, 27.

135: 262 Locomotive, 262T, 812, 810, 817.

138: 253 Locomotive, two 613s, 614.

138E: Same as Set 253, but 253E Locomotive.

142: 4 Locomotive, two 605s, 606.

142E: Same as Set 142, but 254E Locomotive.

144: 262 Locomotive, 262T, two 613s, 614.

181: 262 Locomotive, 262T, 812, 814, 817.

183: 254 Locomotive, 812, 820, 827.

183E: Same as Set 183, but 254E Locomotive.

236: 262 Locomotive, 262T, two 607s, 608.

173: 248 Locomotive, two 629s, 630, 435, one pair 021s, two 184s, 1012X, four 060s, Y Transformer, three 27s, tunnel, and finished train table.

173S: Same as Set 173, but 178 Set, instead of 248 Locomotive, two 607s, 630.

177: 259 Locomotive, 259T, 831, 807.

178: 259 Locomotive, 259T, 529, 530.

179: 252 Locomotive, 831, 804, 807.

180: 259 Locomotive, 259T, two 603s, 604.

236: 262 Locomotive, 262T, two 607s, 608.

239E: 260E Locomotive, 260T, 812, 814, 815, 813, 817.

240E: 260E Locomotive, 260T, 812 with tools, 810, 820, 817.

241E: 260E Locomotive, 260T, two 710s, 712.

292: 248 Locomotive, 629, 630.

296: 253 Locomotive, two 607s, 608.

296E: Same as Set 293, but 253E Locomotive.

Standard Gauge

347: 8 Locomotive, 337, 338.

358E: 400E Locomotive, 400T, 212 with tool set, 219, 220, 217.

360E: 8E Locomotive, 332, 337, 338.

361E: 318E Locomotive, 511, 520, 514, 517.

362: 384 Locomotive, 384T, 309, 312.

362E: Same as Set 362, but with 384E Locomotive.

364E: 9E Locomotive, 424, 425, 426, (Stephen Girard Set).

370E: 392E Locomotive, 392T, 310, 309, 312.

371E: 392E Locomotive, 384T, 511, 514R, 515, 516, 517.

372E: 392E Locomotive, 384T, 424, 425, 426, Pennsylvania Limited (Stephen Girard Set).

386: 384 Locomotive, 384T, 512, 513, 517.

386E: Same as Set 386, but 384E Locomotive.

396E: 390E Locomotive, 400T, 420, 421, 422, The Blue Comet.

405E: Same as Set 364E, plus 921, 917, 155, 915, 80, one pair 223s, 114, 550, 90, 438, 436, 440, T Transformer.

409E: 381E Locomotive, 412, 413, 416, The Oylmpian (State Set).

411E: 408E Locomotive, 412, 413, 414, 416.

423E: 400E Locomotive, 400T, 211, 212, 213, 214, 215, 216, 217.

432E: 400E Locomotive, 400T, 419, 418, 490.

433E: 400E Locomotive, 400T, 412, 413, 416, 20th Century Limited (State Set).

1933

O27 Gauge

Lionel - Ives

1050E: 1651E Locomotive, two 1690s, 1691, 1017.

1051E: 1661E Locomotive, 1661T, 1679, 1680, 1682, 1017.

1052E: 1661E Locomotive, 1661T, two 1690s, 1691, 1017.

1053E: Includes Set 1052E, plus 913, tunnel, mountain, platform.

Mechanical Sets

1525: 1506L Locomotive, 1502, 1811.

1526: 1506L Locomotive, 1502, 1512, 1514, 1517, tunnel, bridge, animal cutout.

1527: 1506L Locomotive, 1502, 1811, 1812, 1813, tunnel, bridge, animal cutout.

1528: 1506L Locomotive, 1502, 1811, 1812, 1813, six 1571s, 1574, 1573, 1560, 1572, one pair 1550s.

NOTE: All 1933 O Gauge Sets, except those with 260E Locomotives, include 068 crossing sign.

O Gauge

135E: 262E Locomotive, 262T, 812 with tools, 810, 817.

144E: 262E Locomotive, 262T, 615, 613, 614.

173E: 259E Locomotive, 259T, 603, 604, 435, two 184s, 1560, four 060s, Y Transformer, tunnel, and spec train table.

179E: 252E Locomotive, 831, 804, 807.

181E: 262E Locomotive, 262T, 812, 814, 817.

239E: 260E Locomotive, 260T, 812, 814, 815, 813, 817.

240E: 260E Locomotive, 260T, 812 with tools, 810, 820, 817.

241E: 260E Locomotive, 260T, two 710s, 712.

242E: 259E Locomotive, 259T, 603, 604.

243E: 259E Locomotive, 259T, 831, 809, 807.

244E: 259E Locomotive, 259T, two 607s, 608.

245E: 262E Locomotive, 262T, 831, 806, 804, 807.

246E: 262E Locomotive, 262T, 602, 600, 601.

247E: 254E Locomotive, 816, 812, 820, 817.

296E: 253E Locomotive, two 607s, 608.

Standard Gauge

342E: 318E Locomotive, 310, 309, 312, (Baby State Set).

358E: 400E Locomotive, 400T, 212 with tool set, 219, 220, 217.

364E: 9E Locomotive, 424, 425, 426, (Stephen Girard Set).

371E: 392E Locomotive, 384T, 511, 514R, 515, 516 with load, 517.

373E: 390E Locomotive, 384T, 332, 339, 341.

374E: 385E Locomotive, 384T, 512, 513, 517.

375E: 385E Locomotive, 384T, 424, 425, 426, Pennsylvania Limited (Stephen Girard Set).

376E: 392E Locomotive, 384T, 420, 421, 422, The Blue Comet.

396E: 400E Locomotive, 400T, 420, 421, 422.

405E: Same as Set 364E, plus 921, 917, 155, 915, 80, one pair 223s, 114, 550, 90, 438, 436, 440, K Transformer, (Stephen Girard Set).

409E: 381E Locomotive, 412, 413, 416, The Olympic (State Set).

411E: 408E Locomotive, 412, 413, 414, 416, (State Set).

423E: 400E Locomotive, 400T, 211, 212, 213, 214, 215, 216, 217.

433E: 400E Locomotive, 400T, 412, 413, 416, 20th Century Limited (State Set).

1934

NOTE: Lionels first scale-detail train set the City of Portland. Chrome and nickel begin replacing brass and copper.

O27 Gauge

Lionel Jr. Sets

NOTE: All Lionel Jr. Sets came with a 1027 Transformer Station combination.

1054: 1681 Locomotive, 1680, 1677, 1682.

1055E: 1681E Locomotive, 1679, 1680, 1682.

1056E: 1681E Locomotive, two 1690s, 1691.

1057: Includes Set 1056E, plus 913, tunnel, trees, finished train platform.

Mechanical Sets

1528: 1506L Mechanical Locomotive, 1502, 1811, 1812, 1813, 1560, 1573, 1574, 1572, six 1571s, pair 1550s, ten MWCs, six MSs.

1529: 1506L Mechanical Locomotive, 1502T, 1515, 1514.

1530: 1506L Mechanical Locomotive, two 1811s, 1812.

1531: 1506L Mechanical Locomotive, 1502T, 1515, 1514.

O Gauge

144E: 262E Locomotive, 262T, 615, 613, 614.

173E: 259E Locomotive, 259T, 603, 604, 435, one pair 021s, two 184s, 1560, four 060s, L Transformer, 88 OTC, tunnel, ten OC and three OS tracks, finished train table.

179E: 252E Locomotive, 831, 804, 807.

181E: 262E Locomotive, 262T, 812, 814, 817.

234E: 259E Locomotive, 262T, 602, 600, 601.

235E: 259E Locomotive, 261T, 655, 654, 653, 657.

239E: 260E Locomotive, 260T or 263T, 812, 814, 815, 813, 817.

240E: 260E Locomotive, 260T or 263T, 812 with tools, 810, 820, 817.

241E: 260E Locomotive, 260T or 263T, two 710s, 712.

242E: 259E Locomotive, 259T, 603, 604.

243E: 259E Locomotive, 259T, 831, 809, 807.

247E: 254E Locomotive, 816, 812, 820, 817.

296E: 253E Locomotive, two 607s, 608.

O72 Gauge

NOTE: 1934 is the first year for O72 Sets.

751E: 752E Locomotive, 753, 754, (City of Portland).

Standard Gauge

358E: 400E Locomotive, 400T, 212 with tool set, 219, 220, 217.

365E: 9E Locomotive, 310, 309, 312.

366E: 1835E Locomotive, 1835T, 310, 309, 312.

367E: 385E Locomotive, 384T, 1766, 1767, 1768, (became Washington Special 1935).

369E: 385E Locomotive, 384T, 514, 511, 515, 517.

371E: 392E Locomotive, 384T, 511, 514R, 515, 516, 517, 81.

377E: 1835E Locomotive, 1835T, 516, 512, 517.

378E: 392E Locomotive, 384T, 424, 425, 426, (Stephen Girard Set).

396E: 400E Locomotive, 400T, 420, 421, 422, (The Blue Comet).

409E: 381E Locomotive, 412, 413, 416, The Olympian (State Set).

1935

NOTE: Lionel begins trains with Remote Control Whistle.

O27 Gauge

Lionel Jr. Sets

1062: 1681 Locomotive with Tender, 1677, 1680, 1682.

1063E: 1681E Locomotive with Tender, 1679, 1680, 1682.

1064E: 1681E Locomotive with Tender, two 1690s, 1691.

1065E: 1700E Locomotive, 1701, 1702.

1066E: Platform Outfit, 1065E Set, 913, tunnel, mountain.

Mechanical Sets

1521: 1508-X Locomotive, 1541, 1542, 1543, catalogued, but not made.

1523: 1508 Locomotive, 1541, two 1542s, 1543, catalogued, but not made.

1532: 1506 Locomotive, 1509, 1515, 1517, Mickey Mouse Train.

1533: 1508 Locomotive, 1509, 1514, 1515, 1517, Mickey Mouse Train.

1534: 1508 Locomotive, 1509, two 1811s, 1812, Mickey Mouse Train.

1535: 1816, 1817, 1818.

1536: Mickey Mouse Circus Train Outfit.

1537: 1508 Locomotive, 1509, 1811, 1812, 1813, 1560, one pair 1550s, warning signal, clock, semaphore, six telegraph posts, Mickey Mouse Train.

O Gauge

266E: 252E, 654, 651, 657.

267W: 616W, two 617s, 618, Flying Yankee.

267E: Same as Set 267W, but no whistle.

269E: 261E Locomotive, 261T, 654, 659, 657.

273W: 265E Locomotive, 265T, 653, 654, 655, 657.

273E: Same as Set 273W, but no whistle.

274E: Same as Set 274W, but no whistle.

274W: 265E Locomotive, 265T, 600, 601, 602, Commodore Vanderbilt.

275W: 255E Locomotive, 263TW, 812, 814, 817.

276W: 255E Locomotive, 263TW, 615, 613, 614.

277W: 260E Locomotive, 263TW, 820, 812, 810, 817.

278E: 264E Locomotive, 261T, two 603s, 604, The Red Comet.

279E: 265E Locomotive, 261TX, 619, 618, 616T.

296E: 253E Locomotive, two 607s, 608, North Shore Limited.

358W: 400E Locomotive, 400TW, 212 with tool set, 219, 220, 217.

365E: 9E Locomotive, 310, 309, 312.

366W: 1835E Locomotive, 1835TW, 310, 309, 312.

O72 Gauge

751E: 752E Locomotive and Post Office, 753, 754, (City of Portland).

751W: 752W Locomotive, 753, 754, (City of Portland).

755W: 250E Locomotive, 250T, 782, 783, 784, The Hiawatha.

757W: 250E Locomotive, 250T, 812, 814, 815, 816, 817.

Standard Gauge

367W: 385E Locomotive, 385TW, 1766, 1767, 1768, Washington Special.
369W: 385E Locomotive, 385TW, 514, 511, 515, 517.
371W: 392E Locomotive, 392TW, 511, 514, 515, 516, 517.
377W: 1835W Locomotive, 1835TW, 512, 515, 517.
378W: 392E Locomotive, 392TW, 424, 425, 426, Broadway Limited.
396W: 400E Locomotive, 400TW, 420, 421, 422.

1936

NOTE: Lionel begins Manual Box Couplers for O Gauge.

O27 Gauge

Lionel Jr. Sets

1066E: 1700E Locomotive, 1701, 1702, 1560, 1029, 1007.
1067E: 1689E Locomotive, 1689T, two 1690s, 1691.
1068E: 1689E Locomotive, 1689T, 1680, 1679, 1682.
1069E: 1688E Locomotive, 1689T, two 1690s, 1691.
1070E: 1668E Locomotive, 1689T, 1680, 1679, 1682.
1071E: 1700E Locomotive, two 1701s, 1702.

Mechanical Sets

1545: 1511 Locomotive, 1516, 1514, 1515.
1546: 1511 Locomotive, 1516, two 1811s, 1812.
1547: 1511 Locomotive, 1516, 1514, 1515, 1517.
1548: 1588 Locomotive, 1588T, 1673, 1674, 1675.
1549: 1588 Locomotive, 1588T, 1512, 1515, 1514, 1517.
1551: 1816W, 1817, 1818.
1552: 1511 Locomotive, 1516, two 1811s, 1812, 1040, six 1571s, 1572, 1574.

O Gauge

267E: 616E, two 617s, 618, The Flying Yankee.
267W: Same as Set 267E, but with whistle.
275W: 255E Locomotive, 263W, 812, 814, 817.
277W: 263E Locomotive, 263W, 820, 812 with tools, 810, 817.
283W: 263E Locomotive, 263W, 615, 613, 614, O Gauge Blue Comet.
284E: 265E Locomotive, 265T, 655, 653, 654, 659, 657.
284W: Same as Set 284E, but with whistle.
290E: 259E Locomotive, 1689T, 651, 654, 657.
290W: Same as Set 290E, but with whistle.
291E: 264E Locomotive, 265T, two 603s, 604, Red Comet.
291W: Same as Set 291E, but with whistle
292E: 264E Locomotive, 265T, 654, 652, 657.
292W: Same as Set 292E, but with whistle.
293E: 249E Locomotive, 265T, 654, 659, 657.
293W: Same as Set 293E, but with whistle.
294E: 249E Locomotive, 265T, two 607s, 608.
294W: Same as Set 294E, but with whistle.
295E: 265E Locomotive, 265TX, 619, 617, 618, The Blue Streak.
295W: Same as Set 295E, but with whistle.
296E: 253E Locomotive, two 607s, 608, North Side Limited.
297W: 238W Locomotive, 265W, 653, 654, 655, 657.
298W: 238E Locomotive, 265W, 600, 602, 601, Torpedo Train.
299W: 636W, two 637s, 638, City of Denver.

O72 Gauge

751E: 752E, 753, 754, (became the City of Portland in 1938).
755W: 250E Locomotive, 250W, 782, 783, 784, The Hiawatha.
757W: 250E Locomotive, 250W, 812, 814, 815, 816, 817.
758W: 752W, two 753s, 754, (became the City of Portland in 1938).

Standard Gauge

358W: 400E Locomotive, 400W, 219, 212 with tool set, 220, 217.
366W: 1835E Locomotive, 1835W, 310, 309, 312.
367W: 385E Locomotive, 385W, 1767, 1766, 1768, Washington Special.
369W: 385E Locomotive, 385W, 514, 511, 515, 517.
371W: 392E Locomotive, 392W, 511, 514R, 515, 516, 517.
377W: 1835E Locomotive, 1835W, 515, 512, 517.
378W: 392E Locomotive, 392W, 424, 425, 426, Broadway Limited.
396W: 400E Locomotive, 400W, 420, 421, 422, The Blue Comet.

1937

NOTE: 1937 Lionel Introduces the Scale Hudson.

O27 Gauge

1067E: 1689E Locomotive, 1689T, two 1690s, 1691.
1067W: Same as Set 1067E, but with whistle.
1068E: 1689E Locomotive, 1689T, 1680, 1679, 1682.
1068W: Same as Set 1068E, but with whistle.
1071E: 1700E Locomotive, two 1701s, 1702.
1072E: 1700E, two 1701s, 1702, one pair 1121s.
1073E: 1668E Locomotive, 1689T, 1679, 1680, 1682.
1073W: Same as Set 1068E, but with whistle.
1074E: 1668E Locomotive, 1689T, two 1690s, 1691.
1074W: Same as Set 1074E, but with whistle.
1075E: 1668E Locomotive, 1689T, 1679, 1680, 1682, one pair 1121s.
1075W: Same as Set 1075E, but with whistle.
1076E: 1668E Locomotive, 1689T, two 1690s, 1691, one pair 1121s.
1076W: Same as Set 1076E, but with whistle.

Mechanical Sets

1545: 1511 Locomotive, 1516, 1514, 1515.
1546: 1511 Locomotive, 1516, two 1811s, 1812.
1547: 1511 Locomotive, 1516, 1514, 1515, 1517.
1548: 1588 Locomotive, 1588T, 1673, 1674, 1675.
1549: 1588 Locomotive, 1588T, 1512, 1515, 1514, 1517.
1551: 1816W Locomotive, 1817, 1818.

O Gauge

232E: 259E Locomotive, 1689T, two 607s, 608.
232W: Same as Set 232E, but with whistle.
233E: 265E Locomotive, 265T, 602, 600, 601.
233W: Same as Set 233E, but with whistle.
234E: 265E Locomotive, 265T, 653, 652, 654.
234W: Same as Set 234E, but with whistle.
235E: 249E Locomotive, 265T, 659, 651, 654, 657.
235W: Same as Set 235E, but with whistle.
236E: 249E Locomotive, 265T, 602, 600, 601.
236W: Same as Set 236E, but with whistle and whistle controller.
237W: 249E Locomotive, 265W, 655, 654, 620, 659, 657.
267E: 616E, two 617s, 618, The Flying Yankee.
267W: Same as Set 267E, but with whistle.
275W: 263E Locomotive, 263W, 812, 814, 817.
277W: 263E Locomotive, 263W, 820, 812 with tools, 810, 817.
283W: 263E Locomotive, 263W, 615, 613, 614, O Gauge Blue Comet.
290E: 259E Locomotive, 1689T, 651, 654, 657.
290W: Same as Set 290E, but with whistle.
295W: 265E Locomotive, 265WX, 619, 617, 618, Blue Streak.
297W: 238W Locomotive, 265W, 653, 654, 655, 657.
298W: 238E Locomotive, 265W, 600, 602, 601, Torpedo Train.
299W: 636W, two 637s, 638, City of Denver.

O72 Gauge

709W: 700E Locomotive, 700W, 792, two 793s, 794, Rail Chief.
755W: 250E Locomotive, 250WX, 782, 783, 784, The Hiawatha.
757W: 250E Locomotive, 250W, 812, 814, 815, 816, 817.
758W: 752W, two 753s, 754, (became city of Portland in 1938).
764W: 763E Locomotive, 263W, 812, 814, 815, 817.
765W: 763E Locomotive, 263W, 820, 812 with tools, 810, 817.
766W: 763E Locomotive, 263W, two 613s, 615, 614.

Standard Gauge

358W: 400E Locomotive, 400W, 219, 212 with tool set, 220, 208, 217.
366W: 1835E Locomotive, 1835W, 310, 309, 312.
367W: 385E Locomotive, 385W, 1767, 1766, 1768, Washington Special.
369W: 385E Locomotive, 385W, 514, 511, 515, 517.
371W: 392E Locomotive, 392W, 511, 514R, 515, 516, 517.
377W: 1835E Locomotive, 1835W, 515, 512, 517.
378W: 392E Locomotive, 392W, 424, 425, 426, The Broadway Limited.
396W: 400E Locomotive, 400W, 420, 421, 422, The Blue Comet.

1938

NOTE: 1938 is the first year for Lionel remote-control couplers. The couplers used open pickups.

OO Gauge

0080: 004 Locomotive, 004W, 0074, 0075, 0077.

0080W: Same as Set 0080.

O27 Gauge

1073E: 1668E Locomotive, 1689T, 1679, 1680, 1682.

1073W: Same as Set 1068E, but with whistle.

1074E: 1668E Locomotive, 1689T, two 1690s, 1691.

1074W: Same as Set 1074E, but with whistle.

1087E: 1664E Locomotive, 1689T, 1679, 1680, 1682.

1087W: Same as Set 1087E, but with whistle.

1088E: 1664E Locomotive, 1689T, two 1630s, 1631.

1088W: Same as Set 1088E, but with whistle.

1089E: 1666E Locomotive, 2689T, 2679, 2680, 2682.

1089W: Same as Set 1089E, but with whistle.

1090E: 1666E Locomotive, 2689T, two 2630s, 2631.

1090W: Same as Set 1090E, but with whistle.

1091E: 1666E Locomotive, 2689T, 2679, 2680, 3659, 2682.

1091W: Same as Set 1091E, but with whistle.

1093E: 1666E Locomotive, 2689T, 2679, 2680, 2682, one pair 1121 Switches.

1093W: Same as Set 1093E, but with whistle.

1095W: 1666E Locomotive, 2689T, 3659, 2680, 2620, 2657, 96 Coal Elevator, one pair 1121 Switches.

O Gauge

175E: 259E Locomotive, 2689T, 2651, 2654, 2657.

175W: Same as Set 175E, but with whistle.

176E: 259E Locomotive, 2689T, two 2640s, 2641.

176W: Same as Set 176E, but with whistle.

177E: 224E Locomotive, 2689T, 2652, 2654, 2657.

177W: Same as Set 177E, but with whistle.

178E: 224E Locomotive, 2689T, two 2640s, 2641.

178W: Same as Set 178E, but with whistle.

179E: 265E Locomotive, 2225T, 2652, 3659, 2657.

179W: Same as Set 179E, but with whistle.

181E: 265E Locomotive, 2225T, 2654, 2660, 2657.

181W: Same as Set 181E, but with whistle.

182E: 225E Locomotive, 2265T, 2600, 2601, 2602.

182W: Same as Set 182E, but with whistle.

183E: 225E Locomotive, 2225T, 2654, 2655, 2657.

183W: Same as Set 183E, but with whistle.

185W: 225E Locomotive, 2225T, 2620, 2654, 3659, 2657, 160.

186W: 238E Locomotive, 2265W, 2600, 2601, 2602, 160, Torpedo Train.

187W: 238E Locomotive, 2225W, 2653, 2654, 2655, 2657.

189W: 225E Locomotive, 2225W, three 3659s, 2657, 97 Coal Elevator.

190W: 226E Locomotive, 2226W, 2613, 2614, 2615.

191W: 226E Locomotive, 2226W, 2815, 2816, 2817.

193W: 226 Locomotive, 2226W, 2812 with tools, 2810, 2820, 2817.

194W: 263E Locomotive, 2263W, 2613, 2614, 2615, O Gauge Blue Comet.

195W: 263E Locomotive, 2263W, 2814, 3859, 2817.

197W: 263E Locomotive, 2263W, 2812, 812T with tool set, 2810, 3859, 2817.

267E: 616E, two 617s, 618, The Flying Yankee.

267W: Same as Set 267E, but with whistle.

295W: 265E Locomotive, 265WX, 619, 617, 618, Blue Streak.

299W: 636W, two 637s, 638, City of Denver.

O72 Gauge

709W: 700E Locomotive, 700W, 792, two 793s, 794, Rail Chief.

755W: 250E Locomotive, 250WX, 782, 783, 784, The Hiawatha.

758W: 752W, two 753s, 754, City of Portland.

759W: 250E Locomotive, 2250W, 2812, 2814, 2815, 2816, 2817.

767W: 763E Locomotive, 2263W, 2812, 2815, 2814, 2817.

768W: 763E Locomotive, 2263W, two 2613s, 2614, 2615.

769W: 763E Locomotive, 2263W, 2810, 2812, 812T with tool set, 2817, 2820.

Standard Gauge

NOTE: No official Lionel names on Standard Gauge set in catalogue for 1938 or 1939.

358W: 400E Locomotive, 400W, 219, 212, 220, 208 tool set, 217.

366W: 1835E Locomotive, 1835W, 310, 309, 312.

367W: 385E Locomotive, 385W, 1767, 1766, 1768, Washington Special.

369W: 385E Locomotive, 385W, 514, 511, 515, 517.

371W: 392E Locomotive, 392W, 511, 514R, 515, 516, 517.

377W: 1835E Locomotive, 1835W, 515, 512, 517.

378W: 392E Locomotive, 392W, 424, 425, 426, (Stephen Girard Set).

396W: 400E Locomotive, 400W, 420, 421, 422, (Blue Comet).

1939

NOTE: 1939 is the first year shielded pickups for remote-control couplers were used.

OO Gauge

0080W: Same as Set 0090W, but for three-rail track.

0080: Same as Set 0080W, but no whistle.

0082W: Same as Set 0092W, but for three-rail track

0090W: 003 Locomotive, 003W, 0044, 0045, 0046, 0047, super-detailed locomotive for two-rail track.

0090: Same as Set 0090W, but no whistle.

0092W: 004 Locomotive, 004W, 0074, 0075, 0077, regular locomotive for two-rail track.

0092: Same as Set 0092W, but no whistle.

O27 Gauge

1073W: 1668 Locomotive, 1689W, 1679, 1680, 1682.

1073: Same as Set 1073W, but without whistle.

1074W: 1668 Locomotive, 1689W, two 1690s, 1691.

1074: Same as Set 1074W, but without whistle.

1087W: 1664 Locomotive, 1689W, 1679, 1680, 1682.

1087: Same as Set 1087W, but without whistle.

1088W: 1664 Locomotive, 1689W, two 1630s, 1631.

1088: Same as Set 1088W, but without whistle.

1089W: 1666 Locomotive, 2689W, 2679, 2680, 2682.

1089: Same as Set 1089W, but without whistle.

1090W: 1666 Locomotive, 2689W, two 2630s, 2631.

1090: Same as Set 1090W, but without whistle.

1091W: 1666 Locomotive, 2689W, 2679, 2680, 3659, 2682.

1091: Same as Set 1091W, but without whistle.

1093W: 1666 Locomotive, 2689W, 2679, 2680, 3659, 2682, one pair 1121 Switches.

1093: Same as Set 1093W, but without whistle.

1095W: 1666 Locomotive, 2689T, 3659, 2680, 2620, 2657, 96 Coal Elevator, one pair 1121 Switches.

1097W: 1666 Locomotive, 2689W, 2620, 3651, 2660, 3652, 2682.

O Gauge

135W: 265 Locomotive, 2225W, 2654, 2652, 2657, Commodore Vanderbilt Special.

135: Same as Set 135W, but no whistle.

138W: 229 Locomotive, 0-2689W, two 2640s, 2641.

138: Same as Set 138W, but no whistle.

139W: 229 Locomotive, 0-2689W, 2654, 2651, 2657.

139: Same as Set 139W, but no whistle.

140W: 224 Locomotive, 2224W, two 2640s, 2641.

140: Same as Set 140W, but no whistle.

141W: 224 Locomotive, 2224W, 2652, 2654, 2657.

141: Same as Set 141W, but no whistle.

143W: 224 Locomotive, 2224W, 2652, 2654, 3651, 2657.

143: Same as Set 143W, but no whistle.

145W: 224 Locomotive, 2224W, 3659, 3652, 2660, 3651, 2657.

146W: 225 Locomotive, 2245W, 2602, 2600, 2601.

146: Same as Set 146W, but no whistle.
147W: 225 Locomotive, 2235W, 3651, 2654, 2657.
147: Same as Set 147W, but no whistle.
149W: 225 Locomotive, 2235W, 2620, 2654, 3659, 2657.
151W: 225 Locomotive, 2235W, 97 Coal Elevator, three 3659s, 2657.
190W: 226 Locomotive, 2226W, 2613, 2614, 2615.
191W: 226 Locomotive, 2226W, 2815, 2816, 2817.
193W: 226 Locomotive, 2226W, 2812 with tools, 2810, 2820, 2817.
194W: 263 Locomotive, 2263W, 2615, 2613, 2614, O Gauge Blue Comet.
195W: 263 Locomotive, 2263W, 2814, 3859, 2817.
197W: 263 Locomotive, 2263W, 2812 with tools, 2810, 3859, 2817,
239B: 227 Locomotive, 2227B, 2655, 2654, 2657X, 169 Controller.
239: Same as Set 239B, but no bell.
241B: 228 Locomotive, 2228B, 2814, 2815, 2817, 169 Controller.
241: Same as Set 241B, but no bell.
267W: 616W, two 617s, 618, Flying Yankee.
267: Same as Set 267W, but no whistle.
299W: 636W, two 637s, 638, City of Denver.

O72 Gauge

709W: 700E Locomotive, 700W, 792, two 793s, 794, Rail Chief.
755W: 250 Locomotive, 250WX, 782, 783, 784, 67, The Hiawatha.
758W: 752W, two 753s, 754, City of Portland.
759W: 250 Locomotive, 2250W, 2812, 2814, 2815, 2816, 2817.
767W: 763 Locomotive, 2263W, 2812, 2815, 2814, 2817.
768W: 763 Locomotive, 2263W, two 2613s, 2614, 2615.
769W: 763 Locomotive, 2263W, 2820, 2812, 2810, 2817.

Standard Gauge

NOTE: 1939 was the last year for Lionel Standard Gauge sets.
358W: 400 Locomotive, 400W, 212 with tool set, 219, 220, 217.
366W: 1835 Locomotive, 1835W, 310, 309, 312.
367W: 385 Locomotive, 385W, 1767, 1766, 1768, (Washington Special).
369W: 385 Locomotive, 385W, 514, 511, 515, 517.
371W: 392 Locomotive, 392W, 511, 514R, 515, 516, 517.
377W: 1835 Locomotive, 1835W, 515, 512, 517.
378W: 392 Locomotive, 392W, 424, 425, 426, (Stephen Girard Set).
396W: 400 Locomotive, 400W, 420, 421, 422, (Blue Comet).

1940

OO Gauge

0080W: Same as Set 0090W, but for three-rail track.
0080: Same as Set 0080W, but no whistle.
0082W: Same as set 0092W, but for three-rail track.
0082: Same as Set 0082W, but no whistle.
0090W: 003 Locomotive, 003W, 0044, 0045, 0046, 0047, super-detailed locomotive for two-rail track.
0090: Same as Set 0090W, but no whistle.
0092W: 004 Locomotive, 004W, 0074, 0075, 0077, regular locomotive for two-rail track.
0092: Same as Set 0092W, but no whistle.

O27 Gauge

1059: 1662 Locomotive, 2203T, 2679, 2677, 2682X.
1061: (Note that this set has two locomotives) 1666 Locomotive, 2689T, two 2640s, 2641, 1663 Locomotive, 2201T, 2679, 2657X, two 1019s, 1039, one pair 1121 Switches, Q Transformer.
1073: 1668 Locomotive, 1689T, 1679, 1680, 1682.
1073W: Same as Set 1073, but with whistle.
1074: 1668 Locomotive, 1689T, two 1690s, 1691.
1074W: Same as Set 1074, but with whistle.
1087: 1664 Locomotive, 1689T, 1679, 1680, 1682.
1087W: Same as Set 1087, but with whistle.
1088: 1664 Locomotive, 1689T, two 1630s, 1631.
1088W: Same as Set 1088, but with whistle.
1089: 1666 Locomotive, 2689T, 2677, 2679, 2682.
1089W: Same as Set 1089, but with whistle.
1090: 1666 Locomotive, 2689T, two 2630s, 2631.
1090W: Same as Set 1090, but with whistle.
1091: 1666 Locomotive, 2689T, 2679, 2680, 3659, 2682.
1091W: Same as Set 1091, but with whistle.
1093: 1666 Locomotive, 2689T, 2679, 2680, 2682, 1121 Switches.
1093W: Same as Set 1093, but with whistle.
1095W: 1666 Locomotive, 2689W, 3659, 2680, 2620, 2657, 96 Coal Elevator, 160, one pair 1121 Switches.
1097W: 1666 Locomotive, 2689W, 2620, 3651, 2660, 3652, 2682.
1099W: 1666 Locomotive, 2689W, three 3651s, 2657, 164 Log Loader, one pair 1121 Switches.

O Gauge

131W: 225 Locomotive, 2235W, 97 Coal Elevator, 3659, 3652, 3651, 2657.
135: 265 Locomotive, 2225T, 2654, 2652, 2657.
138: 229 Locomotive, 2689T, two 2640s, 2641.
138W: Same as Set 138, but with whistle.
139: 229 Locomotive, 2689T, 2654, 2651, 2657.
139W: Same as Set 139, but with whistle.
140: 224 Locomotive, 2224T, two 2640s, 2641.
140W: Same as Set 140 but with whistle.
141: 224 Locomotive, 2224T, 2652, 2654, 2657.
141W: Same as Set 141, but with whistle.
143W: 224 Locomotive, 2224W, 2652, 2654, 3651, 2657.
145W: 224 Locomotive, 2224W, 3659, 3652, 2660, 3651, 2657.
146W: 225 Locomotive, 2245W, 2602, 2600, 2601.
149W: 225 Locomotive, 2235W, 2620, 2654, 3659, 2657.
190W: 226 Locomotive, 2226W, 2615, 2614, 2613.
239: 227 Locomotive, 2227T, 2652, 2656, 2657X.
239B: Same as Set 239, but with bell.
243: 228 Locomotive, 2228T, 2615, 3814, 2817.
243B: Same as Set 243, but with bell.
245: 203 Switcher, 2203T, 2655, 2654, 2657X.
245B: Same as Set 245, but with bell.
247W: 225 Locomotive, 2235W, 2653, 3651, 2656, 2657.
251: 227 Locomotive, 2227T, 2954, 2955, 2957.
251B: Same as Set 251, but with bell.
261W: 226 Locomotive, 2226W, 2810, 3811, 2817.
267: 616, two 617s, 618, (Flying Yankee).
267W: Same as Set 267, but with whistle.
269W: 225 Locomotive, 2235W, 3651, two 2652s, 2657, 165 Magnetic Crane.
273W: 226 Locomotive, 2226W, three 3811s, 2817, 164 Lumber Loader.
291W: 226 Locomotive, 2226WX, 2955, 2957, 2954.
293W: 226 Locomotive, 2226W, 2820, 3859, 2810, 2817.

O72 Gauge

705: 701 Locomotive, 701T, 716, 714, 715, 717.
707W: 700 Locomotive, 700W, 715, 714, 716, 717.
709W: 700 Locomotive, 700W, 792, two 793s, 794, (Rail Chief).
755W: 250 Locomotive, 250WX, 782, 783, 784, (The Hiawatha).
758W: 752W, two 753s, 754, (City of Portland).
768W: 763 Locomotive, 2263W, two 2613s, 2614, 2615.
787W: 763 Locomotive, 2226WX, 2956, 2954, 2955, 2957.
789W: 763 Locomotive, 2226W, 2820, 2812 with tools, 2810, 2817.

1941

OO Gauge

0080W: Same as Set 0090W, but for three-rail track.
0080: Same as Set 0080W, but no whistle.
0082W: Same as set 0092W, but for three-rail track.
0082: Same as Set 0082W, but no whistle.
0090W: 003 Locomotive, 003W, 0044, 0045, 0046, 0047, super-deatailed locomotive for two-rail track.
0090: Same as Set 0090W, but no whistle.
0092W: 004 Locomotive, 004W, 0074, 0075, 0077, regular locomotive for two-rail track.
0092: Same as Set 0092W, but no whistle.

O27 Gauge

1059: 1662 Locomotive, 2203T, 2679, 2677, 2682X.

1061: (Note that this set has two locomotives) 1666 Locomotive, 2689T, two 2640s, 2641, 1663 Locomotive, 2201T, 3651, 2679, 2657X, two 1019s, one pair 1121 Switches, Q Transformer.

1073W: 1668 Locomotive, 1689W, 1679, 1680, 1682.

1073: Same as Set 1073W, but no whistle.

1174W: 1668 Locomotive, 1689W, 1630, 1631

1174: Same as Set 1074W, but no whistle.

1087W: 1664 Locomotive, 1689W, 1679, 1680, 1682.

1087: Same as Set 1087W, but no whistle.

1088W: 1664 Locomotive, 1689W, two 1630s, 1631.

1088: Same as Set 1088W, but no whistle.

1089W: 1666 Locomotive, 2689W, 2677, 2679, 2682.

1089: Same as Set 1089W, but no whistle.

1185W: 1666 Locomotive, 2666W, 2677, 2680, 2672.

1185: Same as Set 1085W, but no whistle.

1190W: 1666 Locomotive, 2666W, two 2640s, 2641.

1190: Same as Set 1190W, but no whistle.

1191W: 1666 Locomotive, 2666W, 2679, 2680, 3659, 2672.

1191: Same as Set 1091W, but no whistle.

1193W: 1666 Locomotive, 2666W, 2679, 2680, 2672, one pair 1121 Switches.

1193: Same as Set 1193W, but no whistle.

1195W: 1666 Locomotive, 2666W, 3659, 2680, 2620, 2672, 97 Coal Loader, one pair 1121 Switches, 1041, 1019.

1197W: 1666 Locomotive, 2666W, 2620, 3651, 2660, 3652, 2672.

1199W: 1666 Locomotive, 2666W, 3651, 3652, 3652, 2680, 164 Log Loader, one pair 1121 Switches.

O Gauge

140: 224 Locomotive, 2224T, two 2642s, 2643.

140W: Same as Set 140, but with whistle.

251B: 227 Locomotive, 2227B, 2954, 2955, 2957, 169X.

261W: 226 Locomotive, 2226W, 2816, 3811, 2817.

267W: 616W, two 617s, 618, (Flying Yankee).

291W: 226 Locomotive, 2226WX, 2954, 2955, 2957.

831W: 225 Locomotive, 2235W, 3659, 3652, 3651, 2757, 97 Coal Loader.

838W: 229 Locomotive, 0-2226W, two 2642s, 2643.

838: Same as 838W, but no whistle.

839W: 229 Locomotive, 0-2226W, 2654, 2651, 2657.

839: Same as 389W, but no whistle.

841W: 224 Locomotive, 2224W, 2812X, 2654, 2757.

841: Same as Set 841W, but no whistle.

843W: 224 Locomotive, 2224W, 2812X, 2755, 3651, 2757.

845W: 224 Locomotive, 2224W, 3659, 2660, 3651, 2758, 2757.

846W: 225 Locomotive, 2235W, two 2623s, 2624.

847W: 225 Locomotive, 2235W, 2755, 3651, 2758, 2757.

859B: 227 Locomotive, 2227B, 2812X, 2758, 2757X, 169X.

863B: 228 Locomotive, 2228B, 2815, 3814, 2757X, 169X.

865B: 203 Locomotive, 2203B, 2758, 2755, 2757X.

865: Same as Set 865B, but no bell.

869W: 225 Locomotive, 2235WX, 3651, two 2652s, 2757, 165 Magnet Crane.

873W: 226 Locomotive, 2226W, 2812, 3811, 3814, 2957X, 164 Log Loader.

890W: 226 Locomotive, 2226WX, two 2623s, 2624, 167.

O72 Gauge

293W: 226 Locomotive, 2226W, 2820, 3859, 2810, 2817.

705: 701 Locomotive, 701T, 716, 714, 715, 717.

707W: 700 Locomotive, 700W, 715, 714, 716, 717.

709W: 700 Locomotive, 700W, 792, two 793s, 794, (Rail Chief).

748W: 763 Locomotive, 2226WX, three 2623s, 2624.

749W: 763 Locomotive, 2226W, 2820, 2812 with tool set, 2810, 2957X.

755W: 250 Locomotive, 250WX, 782, 783, 784, (The Hiawatha).

758W: 752W, two 753s, 754, (City of Portland).

787W: 763 Locomotive, 2226WX, 2956, 2954, 2955, 2957.

1942

OO Gauge

0080W: Same as Set 0090W, but for three-rail track.

0080: Same as Set 0080W, but no whistle.

0082W: Same as Set 0090W, but for three-rail track.

0082: Same as Set 0082W, but no whistle.

0090W: 003 Locomotive, 003W, 0044, 0045, 0046, 0047.

0090: Same as Set 0090W, but no whistle.

0092W: 004 Locomotive, 004W, 0074, 0075, 0077.

0092: Same as Set 0092W, but no whistle.

027 Gauge

1083: 1684 Locomotive, 1689T, 1679, 1680, 1682.

1086: 1684 Locomotive, 1689T, two 1630s, 1631.

1094: 1684 Locomotive, 1689T, 1679, 1680, 1682, pair 1024 Manual Switches.

1096W: 1684 Locomotive, 2689T, 2677, 2679, 2682.

1096: Same as Set 1096W, but no whistle.

1130: 1662 Locomotive, 2203T, 2679, 2677, 2682X.

1131: 1684 Locomotive, 2689T, 2680, 2679, 2682, pair 1024 Manual Switches.

1132W: 1664 Locomotive, 2666W, two 2640s, 2641.

1132: Same as Set 1132W, but no whistle.

1133W: 1664 Locomotive, 2666W, 2677, 2680, 2672.

1133: Same as Set 1133W, but no whistle.

1135W: 1664 Locomotive, 2666W, 2679, 2677, 2758, 2672, pair 1121 Switches.

1136: (Note that this set has two locomotives) 1666 Locomotive, 2689T, two 2640s, 2641, 1663 Locomotive, 2201T, 2677, 2679, 2657X, 1019, 1121, 168, Q Transformer.

1185W: 1666 Locomotive, 2666W, 2677, 2680, 2672, 1041, 1019.

O Gauge

254: 229 Locomotive, 2666T, two 2642s, 2643.

257: 229 Locomotive, 2666T, 2654, 2655, 2657.

853W: 225 Locomotive, 2235W, 2755, 2812X, 2758, 2757.

859B: 227 Locomotive, 2227B, 2812X, 2758, 2757X, 169X.

O72 Gauge

748W: 763 Locomotive, 2226WX, four 2623s.

855W: 250 Locomotive, 2250W, 2815, 2812, 3859, 3814, 2817.

Index

By Cindy Lee Floyd
With the assistance of Fred Schlipf

-C denotes a color plate

Due to Lionel's numbering system, this index treats zeros as digits. Single digits precede double digits and double digits precede triple digits, etc.